BUTTON HERITAGE

REVISED EDITION

BY

ERWINA CHAMBERLIN

AND

MINERVA MINER

Published by

FAULKNER PRINTING COMPANY, INC.

Sherburne, N.Y. 13460

Printed in U.S.A.

In reprinting BUTTON HERITAGE we have made some changes in order to bring prices up-to-date. DeLuxe buttons are becoming more scarce but many beautiful buttons can still be obtained at reasonable prices and the new collector should not be discouraged.

The values that we have given will vary in different areas and will be affected by the condition of the button and its availability.

Examine buttons carefully when you are buying. Some rare buttons have been reproduced. Buy these if you wish but know what you are buying and pay accordingly.

Please use our prices as a guide only.

Erwina Chamberlin
Minerva Miner

FOREWORD

This book has been compiled chiefly for the help of the "Beginning collector" who has had so much difficulty in obtaining a satisfactory reference book.

All buttons are shown in their actual size and were photographed by Fay Edward Faulkner with the exception of the color plates which were photographed by Peter Hollis, Cooperstown, N.Y. and two plates that are by Alphaeus H. Albert.

The prices are, of course, estimated and will be found to vary in different localities. In showing the same button in various sizes, we have shown you the relative value, according to size.

We have tried to keep the text of this book in accord with specifications of The National Button Society, as many years of research have been accomplished by this society. We have used the classifications and terminology accepted by the N.B.S. and the reference N.B.B., which appears often, refers to the National Button Bulletins, from which additional and authentic information can be obtained. We did not consider it necessary to reprint this material but have given you the precise source.

We wish to thank Sally Luscomb, editor of Just Buttons Magazine, which she publishes from the Just Buttons Museum, Southington, Conn., for her information, encouragement and cooperation.

Our thanks also go to many other friends and fellow hobbyists who have so generously loaned us their choice buttons and given us data from their research.

Specifically we thank: Alphaeus H. Albert, Thomas W. Owens, Jr., Zula Fricks, Mrs. Robert Smith, Edith Rodway, Mary Seymour, Mrs. Clarence Reeds, Florence Aberle, Florence Leggett, Mrs. William Crawford, John Whitford, Marion Moxley, Mary Miller, Mrs. Chris Sorenson, Rev. L.L. Twinem, Mrs. James Helgestad, Elsa Ehresman, Gladys Coleman, Floyd and Elizabeth Miner, Mrs. Irene Stribey, Dorothy Lloyd, Mrs. Harold Eby, Mrs. Louis Miles, Mrs. Margaret Knowlton, Esther Woodard, Donald VanCourt, and Donald V. Slayter.

In preparing this book, we have used as references: Button Classics, The National Button Bulletins, and Just Buttons, The Encyclopedia Britannica, Hobbies Magazine, Brewer's Character Sketches, the button books written by Lillian Smith Albert, Dorothy Foster Brown, David F. Johnson, Florence Nicholls, Helen Wegener, Jane Adams and Grace Hornby Ford. We also have found enrichment in the fine articles published in the Button Bulletins from many State Societies.

TABLE OF CONTENTS

Button Heritage

Antique buttons are a heritage from the past that will enrich your life. They can lead to many fascinating hours of historical research, to knowledge of arts and crafts, to the satisfaction derived from beauty and to the pleasure of friendship shared with fellow hobbyists.

We hope that through the pages of this book you will become aware of — or find new joy in — your button heritage.

PLATE 1

PLATE 1

DELUXE BUTTONS

Buttons such as these and some others, pictured under the title of DeLuxe, may seem unobtainable to the new button collector but they are beautiful to look at and interesting to study. After becoming familiar with the different types, one can decide what would most please his personal taste and, by careful planning, can purchase at least one of these better items at intervals, until he has enhanced his collection. The buttons shown and described here are from the collection of Zula Fricks Brown.

1. This is a lovely polychrome painting on ivory, signed by the artist. It is under glass and set in an engraved frame that has never tarnished. $85.00.
2. A very rare Wedgwood floral disk, set in a border of small paste stones. The frame and back are of silver with the shank hall-marked. $150.00.
3. A polychrome painting on ivory of a young lady in a bonnet-shaped chapeau. Exquisite coloring, under glass with small, paste stone border. $85.00.
4. A very early unglazed button with self-shank, having the name, "Wedgwood" impressed in the back. The center medallion is green and in relief. The flower forms on the outer edge are lilac-tinted and also in relief. $75.00.
5. This is a Wedgwood disk of brilliant blue with white figure of a warrior, standing with sword in hand. Copper border. $175.00.
6. This button is similar to No. 4, but is backmarked with the impressions "Wedg-wood" and "England". This marking was adopted about 1892. The center medallion is in relief and lilac-tinted. $75.00.
7. Hand painted polychrome design of basket of flowers on convex, cobalt blue enamel background. The brass border is scalloped and set with paste stones. $45.00.
8. A champleve border with part of the design left without enamel and set with four tiny seed pearls. The center design is of a bird in flight, over flowers and is polychrome painted on white enamel. Beautifully done. $45.00.
9. A monochrome calico transfer on light enamel with a series of contrasting borders. It is a square shape with rounded corners, giving a scalloped effect. The base is silver and quite convex. $35.00.

10. GIRL AT FOUNTAIN, an enamel painting in lovely colors, unusually large with steel studded rim. $50.00.

11. A LIMOGES PORTRAIT HEAD, in lovely colors on turquoise blue. A scalloped border is formed with pieces of gold foil, covered by a transparent glaze. Paste stones are set in each scallop of the border. The back is enameled in cobalt blue. This is called, "counter-enameling". The under coating is given at the same time as the first coating of the face of the button. The counter - enameling prevents the top enamel from flaking, as a result of expansion and contraction. The base of this button is copper. $47.50.

12. This is a fine example of a FOIL PICTURE IN ENAMEL. The metal base is copper and it is enameled on the face, and counter - enameled with cobalt blue. A narrow rim of white enamel was placed between two milled metal edges. The center design and the linked border are of gold foil, the center representing CUPID WITH DOG. The foil pictures and tiny shapes are termed "paillons". They are stamped or cut from thin sheets of foil, applied to the enamel, treated and fired. This type of work requires great skill. Value, $75.00.

PLATE 2

PLATE 2

MORE DELUXE

1. A WEDGWOOD DISK of brilliant blue with a white figure, in the classic style; an 18th century specimen with tin back and gilt rim. $175.00.

2. A Limoges enamel background; outline transfer with polychrome painting, showing girl whose dress is sprinkled with foil specks; called "WHO'LL BUY MY LAVENDER?"; cut steel border. $38.50.

3. Heavy steel frame with cut steel border, enclosing an 18th century WEDGWOOD DISK in medium blue with white relief figures. $200.00.

4. An 18th century button, the background enameled in white and counter-enameled. The scene is done in rose color and enclosed in an embossed, scroll border. Undoubtedly a BATTERSEA ENAMEL. Value $175.00.

5. Slightly convex, square enamel button, counter-enameled on the back. Metallic forms are embedded in the surface and enameled in color, in relief. The background is black, flowers are in two shades of blue, and leaves in lovely greens. A rare specimen. $35.00.

6. Polychrome painting on white enamel background of LADY RIDING BICYCLE; Cut steel border. $45.00.

7. Concave enamel, done in black and white, SAIL BOATS AND SCENE, beautifully painted. Decorative brass border. $25.00.

8. Enamel with polychrome handpainting of HONEY BEE among flowers; green background; cut steel border. $15.00.

9. Small porcelain self-shank polychrome painting of LOVERS, gilt painted rim. $15.00.

10. An oval shaped enamel with a SHEPHERDESS, hand-painted in shades of lavender. Paste diamond border. $38.50.

11. Small Porcelain with self shank, pink background with black and white scene, showing CHERUB CHASING BUTTERFLIES. $12.50.

12. Champleve work showing WARRIOR. An especially deep depression is made for the face which is beautifully enameled in natural colors; other colors used are white, red, light blue and black; a design in black covers the background; cut steel border. $20.00.

13. A sepia transfer on a brick red, glazed, ceramic disk; brass rim and back. $25.00.

14. Small porcelain with a painting of LADY'S HEAD with gold embossed border; self shank. $12.50.

15. An 18th century button, under glass in silver frame, showing black silhouette of LIBERTY CAP AND FLAG, laid on lame fabric. Rare. $38.50.

16. A small enamel, showing scene of HOUSE IN SNOW DRIFTS, done in black, white and pink; cut steel border. $12.50.

All buttons shown here are from the collection of Zula Fricks Brown.

PLATE 3

PLATE 3

PORTRAITS & OTHER DELUXE BUTTONS

All buttons on this Plate, except No. 5, are from the collection of Zula Fricks Brown. After examining these one does not wonder why Antique Buttons are referred to as, "Art in Miniature".

1. A polychrome PAINTING ON IVORY, signed by the artist; set in silver, with paste border. Value, approximately $65.00.

2. Large lithograph, under glass, brass rim; said to be the DUCHESS OF DEVONSHIRE; a fine specimen. $35.00.

3. A polychrome painting on ivory, very similar to No. 1, and done by the same artist. $65.00.

4. A polychrome painting on ivory of a GIRL, IN COLONIAL COSTUME, carrying a jug on her head; under glass in a silver frame made about 1880. $35.00.

5. An eighteenth century "jewel". Green "Sparklers" are set with prongs in a medallion shape, centered and surrounded by "brilliants". Mounted in silver. $35.00.

6. Polychrome painting on ivory, signed by the artist, of MME RECAMIER; under glass in a plain frame. $50.00.

7. An unusual painting of a ST. BERNARD DOG'S HEAD, executed on ivory; under glass with gold rim and lovely olive leaf border of pierced silver. Very rare. $47.50.

8. Large enamel painting in black and white on heavy brass disk; the scene shows BRIDGE AND TOWER; cut steel border. $65.00.

9. An 18th century pearl in frame with paste center; the center portion between pearl and paste jewel is an inset of Eglomese (reverse painting, under glass, done with gold leaf and black enamel, described elsewhere). $35.00.

10. A lovely miniature painting of LOVERS, STROLLING, done in many colors on ivory; under glass with small paste stone border. $25.00.

11. An exquisite IVORY MINIATURE, painted in polychrome, set in silver with diamond paste border. $25.00.

12. Polychrome painting on porcelain with yellow background and PORTRAIT in natural colors. Paste border. $25.00.

13. A metal background with honeycomb design; limoges painting in natural colors, the HEAD outlined by champleve work; cut steel border. $50.00.

14. Black glass, recessed, the SCENE painted on white pigment which fills this recess. Gilt rimmed glass is inserted over the painting and the surface of the glass in incised with fine gold lines which outline and add to the picture; gilt back and beaded gilt border. $25.00.

PLATE 4

PLATE 4

18TH CENTURY AND OTHER FINE TYPES

1. A PORTRAIT OF A LADY, polychrome painted on ivory, under glass, set in silver. $25.00.

2. BACCHUS, god of the vine, polychrome painted on a silver base. The etched design of the border and vine are left without enamel and the rest of the background is filled in with deep wine red. $22.00.

3. Another ORNAMENTAL HEAD, polychrome painted on ivory under glass, set in silver in a similar manner to No. 1. $27.50.

4. Eighteenth century ceramic base with polychrome painted FLORAL decoration. Glazed front, unglazed back with self shank. $15.00.

5. A flat silver button with scalloped edge. The face is enameled black and a ROSE is hand painted on this background. From the collection of Edith Rodway. $35.00.

6. Light blue WEDGWOOD with self shank; white; classical figures in relief. $38.00.

7. Another portrait of a LADY WITH HER DOG, painted with fine detail on ivory, under glass. Set in silver rim with silver back. $38.00.

8. Miniature of a LADY IN BLUE DRESS, polychrome painted on ivory, under glass. $25.00.

9. Miniature of a FRENCH LADY, polychrome painted on enamel background. Repousse gilt border, ornamented with paste jewels. $18.00.

10. A companion button to No. 7 showing the LADY, in elaborate costume, standing in her garden. Polychrome painting on ivory, under glass with silver rim and back. $38.00.

11. This is a hand-made copper "Colonial" button with the face gilded and decorated with a floral design. Most buttons of this type have conventional designs and this is, therefore more unusual. Buttons of this kind were worn in Europe and America from the 17th century 'til well into the 19th century. $25.00.

12. A MINIATURE, painted on ivory, under glass in a jeweler's setting with border in which rhinestones alternate, with faceted black glass "jewels". An eighteenth-century button $65.00.

13. Ceramic with BIRD print transferred in black. Brass rim and back with metal shank. $25.00.

14. This button and No. 16. have high convex glass lenses with SYMBOLS OF THE FRENCH REVOLUTION painted on the reverse of the glass. They have copper rims and tin backs, brass shanks. This button symbolizes the union of Liberty, Equality, Fraternity. The Liberty Cap is conspicious at the top and a motto is written on each side of the design. $50.00.

15. A fine specimen of cloisonne enameling on brass. The fine wires which form the design of the STORKS IN FLIGHT can be plainly seen. These have been left to form the bird's feet and the other areas formed by the "cloisons" are filled with black and white enamel. The background is heavily coated with brick-red enamel. Brass rim. $65.00. This is from the collection of Florence Leggett.

16. See description No. 14. These designs were first outlined on the reverse of the glass and then filled in with color, appropriate for the design. One marvels that such fragile work has survived in this fine condition. $50.00

PLATE 5

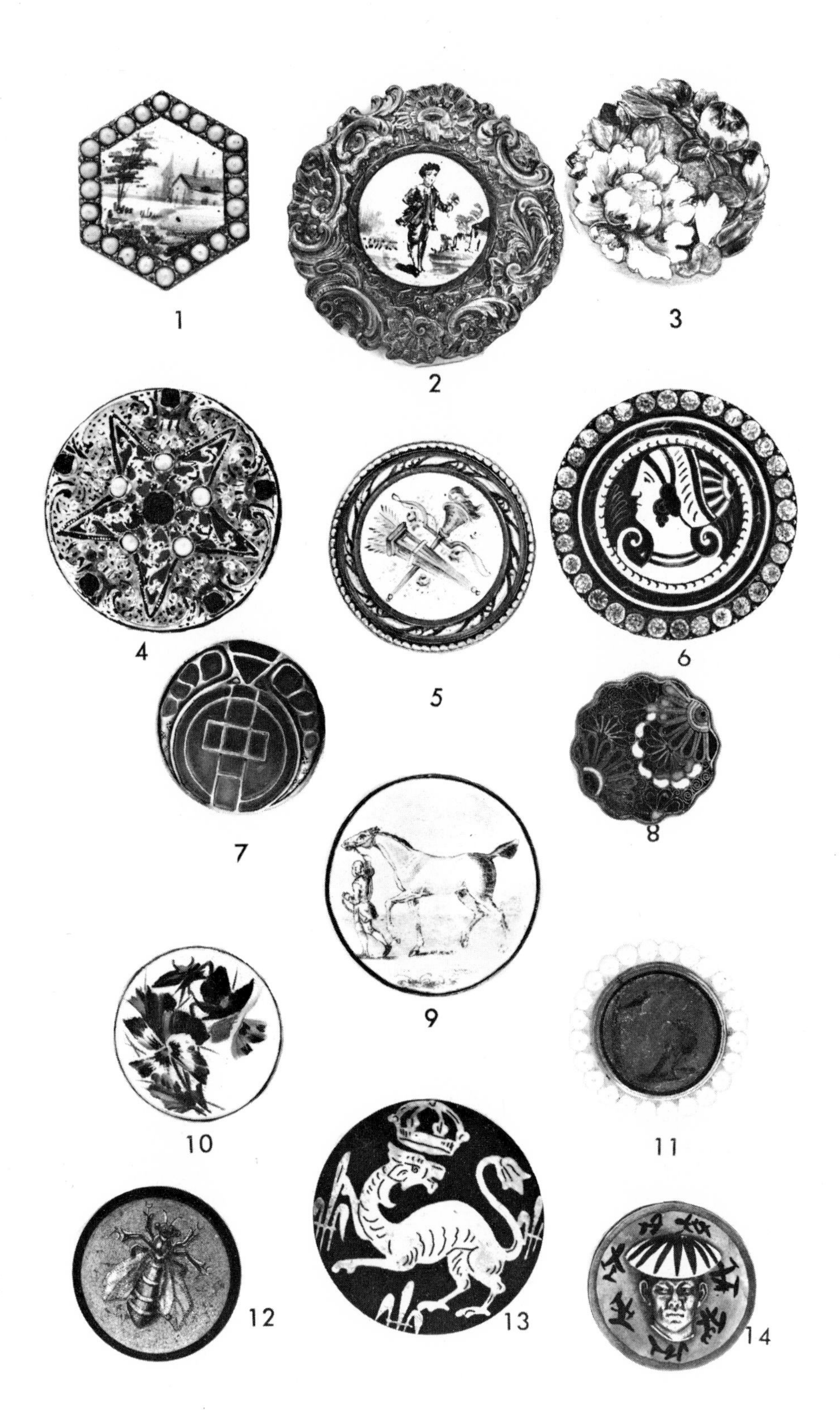

PLATE 5

MORE DELUXE TYPES

1. A hexagon shaped Limoges enamel, with encrusted, turquoise blue border. Such borders are made with drops of enamel, sometimes backed by foil, and fired. They imitate gem stones and can be found in white and ruby, as well as turquoise. THE SCENE OF LAKE AND HOUSE is in lovely colors. Value, $38.00.

   Limoges is a type of enamel painting which derives its name from the locality where it was developed. In painted enamels, a slightly domed metal (usually copper) surface is used and coated, back and front with enamel. This is fired and then becomes a surface for applying other enamels. The process of painting enamel on enameled background was developed at Limoges during the fifteenth century.

2. An outline painting of A BOY HOLDING A BOUQUET, with scenery in the background. This is one of a pair; the other shows a girl, holding a crook. The border is strap-work of the Rococo period. $50.

3. An ORIENTAL BUTTON, of silver, with floral decoration; enameled in beautiful colors and signed on the back. $25.00.

4. Two-toned brass with a STAR in the center; an embossed all-over design, ornamented by turquoise and garnets (semi-precious). The star and rim are outlined with black. Hungarian origin. $25.00.

5. A deep concave center, enameled white, forms a background for a polychrome painting of roses, bow and feather tipped arrows in a quiver; wide gilt, chased rim. $25.00.

6. A GOTHIC HEAD in champleve enameling on silver with a sand glaze. The dark areas are brick red and silver background is allowed to form outlines and a border design. The sand glaze gives a matte finish; set in a paste border. $50.00.

7. PLIQUE-A-JOUR enamel in light shades of green on silver, showing a Latin Cross in the Center:

   Plique-a-jour is a type of enameling which has a foundation, made by soldering together fine wires. The spaces between the wires are then filled with enamel and fired. Buttons made in this manner are very fragile, with a lovely, transparent effect. They are often likened to stained glass windows in miniature. When held to the light, they appear to be translucent. $50.00

8. An Oriental cloisonne enamel with fan designs in pleasing colors of red, blue and green; scalloped border. $20.00. The Chinese excel in the art of cloisonne enameling. Some of the finest cloisonne work has been done on gold. Most of our cloisonne buttons have come from China.

   Cloisonne is said to be the oldest type of enameling. Thin wires are soldered to a metal base and the spaces between the wires are filled with powdered enamel, in colors appropriate for the design which has been formed. The button is then fired several times. This is necessary for, as the powder melts and fuses, there is a resulting shrinkage of enamel, which requires refilling the spaces, till the enamel is level with the top of the wires.

9. A RACE HORSE AND KEEPER. A white background with slightly pinkish tint and outlining done in pinkish sepia. $50.00. Horse racing was an ancient sport and in England it received aristocratic status as early as 1660, when the patronage of Charles II won him the title of, "Father of the British Turf". The type of decoration shown on this button was done during the period of 1753-1756, approximately, at two places in England, Battersea and Bilston. Even museum authorities hesitate to identify these enamel pieces, but this button is undoubtedly Battersea, as Bilston was more crude and this is a beautiful specimen.

10. Hallmarked silver with transparent enamel over an engine turned background. The PANSIES are in lovely shades of purple and yellow and look like real flowers. This is an example of basse-taille enameling which can usually be recognized by its transparent quality. $35.00.

11. This button has a pearl back and border with a center inset of Eglomese, showing the Aesop fable design of "THE FOX AND THE CROW." Eglomese is an artistic skill developed by M. Glomi, a French decorator. Goldleaf was applied to the underside of glass and the design formed by removing bits of the goldleaf. The back of the glass was then painted with black or colored paint which showed at the front, in combination with the goldleaf. In this case, the background is rose colored. $50.00.

12. A paper transfer, with decoration of a Bee; a thread back; early nineteenth century. $15.00.

13. Carved ivory, showing the design of the ROYAL SALAMANDER and the fleur de lis. It is a one piece button and the background and outlining are in sepia. Value, $20.00. The Royal Salamander was the emblem of Francis Premier. (This identity was first given by Lon Twain in J.B. 4-6-138).

14. A lacquered wood button with a CHINESE MAN'S HEAD in very high relief; his hat is lacquered in yellow and black, and the background is turquoise blue, on which are black Chinese characters. French origin. $20.00.

PLATE 6

PLATE 6

HAND WROUGHT BUTTONS

These lovely buttons were made in the eighteenth century, are mounted under glass, have either brass or copper rims, tin backs, and brass loop shanks. They are from the collection of Zula Fricks Brown.

1. A GRISIALLE PAINTING on ivory; CHERUB IN CHARIOT, driving two white horses. Value, about $75.00

   Grisaille means grey in French and a greyed effect is achieved by this type of enameling. It is done with thin layers of white over a base coat of black or other very dark enamel. Fine lines are made through the white to the undercoat with a sharp, pointed instrument to create the desired effect.

2. Grisaille painting on ivory. CARICATURE OF FAMOUS MAN, showing ridiculous side of him and when turned upside down, his pleasant side. $50.00

3. GIRL WITH PITCHER, KNEELING AT COLUMN; an ivory background with blue scrolls in the border; the center is black with the design outlined in sepia. $65.00.

4. A delicate cut-out ivory design of a GIRL FALCONER, placed over a blue background. An exceedingly beautiful specimen. $125.00.

5. A beautiful painting, in colors, on paper, of A SAILING VESSEL. Origin, Portugal. $75.00.

6. A reverse painting, with blue background, of BIRDS SEALING A WEDDING VOW. Value, $65.00. Reverse painting was done on the under side of the glass, as the term implies. Details in the foreground were painted first and the last step was the background. Sometimes, the background was painted on a separate piece of material, and in other instances, the design was backed by a undecorated piece of material, such as foil, ivory, colored paper, pearl, kid, a fabric or whatever satisfied the artist's feeling for what he had created.

7. A gouache painting, on ivory, of A GIRL AND DOG CHASING BUTTERFLIES. The girl resembles paintings of Venus. Value, $75.00

   Gouache is a method of painting in opaque water colour. Highlights are obtained by white or other light colour.

8. A scene, on paper, of THE FRENCH REVOLUTION, titled, "Deliverance a L'Abbaye". This is one of a series of twenty, each different. Value, $50.00.

9. A sepia painting on ivory. A FIGURE, statutary and delicate foliage in the Gothic style. Value, $50.00

10. Reverse paintings of FLOWERS, done in delicate colors, outlined by a black border. Inside the border is a wreath of gold paillons, in leaf and berry shapes. The background is of white kid and the glass used is convex. This is very beautiful and unusual and was obtained in Paris. Value, $65.00.

11. Fixi painting of THE HIDEOUT, under glass. It is rare to find a good speciman, made in this manner. As the word Fixi suggests, the painting has been covered with a thin lacquer and tiny bits of this can be seen, dotting the lens which covers the picture. $45.00.

12. A most unusual button; the design is of A YOUNG BOY DOING GARDEN WORK and it is made of BREAD CRUMBS. It has a metallic background, with concentric waves radiating from the center. Convex lens. This was found in Spain and is a rare specimen. Value, $80.00.

PLATE 7

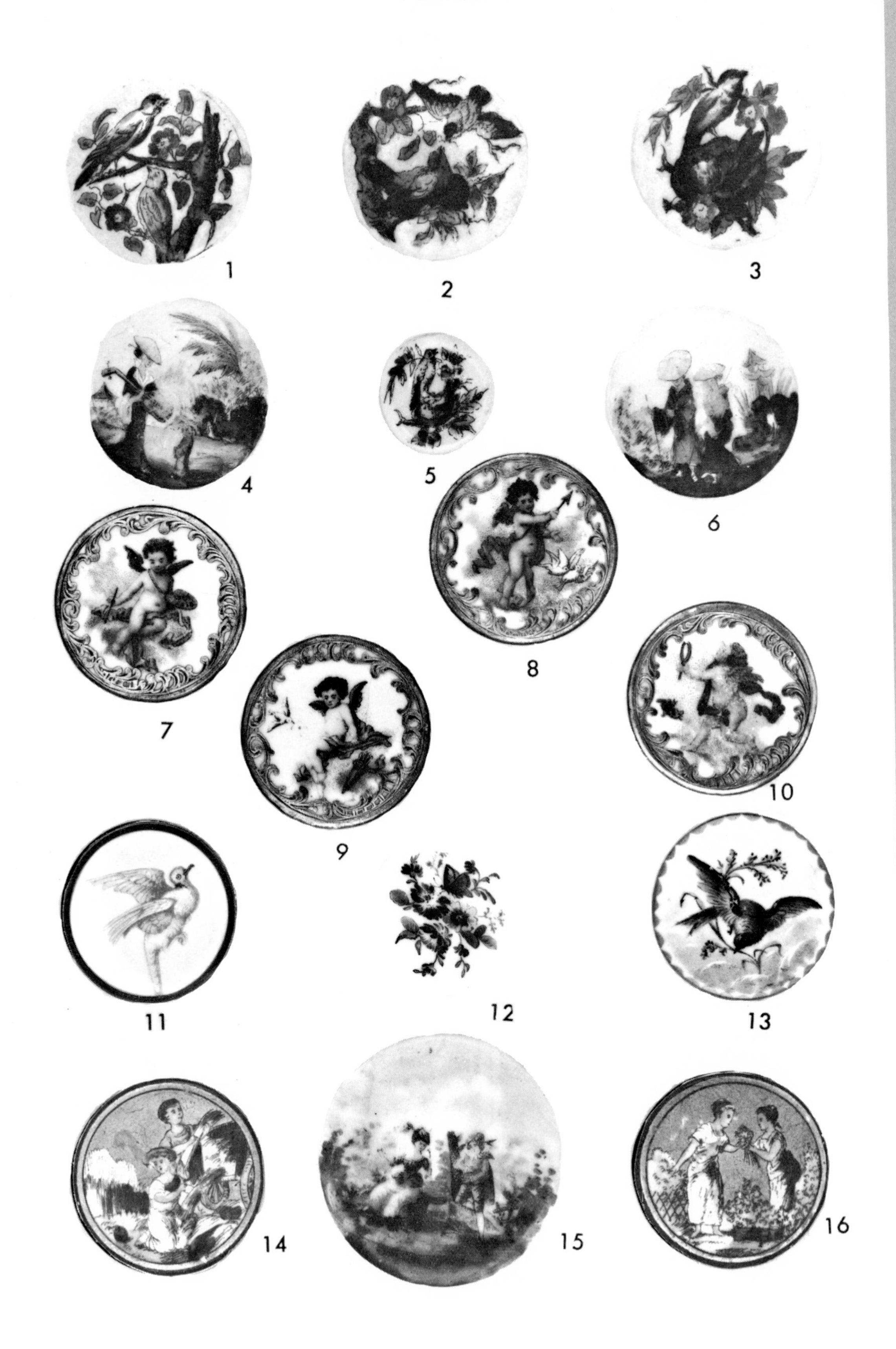

PLATE 7

CERAMICS

The ceramic art is an ancient one, originating with primitive races, who took such clay as could be found, fashioned useful objects from it and baked them in the sun till hard. Eventually, they learned that heating with fire made the objects indestructable; decoration and glazes evolved, and by the eighteenth century fine specimens of ceramic art were being produced. The study of ceramics, its development in different countries and the type of ware produced by each is a fascinating one.

All ceramics are made of baked clay, but there are ceramics which differ in quality and are referred to by different names. However, any button made from clay which has been fired, is a ceramic. The word "porcelain" is applied to certain thin, white, well marked varieties of pottery but with buttons the term is used more loosely.

A fine treatment of CERAMIC BUTTONS by JANE ADAMS can be found in the National Button Bulletin for May, 1956.

1, 2, & 3, from the collection of Agnes Smith are slightly convex ceramic buttons with self shanks with the surfaces painted a light ivory; the BIRD DESIGNS are transferred and polychrome painted in pleasing, naturalistic colors. Value of each, $15.00.

4, 5, & 6 are the same type. No. 5 is another BIRD DESIGN in the small size and 4 and 5 are SCENES WITH FIGURES, apparently Chinese. Value of 4 and 6, $18.00; 5, $10.

7, 8, 9, and 10 are a set, from the collection of Florence Leggett. They are flat porcelain disks with polychrome paintings of CUPID in different attitudes. The rims are made with a lovely running scroll design that is silver encrusted. Value, $35.00 each.

11. A ceramic disk with transfer of BIRD in black and white; brass rim, back and shank. $25.00.

12. Porcelain with polychrome painted FLOWERS AND BUTTERFLY, an 18th century button with three holes to sew through on the back. $15.00.

13. Ceramic, slightly convex with self shank, polychrome painted BIRD, branch and scalloped border. $25.00.

14. and 16 are black and white transfers on porcelain disks with self shanks; the scenes represent different SEASONS. $35.00.

15. A large painted porcelain with self shank, showing a PASTORAL SCENE. $20.00.

PLATE 8

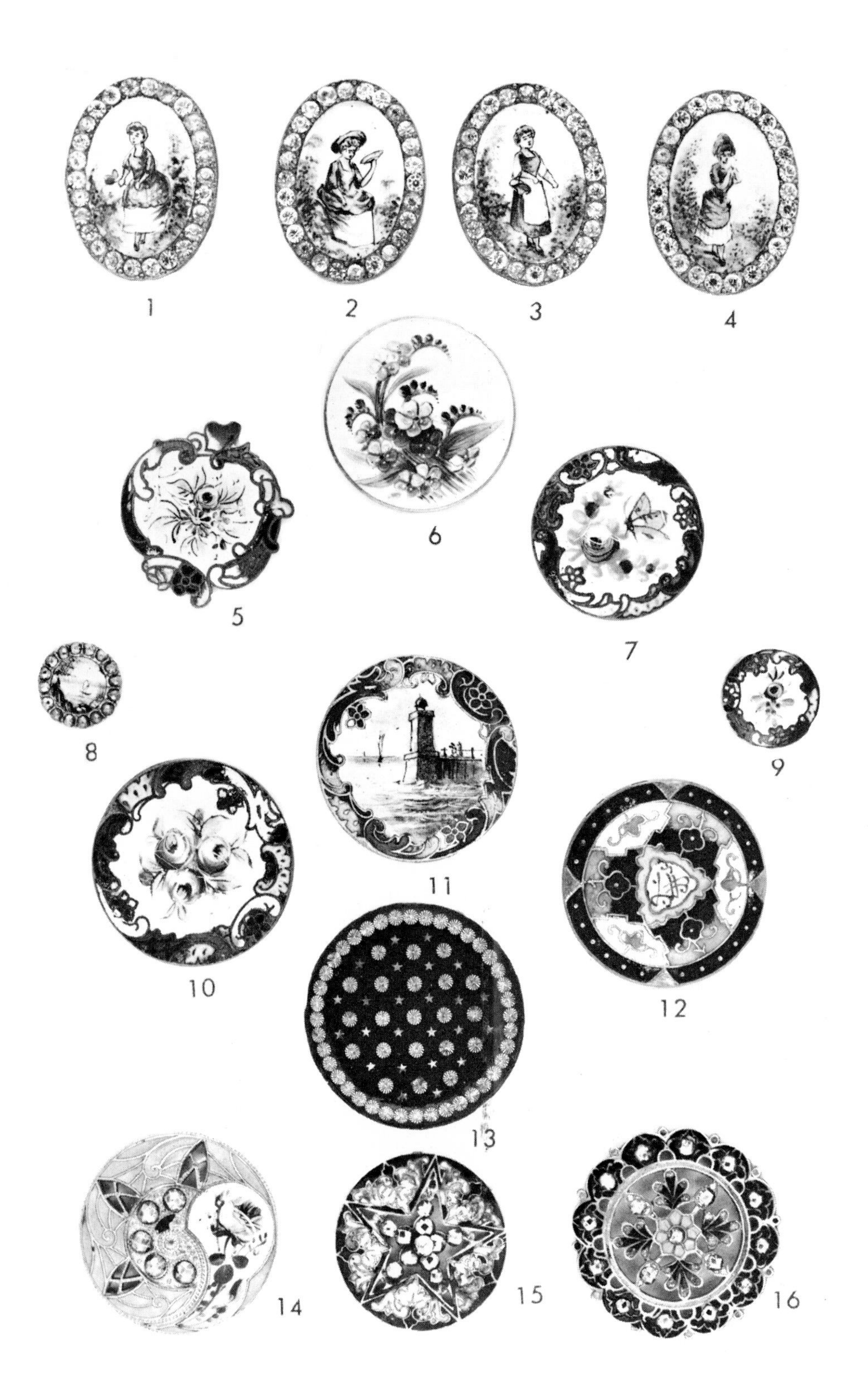

PLATE 8

ENAMELS

Most of the enamels shown here are hand-painted on a hard enamel background. In this type of enamels we find many florals, especially lovely roses, over which a colorful butterfly often hovers. Scenes and figures were also popular. The surface of a painted enamel is usually convex.

1-4. This is a lovely set from the collection of Florence Leggett, which has been called DAINTY MAID. Each is blue and white with border of diamond paste. Value, $38.50 each.

5. An enamel, with hand-painted FLORAL design in pinks, blues and green on white, with a scalloped champleve border. $15.00.

6. A basse taille enamel; transparent enamel applied over an engine turned background with a FLORAL decoration on the surface. This is also from the collection of Florence Leggett. $25.00.

7. Hand-painted polychrome FLORAL WITH BUTTERFLY on a white enamel background; champleve border. $15.00.

8. Another polychrome painting on enamel of a SCENE, showing a sail boat, water, etc., cut steel border. $5.00.

9. A small hand-painted FLORAL on white enamel background with champleve border. $5.00.

10. Hand-painted ROSES on white enamel background with champleve border. $18.00.

11. A hand-painted scene showing LIGHT-HOUSE, with boats in the background, water painted in lovely blue-green with white-capped waves. Champleve border. $35.00.

12. Champleve work, enameled in a geometric pattern with a conventional flower and leaf design used as additional ornamentation. $10.00.

13. Enameled both front and back, this button is decorated with silver paillons, formed in the shape of tiny wheels and applied to the surface of the enamel, then fired. Between the center wheels are tiny gold stars. Fine workmanship. From the collection of Florence Leggett. $38.50.

14. A pierced brass button, enameled and hand-painted with a beautiful stemmed ROSE AND BUD. The center motif is decorated with cut steels. Also from the collection of Florence Leggett. $20.00.

15. Champleve work with a pierced design in the center, STAR-SHAPED and decorated with cut steels. $12.00.

16. Champleve, pierced and decorated with cut steels. $8.50.

PLATE 9

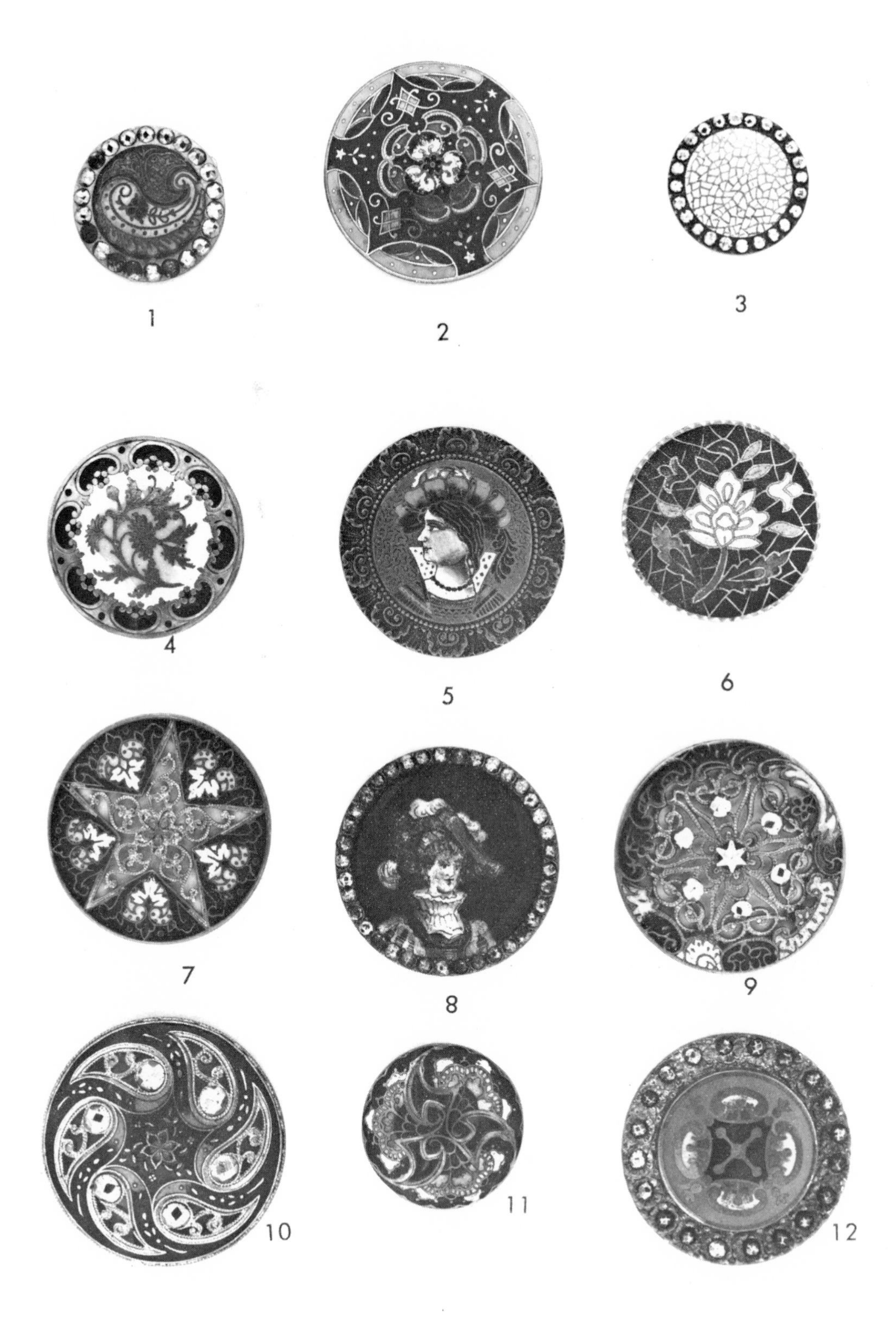

PLATE 9

ENAMELS

Enameling is an ancient art. It is the process of applying powdered glass to a metal base and fusing the two together by heat. Glass and ceramics can also be enameled but most enameled buttons have a metal base.

Several buttons illustrated on this Plate are examples of champleve enameling. Champleve work is done by cutting away troughs in the surface, leaving a metal line raised between them, which forms the outline of the design. The grooves are filled with the powdered enamel, then fused. After this the surface is filed, smoothed and polished.

Cloisonne enameling differs from champleve in only one respect; thin strips of metal are bent and fixed to the outline of the pattern which has been defined on the surface. These strips form a raised outline, giving cells where the enamel is applied, as in the case of champleve.

1. This button is brass and is decorated in imitation of cloisonne; the design is stamped through from the back and painted in blues and yellow; finished with a cut steel border. Value, $8.00.
2. Champleve enameling, the colors in browns and greens; convex, pierced brass. $12.00.
3. A printed design in pink, transferred to a white enamel surface; a white metal button with cut steel border. $8.00.
4. Champleve with polychrome decoration, the gilded brass of the button forms the floral design in the center and the background is filled in with pink and white; the border motif is blue and the tiny flowers have red centers. Paris back. $12.00.
5. A champleve head with skin tones of lovely pinks; red to pink hat with white feather at top, black feather at back. The collar is white and hair, necklace and outlines of costume are filled in with black. There is a wide border with rococo design. From the collection of Florence Leggett. Value, $40.00.
6. Imitation cloisonne enamel; a black background with white, blue, red and two shades of green used for the flower and leaf design. $8.00.
7. Champleve border designs, done in black, blue, white and red enamel. The center is a pierced design and fills in a five-point star. $12.00.
8. A FASHION PORTRAIT enamel. The polychrome painting is done on a black enameled background; the border is of cut steels. Very lovely; an eighteenth century button. Value, $48.00.
9. A pierced brass center, decorated with cut steels; champleve border in lovely blues, pink, white, red and green. $12.00.
10. Cloisonne type, the design having been stamped through from the back, the paisley motifs pierced and decorated with cut steels; the center design and border enameled with black, red, and green. $15.00.
11. Champleve, in tones of pink and red with touches of white; a pierced design radiates from the center motif. $6.50.
12. Faceted cut steels, representing flower centers, form the border of the brass disk which is enameled in beige. The design, the center of which is a cross, has been stamped from the back and sections filled with red, green and blue in imitation of champleve. $8.00.

PLATE 10

PLATE 10

LITHOGRAPHS

Lithography is an art, the process of which was first discovered in 1798. By this process, a picture often in colors, could be reproduced from a smooth, flat, porous stone on which the design had been placed by the use of grease and water in such a way that when the entire surface was inked only certain parts, as desired, would take the ink and print. For color prints, a separate stone was used for each color. Lithograph buttons came into use in the late 19th century. Some have a celluloid covering and some glass. They were often mounted in fancy brass rims, some being ornamented with cut steel borders and some with plastic borders. Some have scenes but more have colored heads of French notables.

1. and 3. are a pair of ANGEL HEADS resembling Reynolds Angels, in delicate colors on gold background under celluloid, set in gilt rims with cut out borders. $25.00 each.
2. A lithograph in pastel colors under glass in a brass rim. Probably the DUCHESS OF DEVONSHIRE as it resembles the portrait of her by Thomas Gainsborough. $35.00.
4. ABBAS II, Hilmi (1874-1944) the last khedive of Egypt, the seventh ruler of the line of Mohammed Ali. He was deposed in 1914 and died in exile at Geneva. In Sepia under celluloid. $6.50.
5. NARR-ED-DIN (1829-1896), Shah of Persia. Black and white on a blue background in a brass rim with no protective covering. $5.00.
6. PRINCESS DE LAMBALLE, close friend of Marie Antoinette. Polychrome lithograph under celluloid in brass rim, set in celluloid with cut out brass border. $6.50.
7. A sepia lithograph under celluloid. $4.50.
8. Possibly another lithograph of PRINCESS DE LAMBALLE, who is described by Paul Gaulot as having an angelic face. $10.00.
9. Another lovely LADY in dainty colors under celluloid with ornamental rim. $6.50.
10. Probably the same LADY as No. 9, a very nicely tinted lithograph under celluloid. $6.50.
11. Polychrome lithograph of a charming LADY, beautifully colored. Under celluloid. $5.00.
12. Marie Antoinette. Nos. 6, 12 and 13 are a set and all three are lithographs mounted alike; same value. $6.50.
13. COUNT FERSEN, long-time friend of Marie Antoinette (See JUST BUTTONS February 1961, Page 47.) $6.50.
14. Polychrome tinted lithograph under celluloid in ornamental brass frame. $12.00.
15. A FLORAL LITHOGRAPH under celluloid with pointed leaf border of brass. $2.50.
16. Another charming LADY. Polychrome tinted, under celluloid. $6.50.
17. COUNT FERSEN. Polychrome tinted under celluloid. $3.50.
18. Polychrome lithograph under celluloid, of a LADY; tinted brass ornamental frame. $8.50.
19. COUNT FERSEN. Lithograph under celluloid with floral brass frame, rimmed by green celluloid and having an outer rim of brass. The button has a metal back and pad shank. $12.00.
20. A lovely colored picture; probably the DUTCHESS OF DEVONSHIRE. Covered by celluloid that is pressed and molded to the face and held in place at the back of the button. $8.00.
21. Another polychrome lithograph of COUNT FERSEN similar to No. 19 but this has a tin back and loop shank. $12.00.

PLATE 11

PLATE 11

HISTORICAL SUBJECTS

Picture Buttons became popular at about 1850 and continued to adorn the dresses and coats of women and children for the rest of the century. The earliest were ornamented with conventional flower, bird, or animal designs. Later, about every popular character of story, song and chronicle was used to decorate a button. Famous paintings and illustrations were copied exactly. Tracing the identities of these and affixing the correct title has been a fascinating pursuit of button collectors. The following plates illustrate many of the different categories.

1. This button is said to represent the UNIVERSE, being upheld by the different races of man. Brass on tin with holly leaf border. $15.00.

2. NAPOLEON III, a prisoner at WILHELM'S "HOKE", after the war of 1870. Brass with fine detail. Value, $8.00.

3. INDIAN HUNTER, as shown in the painting, "THE DEATH OF GENERAL WOLFE" by West. In the painting this Indian is shown, facing in the opposite direction. Pressed brass, tinted, with a tin collet. Value, $27.50.

4. JEANNE HACHETTE, a Frenchwoman who with a small axe, defended the city of Beauvais in 1742. A statue, in her memory stands in Beauvais. Figures of brass are in high relief, applied to a tin background. Value, $8.00.

5. This is called, "FOLLOW WHERE MY WHITE PLUME LEADS" and is said to be Henry of Nevarre at the battle of Ivry. Value $8.00.

6. FALL OF GRANADA, a two-piece pressed brass button with fine detail; tinted tin background. Value $8.00.

7. LION OF LUCERNE. This is a copy of the monument, designed by Thorwaldsen, to commemorate the courage of the Swiss guard who died defending the Tuilleries in 1792. Brass on tin. Value, $3.50.

8. TRUMPITER OF CRACOW. This button was formerly called, "Sentinel of Cracow" but new identity has been given to it by Milla Livingston. (JUST BUTTONS, June 1966). It is a common button and was made in different materials. This one pictured in brass and valued at $2.00. In pewter the value is $.75.

9. TAMMERLANE, THE LAME TIMUR, a renowned oriental conqueror (1336-1405) who won great victories by the sword. Brass with tin back. Value, $6.50.

10. This is a religious button which commemorates the Norman Invasion to liberate Sicily from the Infidels. The shield has the date 1090, three stars and a Latin cross. It is of one-piece brass with shield attached as escutcheon. Value $6.50. (N.B.B., January, 1957)

11. CHARTER OAK, said to represent the hollow oak tree in which the early Connecticut colonists concealed their charter from a tyrannical English governor. The tree is brass, buildings in the back are pewter. Value, $4.50.

12. TEMPERANTIA. This figure is shown in identical pose in the center of a large pewter salver, cast in relief by Francois Briot of Lorraine, 1580-90. The plate is decorated with figures of Minerva and the seven arts, the four elements and TEMPERANCE in the center. (Ency. Brit. 17-Pewter, F3, 1) Pressed brass on a tinted background. Value, $15.00.

PLATE 12

PLATE 12

MINERVA

Mythological characters were favorite subjects portrayed on early picture buttons and one of the most popular, appears to have been Minerva.

Minerva was the daughter of Jupiter and she was, according to legend, born in a strange manner. One day Jupiter had a severe headache and being able to bear the pain no longer, he told Thor to strike him on the head with his hammer. This was done and out sprang Minerva, fully grown and clad in armor, ready to do battle.

She was known as the goddess of wisdom and also as the virgin goddess, having sprung from Jupiter's head. She was patron of the arts, of peace and war, ruler of storms and, in Greek mythology, guardian of Athens. The Greeks called her Pallas Athena and the Parthenon was her temple.

She is usually illustrated, wearing a helmet and aegis and the owl, the cock, the crow and the serpent are her symbols. Her helmet is usually surmounted by a sphinx or a griffin.

1. A brass repousse head, mounted on black stippled horn. Value, $2.00.

2. Minerva is said to have given the olive tree as her special gift to the Greeks. On this button, a lovely front view of her face is framed by olive branches. This is of brass and is mounted on a steel mirror. It has a white metal border of ivy. Value $6.50.

3. Here she is seen wearing the Corinthian helmet with ear guards in place. A one-piece button of silvered brass. Value, $4.50.

4. Another representation made of two-piece brass, an olive wreath decorates the helmet. Value $3.50.

5. This shows the Attic helmet, sometimes worn by Minerva. It fits the head more closely and the visor is turned up. The symbol of the griffin can be seen, which identifies this as Minerva. Value, $3.50.

6. This button has been identified as Catherine of Russia, dressed as the Goddess of War (Minerva). The helmet has an oak wreath, rather than olive leaves and the griffin is replaced by a plume. It is a one-piece button studded with steels and having beautiful detail. Value, $10.00.

7. A brass head, mounted on a wood background with brass border. This is the Corinthian helmet, as shown on a Greek coin. Value, $1.00.

8. A small replica of No. 5. Value $.75.

9. The same head as No. 2 with cut steels in the border and background cut out. Value, $1.00.

10. A small head, like No. 6 with different background and border. Value, $1.00.

11. This head is of brass, mounted on a tinted tin background that gives the appearance of pearl. Value, $3.00.

12. A beautiful button with the head in high relief; one-piece brass with cut steels enhancing the border. Value, $15.00.

13. White metal escutcheon, the head in high relief, applied to a flat white metal background. The Corinthian helmet, very elaborately decorated, is worn. Value, $8.00.

14. A small button showing Jupiter and Minerva. Brass heads on a wood background. Value, $1.00.

14a A brass background, tinted brown, having a sepia tinted milk glass head attached. Value, $12.00.

15. A small button of white metal. Value, $1.00.

16. The head of Athene was first used on coins issued by the City of Athens in 566 B.C. This button resembles a coin. Value, $1.00.

17. Jupiter and Minerva. An escutcheon, mounted on a cut out background. Value, $8.50.

18. A medium sized head of two-piece brass. Value, $1.25.

PLATE 13

PLATE 13

MORE MINERVA HEADS

1. A small black glass intaglio. Value, $1.00.

2. This is of black glass, 1 ¾ inch, and the same as No. 2 on the previous plate. Value, $15.00.

3. A small black glass, cameo type head. Value, $1.00.

4. A caramel glass (opaque glass) center with brass heart border. Part of Minerva's shield is visible. Value, $8.00.

5. A small brass, saucer shaped button with the head in high relief. Value, $.75.

6. Jupiter and Minerva, in the small size; brass heads applied to a wood background; brass rim and tin back. Value, $1.00.

7. This is made of horn, pressed and dyed, backmarked CANE. It has a nice head in high relief, identical to the brass button No. 18, on the previous plate, but is ornamented by a beaded and rayed border. Value, $1.50.

8. The same button as No. 4 in a smaller size. Value, $1.25.

9. The same head as No. 2, but a square, silvered button with a cutout design forming the border. Value, $12.00.

10. Another small black glass, cameo type head. Value, $.75.

11. This is a fine head of pressed horn, showing the helmet with ear guards in place, and is similar to No. 3, Plate 12. It has a textured background and a border of inverted dots. $3.00.

12. Silver lustered black glass, cameo type. Value, $1.00.

13. A square silvered head that might possibly have been a cuff button. Value, $.75.

14. A small intaglio head of transparent amber glass. Value, $1.00.

15. The same as No. 7 in a large size. Value, $3.50.

16. An escutcheon type brass head on black glass, having a brass border with the Greek key design. Value, $2.00.

17. The large size of No. 6. Value, $6.50.

18. A brass escutcheon on pearl, the head very similar to No. 3, Plate 12, but facing left. Value, $2.00.

19. The front view again in a small brass button. Value, $1.00.

20. Sepia tinted milk glass; a cameo type head. Value, $1.00.

21. Caramel glass; otherwise identical to No. 20. Value, $1.00.

22. The front view, brass, mounted on flat steel. Value, $1.00.

23, 24, and 25 are identical heads but No. 23 is of black glass, 24 is of milk glass, tinted with green and gold, and 25 is of custard glass. Value of each, $15.00.

PLATE 14

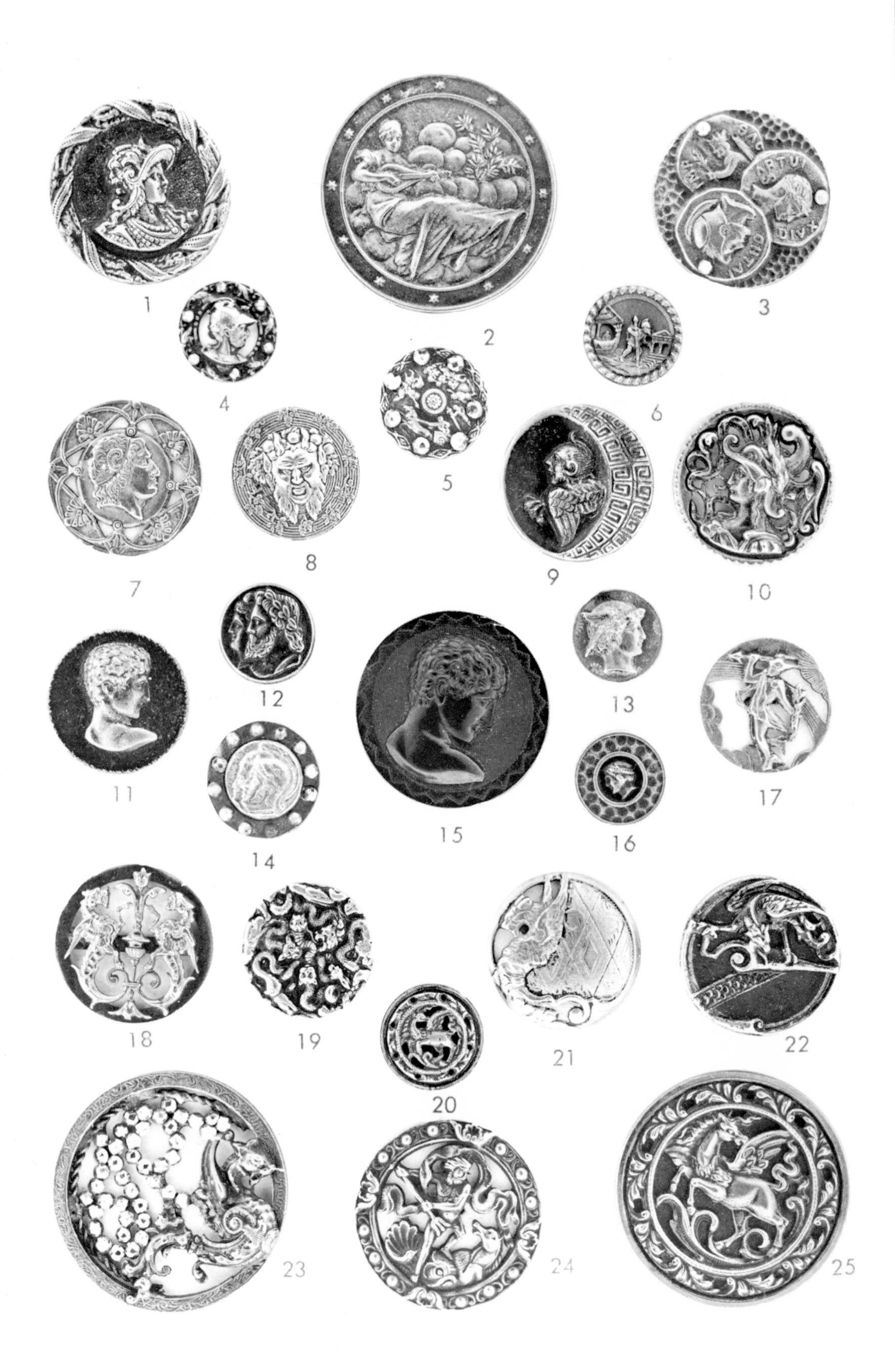

PLATE 14

MYTHOLOGICAL CHARACTERS & CREATURES

The world of mythology never fails to intrigue both young and old. As you can see, it offered a wealth of material for button collectors. Through the study of these buttons, collectors take fascinating journeys into the ancient world and learn or recall the legends of early people, in which are recorded their explanations for their origins and for their beliefs.

1. A woman's head in relief on a darkened brass background. The interesting part of the design is the back of the hat which is a grotesque mask. Dorothy Foster Brown in "Button Parade" calls this, "THE AMAZON". The Amazons were a warlike race of women in Greek mythology who helped the Trojans in the Trojan War. $4.00.
2. This lady should be classified with MUSICAL SUBJECTS for although she seems to be living in the clouds, she has never been accurately identified as a mythological character. The instrument appears to be a lute, which is said to have been invented by Mercury. Stamped brass with a star border. $6.50.
3. THE TRIUMVIRATE, made with three coin heads in relief on a one-piece background. Each coin is decorated with one cut steel which appears to hold the coin in place. A Triumvirate is a government by three men. There were two such governments in ancient Rome. $3.00.
4. AJAX, Grecian warrior. His Greek helmet is very similar to those often worn by Minerva. One-piece brass with pierced design. Border decorated with cut steels, alternated with fabulous animals which are similar to the helmet decoration. $1.25.
5. THE TRIUMPH. A convex, highly silvered, brass button. The stamped design pictures chariots and foot soldiers, indicating a successful battle. Cut steels enhance the border. $2.00.
6. RETURN OF ULYSSES. A pierced brass design. Twisted rope border with steel liner. Background tinted. Rare. $2.00.
7. A one-piece stamped brass button with pierced border which has been called, Bacchus, but more recently identified by Rachel Price Lynn as ALEXANDER THE GREAT. $1.75.
8. BACCHUS (DIONYSUS), this time crowned with fruit and looking somewhat ribald. One-piece stamped brass. Bunches of grapes form a border. $2.00.
9. A HARPY. These were revolting creatures, filthy, greedy and bad smelling. They were winged monsters with a woman's face and body and the wings, tail, and claws of a vulture. Part of the all-brass, pressed design is concave, holding the harpy's head and shoulder. The rest of the button's face is filled in with the Greek key design. $2.50.
10. This head personifies "DRAMATIC ART" and should be classified with HEADS. Pierced brass, set in a white metal rim. $2.00.
11. HERMES and MERCURY are the same character, Hermes being the Greek name and Mercury the Roman. This design is taken from the ancient Greek statue of Hermes by Praxiteles, a Greek sculptor. Pressed brass in very high relief. $2.00.
12. JUPITER AND HERA, his wife who was Queen of Heaven. One-piece brass. $1.00.
13. MERCURY, messenger of the gods. The wings on his hat and heels helped him move, "with the speed of the wind or even thought, itself". One-piece stamped brass. $1.00.
14. Two Greek COIN-TYPE HEADS, the one in the foreground wearing a Greek helmet. Inscription at the side, "Helena". $1.00.
15. HERMES. The same head as No. 11, made of black pressed horn. The statue from which this design was copied was so beautiful that it has made Praxiteles famous through the ages. The profile shows the Greek nose, which was considered beautiful by Greek sculptors. The border is the zig-zag design, sometimes called the chevron border, which was used by early Greek artists and achitects. $3.50.
16. Another head of MERCURY, with winged cap. One-piece with pressed brass border. Escutcheon type head. $1.00.
17. A pierced brass design showing a full figure of MERCURY, similar to the statue "The Flying Mercury" by Giovanni da Bologna. He is holding Caduceus, his magical wand. It had the power to make Mercury invisible, to increase his speed and to end conflicts. Mercury was also the god of health and this caduceus is used as an emblem by the medical profession, and is the insignia of the U.S. Medical Corps. $2.00.
18. A delicately pierced design of gilded brass with the URN in the center and a dragon on either side, applied to a steel rim having a bar behind the design to which the shank is attached. $2.00.
19. SEPS, mythical animals of the composite type, having snakes' bodies and the heads of other animals such as can be seen here: rooster, rabbit, fish and snake. The creatures are in high relief against a darkened background. Two-piece, back-marked, "T.W. & W." $2.00.
20. PEGASUS, the winged horse which sprang from the dead body of Medusa and was tamed by Minerva. Pierced brass, mounted on a darkened, concave background, with tin rim. $1.00.
21. A one-piece brass button, engraved and pierced showing a GRYPHON. $1.75.
22. A DRAGON of pierced brass, attached to the rim which has a steel liner. Concave brass background, darkened. $1.50.
23. A gold-plated DRAGON. Pierced design with riveted cut steels filling the remaining space, in curves that compliment those of the dragon. Rim and dragon are finely chased. $4.50.
24. NEPTUNE, god of the sea, carrying his trident and riding a dolphin. The pierced design also shows a sea horse. Silvered brass. $2.50.
25. PEGASUS, the same design as No. 20 but having a brass rim and wide leaf border. $7.00.

PLATE 15

PLATE 15

FAIRIES & CHERUBS

A fairy is described as an imaginary being of graceful and tiny human form. A cherub is the representation of a winged child. Cherubs, cupids and fairies had a prominent place in Victorian decorative art.

1. PUCK OR ROBIN GOODFELLOW. In "Midsummer Night's Dream" Shakespeare represents him as, "A rough, fawn-faced, shock-pated, mischievous little urchin". A cut out design, attached to the rim, over a darkened brass background. $3.75.

2. ARIEL, in Shakespeare's "The Tempest", an airy spirit, able to assume any shape, or even to become invisible. White metal, pierced with a tinted background. $2.25.

3. FAIRIES AT ST. CUTHBERT'S WELL. There is an old enamelled drinking goblet preserved at Eden Hall, Cumberland, the seat of the Musgrave family, perhaps of the 10th century. In the grounds of Eden Hall is the spring called St. Cuthbert's Well and the story is that one of the early Musgraves surprised the fairies making merry at the well. He seized the goblet from the fairy king who acknowledged his defeat but warned him, "When this cup shall break or fall, Farewell the luck of Eden Hall". The button has fine detail and is of two-piece, pressed brass over a darkened background. $4.00.

4. This is another interpretation of "ARIEL". In Shakespeare's "Tempest", Ariel's last song ends, "Merrily, merrily shall I live now, Under the blossom that hangs on the bough". These lines seem well illustrated here. The button is of brass with decoration in high relief and a very exceptional border of astonishing animals. $6.50.

5. FAIRY AND BUTTERFLY. The insect is nearly as large as the human-like figure, therefore we conclude that it represents a fairy. One-piece pierced brass. $1.75.

6. This FAIRY has changed its human extremities for a mermaid-like tail. Two-piece pressed brass in low relief. $1.75.

7. A FAIRY-LIKE FIGURE flitting through the grass and leaves. One-piece pierced brass, tinted. $1.25.

8. FAIRY FLYING; two-piece pressed brass. $1.00.

9. OBERON AND TITANIA, characters in "Midsummer Night's Dream" by Shakespeare. Oberon, king of the fairies is anointing the eyes of his sleeping wife, Titania with an extract which will make her fall in love with the first object she sees when she awakens. $1.50.

10. FAIRY seated on flower. One-piece pierced brass. $.75.

11. Called, "CUPID AT THE COLUMN". Two-piece pressed brass. $1.25.

12. A FLYING CHERUB. This is of cut-out brass, the cherub is beautifully formed and attached to the scroll border. $.75.

13. CHERUB WITH DOVE. Two-piece pressed brass. $1.00.

14. THREE CHERUBS WITH GOAT. Concave with figures in relief. $2.00.

15. CHERUB WITH BIRDS. Two-piece tin in low relief, tinted pink. $.75.

16. THREE CHERUBS MAKING WINE. Two-piece pressed brass. Scarce. $8.00.

17. CUPID RIDING ON A DOLPHIN, the design probably borrowed from Thorwaldsen. One-piece pressed brass. $1.00.

18. CHERUB IN GARLAND SWING; one-piece pressed brass. $2.00. This is often found in white metal and is valued at $1.00.

19. CHERUB RESTING IN ROSE BUSH; two-piece pressed brass. $1.75.

20. ROBBING THE BIRD'S NEST. Pierced brass design on darkened background. Scarce. $4.00.

21. PLAYING WASHDAY. A scarce tin rimmed brass button. $6.50.

PLATE 16

PLATE 16

GNOMES & CUPIDS

Cupid was of course a mythological character, the god of love, son of Venus. He is represented as a small winged boy, carrying a bow and arrow. For ages poets and artists have used cupid as a favorite theme and since button designers acquired much of their inspiration from art and story, it is only natural that we find this little fellow who symbolizes Love, pictured in many different ways on buttons of all materials. Some are quite rare but many are plentiful.

Gnomes or dwarfs are not found so often.

Sometimes careful observation shows that a small figure which at first appears to be Cupid, has hoofs instead of human feet. This is Pan, the god of flocks and pastures. He is often represented with goat ears, legs and feet.

1. IMP OF PAIN. This button was identified from an old wood cut which depicted pain. Two-piece pressed brass, pierced design with pine cone border. $6.50.

2. CUPID AND SEA HORSE. Cupid is gleefully riding and urging the seahorse on with a trident. One-piece pierced design with Greek key border. $2.00.

3. GNOME, WATERING THE TOADSTOOLS. Wood background with cut out design and rim of brass. Scarce. $2.00.

4. A GNOME riding what appears to be a quiver. Brass with tin rim. $2.00.

5. RUMPELSTILTSKIN from a fairy story by the Brothers Grimm. This wicked dwarf helps the young queen carry out a deception which had led the king to marry her. In payment, he demands that the queen guess his name in a certain length of time or give him her beautiful baby boy. On the last day she discovers the name and frees herself. The button can be found in various constructions. This one, more scarce than others, has a screen back and silvered rim. Picture and screen are brass. $4.50.

6. GNOMES cooking over brazier. Two-piece pressed brass. Scarce. $1.50.

7. LOVE, RULER OF EARTH. From a drawing of Thorwaldsen (N.B.B. November, '57). Two - piece pressed brass. $2.75.

8. OVER THE WALL, an all brass specimen which is not common. $1.00. It can be found often in white metal with a tin rim. Value in the large size, $2.00.

9. YOUNG LADY DEFENDING HERSELF AGAINST LOVE, described on Plate 85 (T.W. & W.) No. 10. This is sometimes called, "Cupid and Venus" but it is an exact reproduction of the painting by the above name. (N.B.B. May, '59) $3.00.

10. This is correctly called "CUPID AND VENUS", one-piece pressed brass. $1.00.

11. Called, "VENUS TEASING CUPID". Two-piece pressed brass. $3.50.

12. CHERUBS FORGING MARRIAGE CHAINS. A brass button with figures of white metal. $2.00.

13. CUPID PLOTTING, two-piece pressed brass picture over a tin mirror background. $.75.

14. Called MARRIAGE BOAT, pierced design of brass over darkened background, scalloped design on border. $2.25.

15. CUPID THE LION TAMER. Another adaptation from Thorwaldsen; pierced design of brass over steel mirror. Wide pine cone border. $.75.

16. CUPID AND ERATO, muse of lyric poetry. Pierced brass design over darkened background, brass rim. $1.25.

17. CUPID WITH SCROLL, stamped brass, two-piece. $3.50.

18. CUPID PIPING TO A DOG who is sitting up. Two-piece pressed brass. $.75.

19. MASQUE OF MEPHISTOPHELES who impersonated the devil in the Faust legend. Cherubs form part of the cut-out design on each side. $2.50.

20. CUPID WITH TORCH. Cut-out design with rolled under rim, brass. $1.00.

21. CUPID AND HEBE, the goddess of youth, pierced white metal design in relief, brass rim. $6.50.

22, 23 and 24. PAN, THE LION TAMER. These button designs are all adaptations from Thorwaldsen's drawings in which the god of love is represented as being able to tame even the most ferocious beasts. 22 and 23 have a pierced design with cut steel decorated border. 22. $3.00; 23. $6.50. 24 is more common and has a white metal design applied to a darkened brass background, the dotted rim has a steel liner. $2.50.

PLATE 17

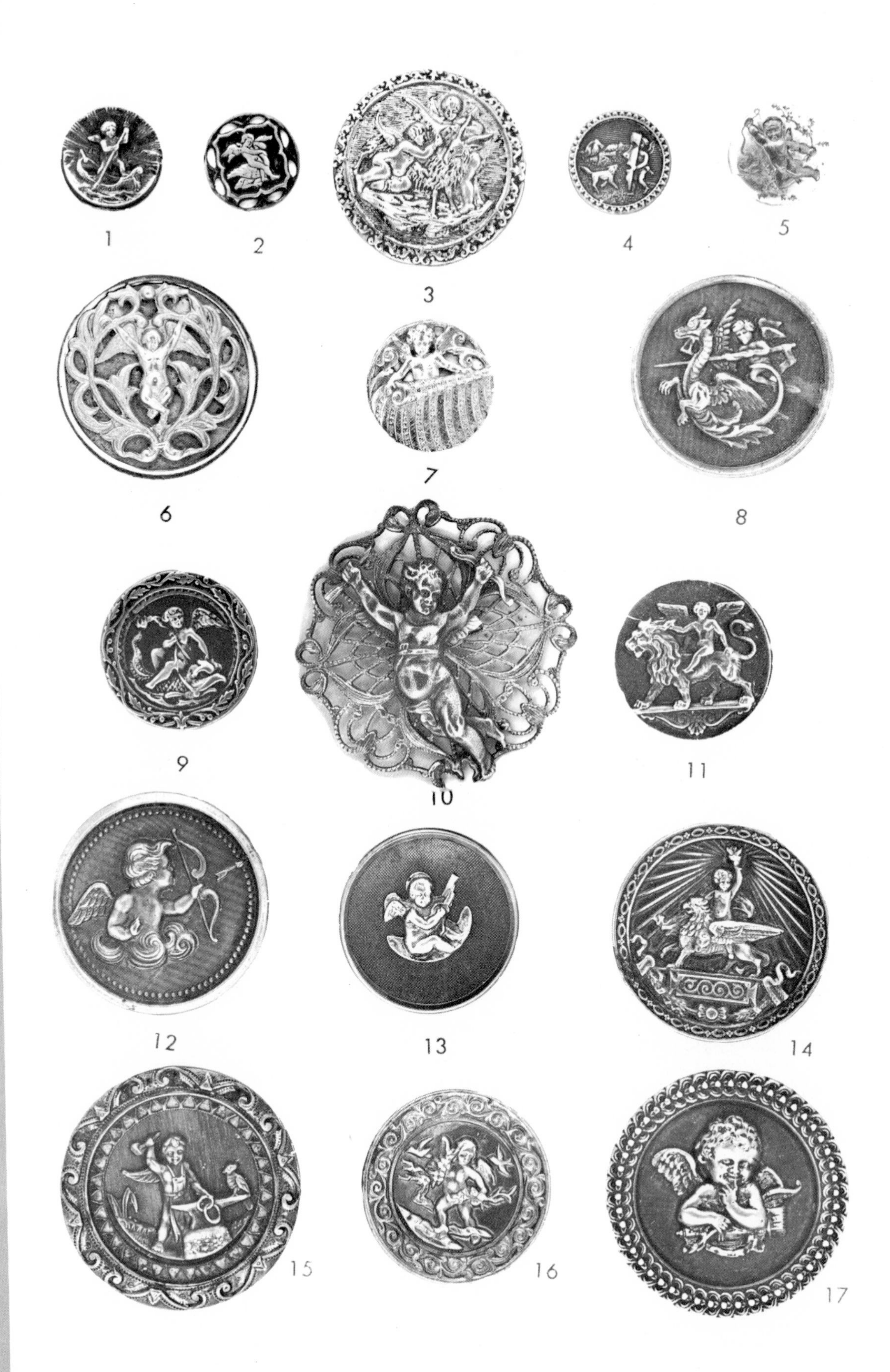

PLATE 17

CUPIDS & CHERUBS

The use of the cupid in art is not only decorative but usually symbolical - as can be seen with button designs. The theme often seems to be the Success of Love. "The only power that endures is love, all else is transitory."

1. CUPID ROWING, a sunburst and temple are in the background and the boat and cupid are in high relief, on this one-piece button. If turned upside down, the boat is discovered to be in the shape of a dolphin. $1.25.

2. CUPID CARESSING A SWAN, the design taken from a bas-relief by Thorwaldsen. One-piece brass, low relief with a square center and pierced border. $1.25.

3. CHERUBS WITH CORNUCOPIA AND GOAT. Two-piece pressed brass in high relief. $3.00.

4. CUPID FIGHTING A DOG, WITH MASK. One-piece pressed brass. $1.00.

5. CUPID WITH A BEE ON A LEASH. An intaglio design on a two-piece brass button. Intaglio designs are seldom found on brass buttons. $1.00.

6. "FAT OL' CUPID." A cut out brass design over a white metal background. Rolled rim. $2.00.

7. CUPID WITH SCROLL. One-piece stamped brass, silvered. The design above the scroll is pierced. $1.75.

8. CUPID SLAYS "JEALOUSY". Jealousy represented by a dragon. Two-piece brass, design in relief on brown-tinted brass background, brass rim. $3.00.

9. CUPID RIDING A DOLPHIN. A two-piece button with cut-out brass design mounted on dark background with narrow steel liner and leaf border. This design resembles a Thorwaldsen drawing also. $2.00.

10. CUPID TRIUMPHANT. A beautiful pearl button with cut out design in very high relief, superimposed. Fine. $20.00.

11. CUPID, THE LION TAMER, from a Thorwaldsen design (N.B.B., Nov. '57). One - piece pressed brass. $2.00.

12. CUPID FINDS A VICTIM. Two-piece brass, the cupid in very high relief. $3.50.

13. LUTE PLAYER. Brass cupid applied to a pebbled brass background, slightly concave, brass rim. This same design can also be found on pearl. $2.00.

14. CUPID WITH TORCH on winged lion (a fabulous animal). Rays of light from the torch are indicated on the background and the design doubtless symbolizes the power of love. It is a design with elaborate and fine detail. $6.50.

15. This has been called HYMEN, the god of marriage, also CUPID AT FORGE. The cupid is wearing an apron and acting as a blacksmith, hammering out links for a chain which are thought to be marriage links. A love bird watches him. It is a fine button, having a wood background and wide scroll border. The cupid design is attached to an inner saw tooth border which is placed over a steel liner. The brass parts have a deep brown tint. $6.50.

16. CUPID WITH GARLANDS AND LOVE BIRDS. Two-piece brass without rim. $3.00.

17. SMILING CUPID (N). The design is in very high relief applied to a dark metal background enclosed in an elaborate border. $8.00.

PLATE 18

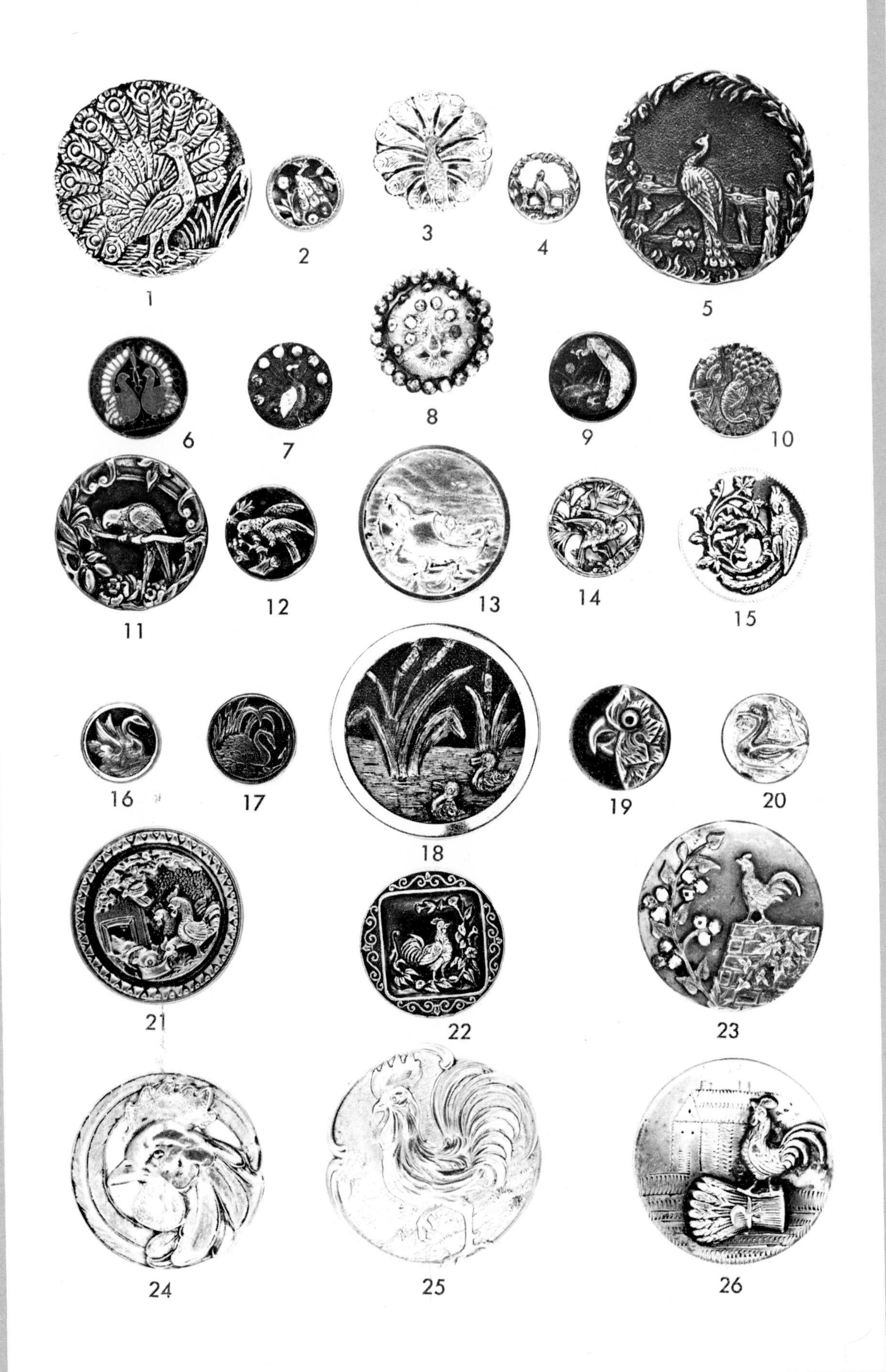

PLATE 18

DOMESTICATED BIRDS

The birds shown in this plate have been removed from their natural surroundings at some time and taught to live with man.

The peacock, parrot and swan have been domesticated chiefly for their ornamental beauty while fowl of all types, of course, provide food. It can easily be seen that all have artistic lines which, even without adding the natural colors of their beautiful plumage, are very decorative.

1. A two-piece tin button with all detail of the peacock's tail feathers nicely shown. The background is tinted black and a bit of foliage resembling cattail leaves gives balance. $3.50.

2. A small saucer-shaped brass button, brass PEACOCK with tail folded, cut steels representing the eyes of the tail feathers and the flower. $1.00.

3. Another two-piece PEACOCK, front view with spread tail. $2.25.

4. PEACOCK ON THE FENCE, pressed brass. $1.00.

5. The same as No. 4 in the large size. $3.50.

6. Champleve Enamel in polychrome of two PEACOCKS. $4.50.

7. One piece white metal forms this PEACOCK. The cut steels in the tail feathers are tinted alternately blue and brown. $1.00.

8. Another PEACOCK of tinted white metal; tail feathers ornamented with cut steels. The center is quite convex and the border is of cut steels. $2.00.

9. TALL PEACOCK ("N"), a one-piece tinted button of brass. $2.00.

10. An oriental lady holding a fan looks from a small window at this peacock. Two-piece brass. $1.50.

11. A PARROT on a natural perch which is attached to a cut out border of flowers and foliage. Brass design over a darkened brass background. $1.25.

12. A PARROT of brass on a purple tinted concave background, two-piece. $.75.

13. DUCK WITH SIX DUCKLINGS, three swimming with the mother, three inside a floating Dutch shoe. $3.50.

14. TROPICAL PARROT in natural habitat. Cut out brass. $.75.

15. White metal concave button with applied PARROT and spray of foliage. Two-piece. $.75.

16. A brass SWAN, tin collet. Two-piece. $.75.

17. A brass SWAN floating on water, cat tails drooping over her. Brass on tinted background. $1.00.

18. DUCKS on a pond with large cat tails. White metal tinted blue, with shiny tin border. $2.50.

19. PARROT HEAD of brass in high relief on a flat brass background which is tinted red. The parrot has a paperweight eye of yellow glass with a black center. $3.50.

20. SWAN in high relief; white metal; T.W. & W. back-mark. $.75.

21. Breakfast for one. The HENS AND ROOSTER are very much interested in the dog's food but he is not going to allow any further investigation. A pressed brass design with geometric border design. Two-piece. $4.50.

22. ROOSTER IN TRUMPET VINE. The rooster and vine are in a square concave portion, framed by a border design which is repeated on all four sides. Two-piece brass. $2.50.

23. THE COCK THAT CROWED TWICE. This is accepted as a religious symbol. Ivy has been held sacred and the rooster stands on an ivy covered roof with an attached spray decorated with cut steels, all applied to a slightly concave brass button. $6.50.

24. A pierced brass one-piece button showing a ROOSTER HEAD, tinted in natural colors with a tail feather curved to form a border. $8.00.

25. STRUTTING ROOSTER. A convex, one-piece button showing tree and tufts of grass in the background. The rooster's tail forms part of the border and a raised and divided scroll which curves in a comparable manner completes the border. $8.00.

26. A concave one-piece brass button with a ROOSTER, STANDING ON A SHEAF OF WHEAT, applied. This has been called, "The Cock That Crowed in the Morn" as told in the nursery rhyme, "The House That Jack Built". This seems like a good name as a house is etched in the background. $10.00.

    A similar button was made with a rabbit standing on the sheaf of wheat and a half moon etched in the background.

    Another shows a dragon fly resting on the wheat and cupid riding the dragon fly. By diligently searching you might find a complete series with this motif.

PLATE 19

PLATE 19

BIRDS

So many buttons have been decorated with birds that there are innumerable ways in which they may be classified and mounted. There are birds that can easily be identified, such as owls and cranes, and birds that are only an artist's conception of a decorative motif. There are birds in flight, birds with nest, papa and mama birds, mythological birds, birds of the Bible, birds that illustrate Fables, birds referred to in poetry and prose, different birds in one material, and birds in many different materials. This category with such a variety of subject matter makes a good place to start ones' button collection, but it also affords an opportunity for a highly specialized collection, including buttons that show many interesting subjects, materials, and techniques.

1. THREE CROWS ON A BRANCH. This is a pierced brass design, in one-piece with the rim which represents a curved branch. Under this is a tinned metal liner and the background is slightly concave, darkened metal. $2.50.

2. BIRDS AT THE FOUNTAIN, a charming pressed brass design which is in one piece with the turned under rim. $2.00.

3. TWO TROPICAL BIRDS evidently of the parrot family, a cut out design, attached to the border, tin liner under rim, darkened background, two-piece. Scarce. $1.50.

4. We believe this bird is supposed to represent a HUMMINGBIRD, although it is not the Rubythroat with which we are familiar east of the Mississippi. He appears to be sipping nectar from a flower and the tiny nest might well belong to a hummingbird, so possibly the artist needed larger proportions to fill his space. A one-piece pierced brass design. $1.25.

5. BIRDS AND BIRDHOUSE. This is an unusual button as it is made of molded opaque glass in the rare color, now designated as chocolate. The Background has a dull finish while the design and border have a bright finish, giving contrast. $15.00.

6. BIRDS IN TRELLIS. This is a scarce design, delicately pierced and attached to the collet, in the same manner as 1 and 3. $1.25.

7. This BIRD IN FLIGHT is of brass in high relief against a tinted background which has a typical Victorian design of flowers and grasses. It is finished with a nice twisted rope and ribbon border. $3.50.

8. Another BIRD IN FLIGHT, one-piece pressed brass, bird in high relief against a background of foliage, metal back. $.75.

9. BIRD WITH WREATH, a lovely pierced background with silver and gilt finish has a drum-like shape mounted in the center and the bird and flower decoration is applied to this. $3.50.

10. BIRD ON A BRANCH, a pierced design is mounted over a very brightly tinned background. There is also a mirror liner under the pierced circles in the border. This construction is quite unusual. $1.50.

11. FOUR SWALLOWS DRINKING. The pierced design, circled by a brass rim is mounted in a wide steel border under a brass, sawtooth outer border. This border and the bird design have a purple tint. $2.50.

12. BIRD ON PERCH. Brass design on tinted background with brass border and liner. $1.75.

13. THREE SWALLOWS, pierced design, tinted background, steel mirror liner. $3.50.

14. THREE BIRDS UNDER AN UMBRELLA, an all time favorite made of pressed brass, in high relief, two-piece. $6.00.

15. CREEPERS, small brown birds that climb trees (identified by Helen Wegener), two-piece pierced brass, design attached to rim, steel liner and darkened background. $3.50.

PLATE 20

PLATE 20

ROOSTERS

The rooster is a favorite character in children's stories and rhymes. He was one of the symbols of the goddess Minerva and the silhouette of the strutting cock has always seemed to create decorative interest. An outstanding example of American folk art is the weather vane and here the rooster is unsurpassed as a decorative object. The great painter Picasso is quoted as having said, "Cocks have always been seen but never as well as in American weather vanes."

It was only natural that this proud bird should be used also as a decorative motif on picture buttons. Although they are not too plentiful, quite a variety can be found as the two accompanying Plates will show.

1. This ROOSTER has his beak open and appears quite angry. The head is in high relief on a brass background with a decoratively arranged border of brass feathers. $2.00.

2. A pleasanter fellow; a raised head on slightly convex brass background. Value $8.00.

3. A head inside a tail-feather border; white pierced metal. Value, $2.50.

4. The same as No. 1 in the large size. Value, $6.50.

5. This is a small brass head with cut out border, ornamented by cut steels. The rooster's mouth is open and he is holding a red glass ball which looks like a cherry. This is considered to be a Fable button and has been named, "THE COCK AND THE JEWEL" from Aesop's fable by that name. Value $3.50.

6. A head in high relief; an ANGRY ROOSTER similar to No. 4; brass. Value $6.50.

7. Cockerel; a two-piece brass button, tinted black. Value $2.50.

8. This is an Ashlee button (N.B.B., July '62); the brass rooster is applied to an extra large concave wood background; very ornamental. Value $8.00.

9. Vegetable ivory; a proud rooster who looks like an Orpington. Value $2.50.

10. SERENADING ROOSTER, playing a guitar and apparently singing. This is a two-piece button of silvered brass, back-marked, "Paris, T.W. & W." Value $12.00.

11. WILD COCK'S HEAD. The head is in very high relief with three cut steels in the crest. All brass. Value $15.00.

12. A crest button of two-piece brass, back-marked "Scovill Mfg. Co., Waterbury." $2.50.

13. CHANTECLER; rooster in relief; two-piece brass. Value $4.50.

14. A steel cup with a steel rooster's head. The comb and collar are of brass. Value $1.00.

15. THE COCK THAT CROWED IN THE MORN. The sun is rising and the sky is tinted white. Value $8.50.

PLATE 21

PLATE 21

ROOSTERS

1. ROOSTER EATING GRAPES. A brass two - piece button with a cut out border over a steel mirror liner. Value $1.50.

2. LARGE MINERVA HEAD with helmet surmounted by rooster head; the rooster's wings and long ornamental tail feathers also form part of the helmet decoration. The head is of brass on a brass background that is tinted green. Value $8.50.

3. THE COCK THAT CROWED THRICE. The design is of brass, applied over a background that is tinted dark blue. This button can be found in a larger size and is sometimes classed with RELIGIOUS SYMBOLS. The vine growing on the wall is ivy and the ivy has religious significance as well as the title of the button. Value, $1.50.

4. A large brass head on a wood background with rolled brass rim. Value $6.50.

5. Another version of "THE COCK THAT CROWED IN THE MORN." One-piece silvered brass button with rooster in high relief. Value $8.50.

6. A small two-piece brass button with a ROOSTER STRUTTING toward the left. Value $2.00.

7. Another Ashlee rooster, applied to a celluloid background. (N.B.B., '62). Value $8.00.

8. Crest button, back-marked, "Firmins, London". The motto says, "Virtute et Labore." $2.00.

9. A black glass button with painted roosters. Value $1.75.

10. The small size of No. 14. Value $1.50.

11. A black horn button with rooster tinted in natural colors. Value $3.50.

12. A one-piece concave brass button with rooster in high relief. Value $8.00.

13. Black horn button with the head in a convex center, enameled in red and two shades of blue and enclosed in a gold border. Value $15.00.

14. HEN ON THE FENCE. A pierced brass design over a wood background. Value $6.50.

15. A small brass head, ornamented by cut steels and a pierced stem and leaf design over a darkened brass background, slightly convex. Value $1.50.

PLATE 22

PLATE 22

OWLS

The owl is a well known character is story, verse, and legend. As everyone knows, he is a nocturnal bird of prey and there are few of us who have not heard the screams of our common screech owl at night. Owls are distinguished by their large head and eyes, short, hooked bill and strong talons. Their plumage is very soft which makes their flight almost noiseless. The eyes of an owl are especially adapted for night "viewing" and their position in the head, different from that of other birds, gives him a quizzical expression which is very appealing. This and the roundness of the head makes the owl very pleasing as a button design.

The buttons shown on this Plate are from the collection of Elsa Ehresman. You will find others on different Plates. Many Owl buttons have been given special names by Florence Nicholls and we use the names here.

1. This one, sitting on a branch in foliage, is called, "Timid Owl." A two-piece, pressed brass button. Found also in larger sizes. $2.00.

2. COCKY SCREECH OWL. Brass owl and flowers are attached to a concave background. $6.50.

3. The same as No. 2 in a small size. $1.00.

4. This is an OWL HEAD with two holes to sew through in place of eyes. $1.00.

5. SURPRISED OWL. Two-piece pressed brass with border. $1.00.

6. OWL'S HEAD in high relief with glass eyes. $3.00.

7. OWL ON GATE. A brass design trimmed with two cut steels and applied to a concave, one-piece background. $1.00.

8. MOTHER AND BABY OWL sitting in crescent moon. A white metal design on darkened brass. $1.00.

9. A brass owl with head turned, superimposed on a white celluloid background. Two-piece. $2.50.

10. EAGLE OWL'S HEAD, this large pressed brass design, high and convex, completely covers the face of the button. $6.50.

11. PEWTER OWL HEAD on concave background. $2.00.

12. The medium size of No. 10. $3.00.

13. An owl sitting on crescent moon. Brown composition, ribbed background. $.75.

14. "THE OWL WITH THE GOO-GOO EYES", on a branch. A pewter design, applied to a concave, mottled and darkened brass background. Border design in relief. $1.00.

15. This OWL WITH WINGS SPREAD is a 20th century button. The face is pressed brass rolled over the back. $.75.

16. Brass owl, superimposed on concave brass background, which has etched branch and limb. One-piece. $2.00.

17. FAT HORNED OWL. A pressed brass rim. This owl is very desirable as he has yellow glass eyes that look very natural. Tin back. $8.50.

18. OWL in pewter, crescent moon and star in brass on darkened brass background. Raised rim. $.75.

19. The same as No. 14 in the large size. $6.50.

PLATE 23

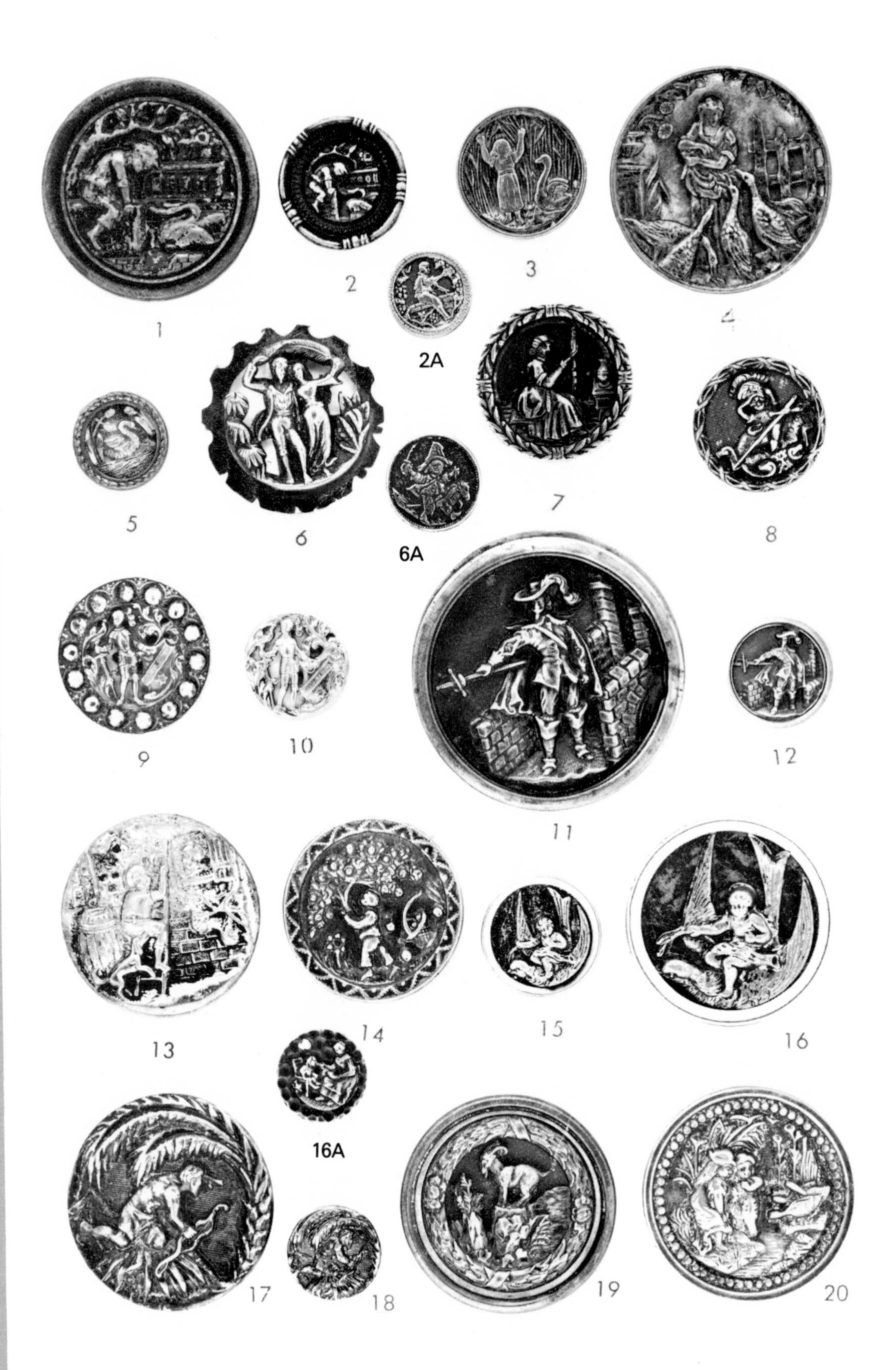

PLATE 23

STORIES

1. This has been named, "THE GOOSE THAT LAID THE GOLDEN EGG". Pewter design, darkened, steel mirror, brass collet. $6.50.

2. The same design as on No. 1 but all brass, the design pierced, showing blackened background. $2.50.

2a. STEALING GRAPES, pressed brass, pierced with darkened background. $2.00.

3. "PRINCESS WITH SWAN BROTHER", from the Fairy Tale of the princess Elsa whose brothers were changed into swans by their wicked stepmother. Two-piece, stamped brass with design in relief. $3.50.

4. "GOOSE GIRL". Two-piece, the design cut out and attached to collet. All brass, the design tinted with purple and the background with green. Buttons that have had more use might not have this original tint. $12.00.

5. "THE UGLY DUCKLING". As No. 3, this button is named from one of Hans Christian Anderson's Fairy Tales. One-piece concave molded pewter in a brass frame. Can be found in the large size also and is often tinted. This size $.75.

6. PAUL AND VIRGINIA; characters from the French story of the same name by Bernardine St. Pierre, published in 1788. The story has been made into plays and operas also, and the button can be classified with operatic buttons as well as stories. These figures are of brass, pierced, set in steel frame. $6.50.

6a. PLAYING SOLDIER, a small boy riding a Hobby Horse, brandishing a sword and wearing cocked hat (paper). the hat worn by this boy illustrates the ancient Japanese art of origami (folding flat pieces of paper into three dimensional objects.) Tin with darkened background, raised figure. $1.00.

7. "MARGUERITE AT SPINNING WHEEL". Heroine of Gunod's FAUST, this is also an operatic button. Pierced brass, tinted, with darkened background and leaf border. $4.00.

8. "PLAYING HERO". Child is astride a saddle and has sword and equipment. $2.00.

9. "KING ARTHUR WITH SWORD EXCALIBUR AND SHIELD PRIDWIN". One-piece, pressed brass, silvered, pierced, border set with cut steels. $2.00.

10. Same as No. 9 in smaller size without cut steel border. $1.00.

11. "D'ARTAGNAN" principal character in "The Three Musketeers" by Alexander Dumas. On the button, D'Artagnan is seen surrendering his sword because he has engaged in duelling, forbidden to a member of the King's Guard. Pressed brass, figure in high relief. Very scarce. $25.00.

12. The same as No. 11 in the medium size. $5.00.

13. A white metal button, stamped, two-piece, said to be TOM SAWYER RUNNING AWAY FROM HOME. $4.00.

14. "SHAKING THE APPLE TREE", two-piece brass. $4.00.

15. "LITTLE THUMB" or "Little Tiny" riding the swallow. A character from a fairy tale by Hans Christian Anderson. Little Tiny fell into a hole from which she thought she could not escape but the Swallow carried her to safety. Brass in high relief with tin collet. $2.00.

16. The same in the large size. $4.50.

16a. "PORRIDGE TIME". Brass escutcheon on hammered brass background. One-piece. $2.00.

17. "ROBINSON CRUSOE", from the story by the same name written by Daniel Defoe in 1719. Two-piece pressed brass. $6.00.

18. The same as 17, small size. $1.00.

19. Called, "ROBINSON CRUSOE'S GOAT". Pressed brass, steel liner, brass collet. $8.00.

20. "HANSEL AND GRETEL", from one of Grimm's fairy tales, made into an opera by Engelbert Humperdinck with the libretto written by Adelheid Wette. Hansel and Gretel were sent into the woods by their cross stepmother and told to gather berries. The button pictures them beside the brook which they could not cross and Gretel is begging the ducks to take them across on their backs. In the opera she says, "Oh there are some ducks. Perhaps they will carry us across." So she sings, "Hansel and Gretel here we stand. Will you take us over on your backs to land?" Stamped brass, two-piece. $4.50.

PLATE 24

PLATE 24

STORIES & KATE GREENAWAYS

Kate Greenaway, born at Hoxton, England, March 17th, 1846, was the daughter of a prominent wood engraver. She loved to help her father when she was a child, drew pictures on her slate when very young and began to study art at eleven years of age. Her first exhibit was held at the Dudley Galleries in England in 1868. Her drawings of child life became very popular and her style was widely imitated. One of her most successful books for children was "Under the Window". Many of the buttons called, "Kate Greenaways" have designs copied from the illustrations in this book. For more information see N.B.B., November, 1949.

1. HOOKING A SNAIL, a typical K.G. bonneted girl of two-piece pressed brass. Scarce. $2.00.

2. MISS PATTY AND HER PLAYMATES. This little girl is the same as shown in K.G.'s picture " 'Shall I sing?', says the lark". Two-piece pressed brass in high relief, the design pierced over a darkened background, tin rim. $4.00.

3. SPRING, from a K.G. print by this name (1883 Almanac); one-piece convex brass with applied design. $2.50.

4. THE TRUMPETER, from "Pipe Thee High", two-piece tinted brass with design in relief. $4.00.

5. SUMMER, also from the Almanac. This is one of the most common of the K.G. buttons. It is found with metal design on pearl, on brass and steel; various sizes. $2.00.

6. THE WAITS. This is thought to represent children singing in the street at Christmas time and hoping to receive gifts of food and other goodies. The girl's costume is very similar to those found in K.G. drawings. Two-piece pressed brass. $6.50.

7. and 8. Both called "AT THE WELL." The children are dressed in the K.G. manner; both buttons are of stamped brass with slightly different designs and rims. Value of 7, $12.00; 8, $4.00.

9. and 10. BO-PEEP from K.G.'s "Mother Goose". No. 9 has a pierced brass design on metal. No. 10 is a T.W. & W. button. This picture is not as clear as on No. 9 but this firm discontinued business over 100 years ago, which establishes the approximate age of the button and makes the value slightly more. $1.50 and $2.50.

11. KING ARTHUR with Excalibur (sword) and Pridwin (shield). Pierced metal with cut steel trim; also found in medium size. $6.50.

12. LITTLE MISS PATTY AND MR. PAUL from K.G.'s, "The Garden Wall". Two-piece, pressed brass. $2.00.

13. and 15. BLONDEL, STROLLING MINSTREL. Blondel was a favorite minstrel at the court of Richard I (Coeur de Lion) who, after leading a crusade to the Holy Land, was captured on his way home and confined in the castle of Durenstein on the Danube. His whereabouts were unknown in England for some time and the story is told that Blondel strolled from castle to castle in Austria, singing a song that he and Richard had composed. It is said that eventually he came to the right castle and was heard by his master who came to a window and made himself known. Richard was in time released for a very high ransom. No. 13 is the more scarce button; it is a two-piece with the pierced design over a tinted background. $3.50. No. 15 is stamped brass, two-piece, tinted; tin rim. $6.50.

14. HOP O' MY THUMB riding the butterfly. This character is from a nursery tale about the adventures of a tiny boy, no larger than his father's thumb. Brass rim and darkened brass background with white metal design. $2.00.

15. See No. 13, above.

16. HANSEL AND GRETEL, shown with different border on previous Plate. $4.50.

17. THE PIED PIPER from the poem by Robert Browning. The rats at the piper's feet, the river Weser and Hamlintown in the distance can be plainly seen. This version has a steel liner behind the cut-out moon. Slightly concave stamped brass with background darkened. Scarce. $18.00.

18. RADLAUF THE MILLER, from an old fairy story. Pierced brass design on tinted background. $3.00.

19. This is said to illustrate a scene from SNOW WHITE AND THE SEVEN DWARFS, the dwarfs are supposedly carrying lilies of the valley to place on the casket of Snow White, before the evil spell was broken. Two-piece stamped brass. $7.50.

20. This is known as EASTER PARADE, a descriptive title. The cart appears to be made of half an egg shell and in the background is a bunny. Two-piece stamped brass with a design in relief, tinted. $2.00.

21. THE TRUMPETER, a K.G. design, a one-piece concave button with engraved background, the pierced design of white metal. $2.50.

22. and 23. This button has been called RIP VAN WINKLE but some classify it with Fable buttons and name it, "The Peasant of the Danube" and it is said to resemble an illustration by M.M. Pauguet and Henry Emy found in an edition of LaFontaine. (See N.B.B. September, 1952). Stamped brass, design in relief, tinted. Small, $2.00. Large, $15.00.

PLATE 25

PLATE 25

CHILDREN

1. A Kate Greenaway GIRL WITH BALLOON; superimposed on concave brass background; flower, leaf and stem also superimposed and cut steels used as additional decoration. $12.00.

2. JOHNNY WITH VINE, same boy as No. 3. This design is taken from UNDER THE WINDOW, a Kate Greenaway Book. The button is of white metal with boy and vine superimposed and cut steels applied. Value, $40.00.

3. JOHNNY AND BALLOON from K.G.'s "For What Are You Longing You Three Little Boys?" A boy companion to No. 1. Same construction and value. $15.00.

4. BOY WITH HIGHWHEELER. Two-piece pressed brass. $2.00.

5. LITTLE GIRL PLAYING WITH DOG. Two - piece pressed brass with floral border. $2.00.

6. HENNY PENNY, the little chicken who thought the sky was falling. Brass with steel liner. Value $7.50.

7. CATCHING BUTTERFLIES. Pressed brass. Value $2.50.

8. PLAYING GROWN UP. Two-piece pressed brass with tinted background. Value, $2.50.

9. HOOP ROLLING. Two-piece brass, pierced, showing contrasting background. Value, $12.00.

10. BUSTER BROWN AND TIGE; comic strip characters. One-piece pressed brass. Very scarce. Value, $27.50.

11. BATTLEDORE AND SHUTTLECOCK. Tin collet, pressed brass center with figures in relief. Value, $4.50.

12. LITTLE PETER, the boy who plugged the dike with his finger. Pressed brass design applied to concave button - cut steels that represent nails. Value, $10.00.

13. THE UGLY DUCKLING. This is from Hans Christian Anderson's Fairy Tales. A one - piece concave button with tinted background and highly polished design. Value, $6.50.

14. THE GIANT of "JACK THE GIANT KILLER". A large superimposed brass figure with ivy leaf border; cut steels in the border. Value, $12.00.

15. RED RIDING HOOD, from Grimm's Fairy Tales. A rare button. The design is of pierced brass over a tinted background, with an elaborate border. Value, $18.00.

16. RED RIDING HOOD in this representation has stopped to pick flowers for her grandmother. One-piece with raised design in fine detail; tinted. Value, $15.00.

17. Another version of LITTLE RED RIDING HOOD called RED RIDING HOOD AND THE WOLF WITH UPRAISED PAW. Two-piece, pressed brass. Value, $18.00.

PLATE 26

1 2 3 4 5 6 7 8 9 10 11 12 13

PLATE 26

CHILDREN

1. PORRIDGE TIME. One-piece stamped brass with figures in high relief. Blue steel border. Scarce. Value, $15.00.

2. This has been named, SEVEN AT ONE BLOW (N) from the story of the little tailor claimed to have killed "seven at one blow" but failed to say that the "seven" were flies. Its construction has the appearance of an Ashlee button (N.B.B., July 1962). Value, $8.00.

3. LITTLE COLONEL'S HERO. The figure is in relief on a stamped brass background that is engraved and tinted. Value, $15.00.

4. LITTLE SLEEPER; also known as DICK WHITTINGTON AND HIS CAT. Two-piece pressed brass. Scarce. Value, $15.00.

5. DOG-FACED BOY, evidently a circus act is illustrated here. Two-piece, tinted brass. Value, $3.50.

6. THE SINGING LESSON. This button has been identified by Lodema Collamore (J.B., June, 1956) from an old trade card on which she found the same picture and which said the lesson was being given by Ichabod Crane, teacher in Irving's, "Legend of Sleepy Hollow". Two-piece pressed brass. $6.50.

7. STOLEN PORRIDGE. Two-piece brass, figures in very high relief. Scarce. $12.00.

8. CHILDREN'S CIRCUS. One-piece, pressed brass with ball and trapeze-ends of faceted steel. Value, $12.00.

9. ESMERALDA AND HER GOAT. Esmeralda was the dancing gypsy girl in the story NOTRE DAME de PARIS by Victor Hugo. The cathedral of Notre Dame where Quasimodo, the hunchback bell ringer, hid Esmeralda can be seen in the background. A one-piece brass button. This button can be classed with "Opera" as the story formed the basis of a light opera by Dargomizsky. $35.00.

10. HAIR PULLING. A stamped brass, two-piece button with children and chairs in high relief. Value, $20.00. This is sometimes found, showing a doll lying on the floor and is valued at $25.00.

11. CREEPING BABY. Two-piece pressed brass, repouse border. Value, $15.00.

12. VICTORIAN GIRL with Japanese parasol laughing at her dog. Two-piece brass flat metal rim. $4.50.

13. BLIND MAN'S BUFF, a children's game of the Victorian Era. Two-piece brass with much detail. Scarce. $15.00.

PLATE 27

PLATE 27

FABLES

A fable is a short story in which animals and sometimes inanimate things, speak and act like people. Their conduct is supposed to teach an object lesson. A true fable always ends by stating the moral.

Aesop, who lived during the eighteenth century B.C., is probably the most celebrated fabulist of all time. The French poet Jean De La Fontaine is also well known for his fables, first published in 1668. These have been translated into English and illustrated by many different artists. The following Plate shows how these stories and pictures inspired the designs of various buttons. Others can be found.

Fables in sooth, are not what they appear
Our moralists are mice, and such small deer
We yawn at sermons, but we gladly turn
To moral tales, and so - amused - we learn.

1. THE HARE AND THE FROG, from the Adventure of Reynard the Fox. Two-piece with brass, applied design. White metal rim. Value, $12.00.

2. THE WOLF AND THE STORK. One-piece solid metal, Paris back. The exact design is found in the 1879 edition of LaFontaine's fables, the illustrator is J.J. Grandville. Value, $3.00.

3. THE TWO RATS, Aesop. Sometimes called, "The Country Mouse and the City Mouse". Two-piece stamped brass. Rare. $25.00.

4. REYNARD THE FOX, distinguished as a pilgrim with book and staff. He sits at the gate of his castle, Malepartus, in wait for an unsuspecting victim passing along the road. Two-piece tinted metal. $12.00.

5. THE FISH AND THE SHEPHERD WHO PLAYED ON A CLARINET, LaFontaine; illustrated by Dove. Two-piece metal. $8.00.

6. THE EAGLE AND THE STAG, Pilpay. "It is better to hunger and thirst in safety than to seek an easy way to abundance". A wood back button with brass design. $3.00.

7. THE FOX AND THE GRAPES, LaFontaine's Fable. Two-piece metal with darkened background, a scarce design. $8.00.

8. THE FOX AND THE STORK, LaFontaine. Two-piece pressed brass. $6.50.

9. THE FOX AND THE GRAPES, a more common design than No. 7 but the pierced design is placed over a velvet background making the button more unusual and very attractive. $6.50.

10. THE KID AND THE WOLF, Aesop. A button with large, well defined figures; all brass. $6.50.

11. GOAT ON THE CRAG, Aesop's fable of the goat and the lion. $6.50.

12. THE PREACHING FOX. Reynard is wearing the vestments of a monk. He tells the fowls he has sworn never to eat meat again and of course he soon has a good meal. Yellow and white metal. $3.50.

13. THE FROGS DESIRING A KING, LaFontaine. Two-piece brass button, extra large size, with design in high relief. $8.00.

14. LION IN LUSH VALLEY, Aesop. A two-piece button, pierced design on darkened background, brass rim. $3.00.

15. THE LION AND THE SNAKE, LaFontiane. The story begins, "The lion saw the snake basking in the sun". Two-piece tinted brass. Value, $15.00.

PLATE 28

PLATE 28

RELIGIOUS SUBJECTS

1. "SHEPHERD DRIVING HIS FLOCK", a Thorwaldsen design. One of four picture button designs taken from a frieze depicting The Triumphal Entry of Alexander the Great into Babylon. (N.B.B., November, 1957). One-piece pressed brass. $6.50.

2. "MADONNA AND CHILD" from Raphael's "Sistine Madonna". One-piece, pressed brass in high relief. $20.00.

3. "JESUS AND THE WOMAN OF SAMARIA" at Jacob's Well. This is of early silver, not hall-marked. Rare. $15.00.

4. This is also called "WOMAN OF SAMARIA." Two-piece pressed tin with steel liner showing between openings in the heart design of the border. Also rare. $15.00.

5. "ITALIAN STREET VENDOR", selling an angel figurine. Two-piece pressed brass. Rare. $8.00.

6. Probably HUBERT being forbidden by God to kill the stag, which can be seen in the background. Two-piece pressed brass in high relief. Rare. $12.00.

7. An OPEN BIBLE with a bordering inscription which says, "In God We Trust". One-piece pressed brass in low relief, Circa, 1830-40. Political. Rare. $10.00.

8. "DAVID AND GOLIATH". The sling shot can be seen plainly in the boy's hand. Pressed brass picture with a tin rim. $15.00.

9. "ISABELLA THE CATHOLIC", (1451-1504), a courageous queen who took part in the War with the Moors in 1492. The armor that she wore is preserved at Madrid. She is said to have fitted out, at her own expense, the ships in which Columbus discovered America. A one-piece, pierced brass button with the head in very high relief, applied and the rim is of tin. $8.00.

10. "A CRUSADER OF THE HOLY GRAIL". two-piece stamped brass, tinted. The background is of steel. $6.50.

11. "MOSES BEING WATCHED OVER BY MIRIAM". Pressed, pierced, white metal design over brass background which is tinted. Two-piece with brass rim. Beautiful and rare. $35.00.

12. CHERUB, a dainty polychrome painting on porcelain, set in paste rim. Very scarce. $35.00.

13. THE GOOD SAMARITAN. Pressed horn, black, in relief. $25.00.

PLATE 29

PLATE 29

SYMBOLIC, RELIGIOUS, & WINGED

This Plate starts with symbolic and religious buttons and ends with winged subjects, most of which are angels.

Angels are spiritual beings, having immortal life and supposed to form a connection between the seen and the unseen worlds. One can, of course, place ones' own interpretation on the Bible but Angels are part of our Biblical heritage and are found both in the Old and in the New Testament. Although we have "fallen Angels", banished from Heaven, and known as Demons or Devils, and Angel is usually represented as a white-robed, winged figure with human form and is supposed to personify Goodness, Love, Truth and Purity.

Assemblying a "frame" of Angels is especially appropriate at Christmas time and it can occupy a prominent place in ones' Christmas decor but Angels make a lovely display at any time. Angel buttons can be found in many materials, including enamels, porcelains, Wedgwood and carved pearl but the supply seems limited. Cherubs, who are "lesser" Angels may be added to the arrangement. However, Cupid must not be confused with Cherubs and substituted for one, as this winged fellow belongs in Mythology. Several Cupids were used on this Plate to symbolize Love but Angels are not symbols.

1. A pierced brass design of a PEACOCK. Two-piece brass. It symbolizes Pride and also The Resurrection, (when a peacock loses his tail feathers, he gains new ones that are more beautiful than the old.) $1.00.

2. The same design with a shiny metal liner behind the "eyes" in the peacock's tail. .75.

3. Called, "KNIGHT OF THE HOLY GRAIL". A brass design, attached to the rim and placed over a velvet background; two-piece. $4.00.

4. A DOVE OF PEACE. Two-piece with bird in relief. $.50.

5. SWALLOWS IN FLIGHT. In Bible times, the swallow was considered sacred because so many nested in the temples. Pressed brass. $1.00.

6. Called, "THE HEJIRA" or, " THE FLIGHT OF MOHAMMED FROM MECCA"; a pierced brass design with darkened background. $.75.

7. ST. GEORGE AND THE DRAGON; white metal design on a concave, one-piece button. $1.00.

8. A child and lion, identified by Nicholls as, THE PEACEABLE KINGDOM. A one-piece white metal button. $2.00.

9. and 10. THE TREE OF LIFE. White metal design on a darkened background; tin rim; two-piece. $.50 and $2.00.

11. BUDDHA. One-piece pierced brass, gilded with cut steel trim. Buddhism, a religion of eastern Asia, founded by Gautama, the Buddha, teaches self-denial, virtue, wisdom, and the attainment of happiness through obedience and freedom from earthly passion. $1.00.

12. WALLS OF JERICHO, a pierced, white metal design with brass background and rim. $1.75.

13. CHERUB WITH CORNUCOPIA. A white metal design, superimposed on a tinted background; pierced brass border. $2.00.

14. HEAD OF CHERUB. One-piece pressed brass. $1.00.

15. CHARLEMAGNE AND THE WARNING ANGEL. Stamped brass figures, superimposed on a dark, stippled brass background. Brass rim. The Angel is warning Charlemagne to return to his endangered kingdom before it is lost. $3.50.

16. A head, probably of a SAINT, with a pierced design of two angels, supporting the framed head. The Angel's wing-tips meet at the top of the design. Two-piece brass. $1.50.

17. CUPID ASCENDING; brass figure, attached to border, over a nickel crescent and tinted tin background. $1.00.

18. A LYRE, symbol of Peace. It is a harp-like instrument which was used by the ancients to accompany singing or recitation. A two-piece white metal button with applied rim, the instrument in relief on a pebbled background. Backmarked, "D. Evans & Co., Extra." $1.00.

19. and 20a. ANGEL ON THE WALL, in two sizes. Two-piece pressed brass. $2.50 and $1.00.

20. CUPID WITH TORCH, lighting the world with LOVE. Pressed tin, two-piece. $.50.

21. Two figures in high relief with LYRE between them. Two-piece white metal. Called, "HOLY MUSIC". $1.00.

22. Lovely winged ANGEL HEAD. Convex silver. $6.50.

23. and 24. ANGELS. Brass, superimposed on a darkened background. This button has been called, "The Dancing Cupid" but we believe the wings are Angel wings. $2.50 and $4.50.

25. AN ANGEL HEAD. Two-piece stamped brass. $3.00.

PLATE 30

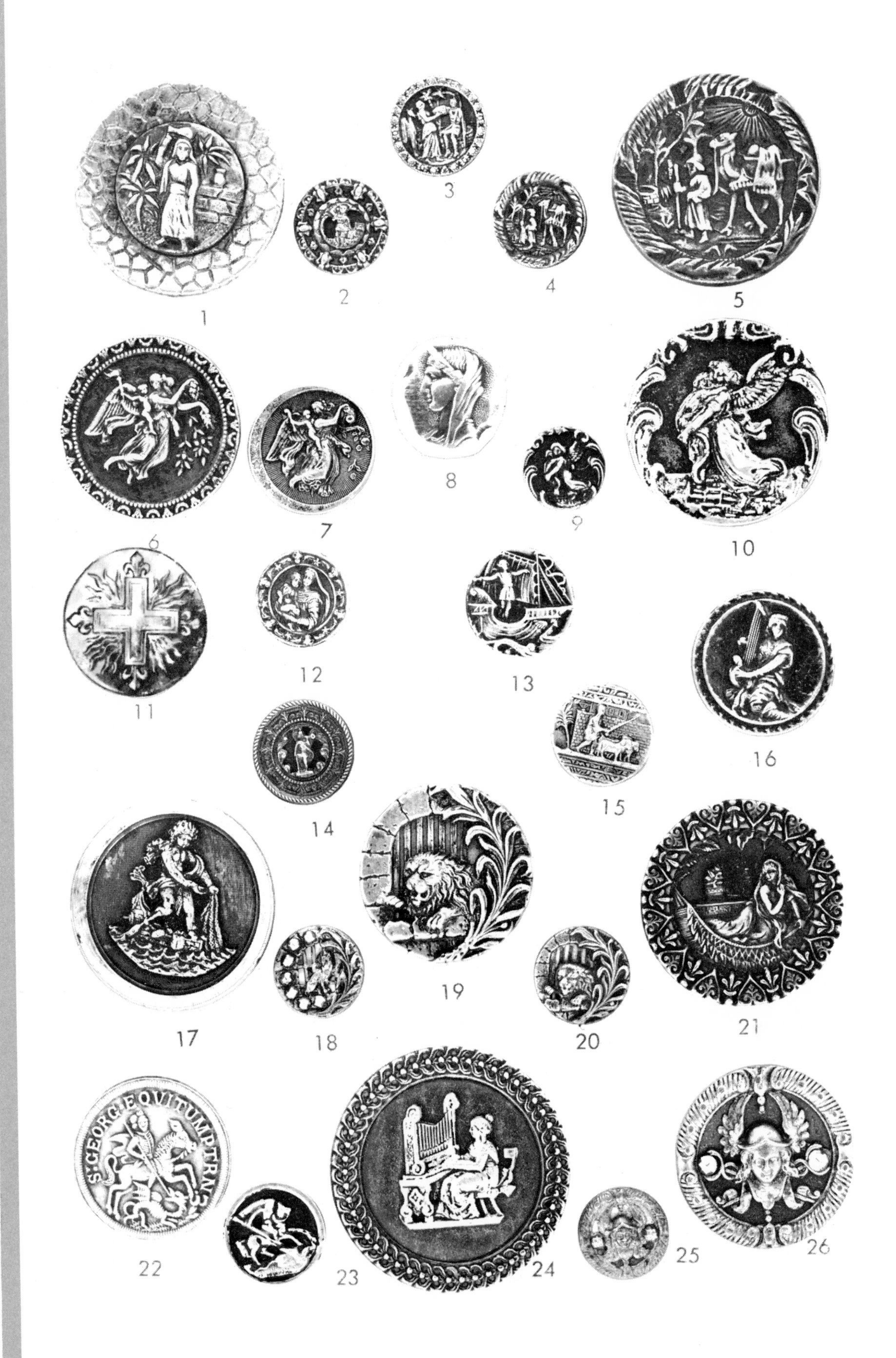

PLATE 30

RELIGIOUS SUBJECTS

1. REBECCA AT THE WELL. Two-piece, stamped brass, tinted, $6.50.

2. REBECCA AT THE WELL, also, but a slightly different design. $1.00.

3. REBECCA AND ELIEZER AT THE WELL. A pierced brass design over a darkened background. This can also be found in small and medium sizes but it is rare in any size. $2.50 for the small size.

4. and 5. ELIEZER AT THE WELL. Eliezer, the servant of Abraham, in the Biblical story of the Old Testament, is seen here just arriving at the well. He meets Rebecca, and because of her great kindness, chooses her as a wife for Isaac, Abraham's son. It is a two-piece, pressed brass button with tinted background and an ornamental border. $4.00. Small, $.75. With tin border, $1.50.

6. and 7. MORNING. This is an almost perfect copy of a design by Bertel Thorwaldson, which was called by that name. It was such a popular design that it was not only copied by button makers, but by cameo cutters, ceramicists and silversmiths. (N.B.B. November 1957). Two-piece pressed brass; No. 7 has a crescent shaped border, decorated with stars. Values of No. 6 and No. 7, respectively; $6.50 and $3.50.

8. QUEEN ESTHER. Silver, stamped in one-piece, not hallmarked. $3.00.

9. and 10. THE ANGEL OF PEACE. Pierced brass design over tinted background. Shown in two sizes. This was identified from a painting by Wm. Kaulbach, who originally entitled it, "Guardian Angel". $2.00 and $8.00.

11. THE CROSS FLEURETTE, two-piece pressed brass. The many different crosses have religious significance. The various types can form an interesting collection. Two-piece pressed brass. $1.00.

12. MADONNA AND CHILD, a bust of Raphael's "SISTINE MADONNA". One-piece pressed brass. Scarce, especially in this size. $4.50.

13. This boat has a WINGED FIGUREHEAD. Figure heads were used by the ancient Romans, who carved images of their favorite gods and placed them on their boats, hoping to gain their favor and have good luck on the sea. We have not positively identified the type of this boat but the figurehead has religious significance. Pressed brass. $2.50.

14. ANGEL GABRIEL. Pierced brass, black-tinted metal background. $2.00.

15. THE SHEPHERD DRIVING HIS FLOCK, from a Thorwaldson frieze depicting, "Alexander's Triumphal Entry Into Babylon. Two-piece pressed brass. $2.00.

16. THE HARPIST. Two-piece pressed brass. This could also be classed with musical buttons. "Praise the Lord with the Harp". It is a symbol of worship and praise. $3.00.

17. Called, "ST. PETER, casting his nets." A grey-tinted brass background with pierced, white metal figure, applied. Brass rim. $12.00.

18., 19., and 20. THE LION'S DEN. The palm frond curls upward, forming a half border. The palm branch is a religious symbol of Victory. This design might have been inspired by the story of, "Daniel in the Lion's Den". No. 18 is a one-piece pressed brass button. $1.25. 19 and 20 are two-piece with tinned bars as parts of the background design. $3.00 and $1.50, respectively.

21. CLEOPATRA was the name given this button in advertisements at about 1890. After the loss of the battle of Actium, Cleopatra killed herself with an asp. One can be seen near the edge of the hammock. A two-piece pressed brass button with heart-border. Quite plentiful. $3.50.

22. ST. GEORGE AND THE DRAGON. The legend of St. George has been represented by Raphael and many other great artists. The dragon symbolizes evil and the slaying by St. George represents the triumph of Christianity over Paganism. Stamped white metal. $2.00.

23. Another representation of ST. GEORGE AND THE DRAGON. Two-piece pressed brass. $.75.

24. Called, "ST. CECELIA AT THE ORGAN". The legend of Cecelia has inspired many masterpieces of art, literature and music. She is the patron saint of Music and of the Blind. A stamped brass button with design in relief on a dark background. $25.00.

25. and 26. MERCURY, shown in two sizes. Although this head resembles an angel and has been called one by some collectors, it is not. The wings are attached to the cap, instead of the shoulders and close inspection shows two of the Caducei of Mercury, crossed behind his head. There is a cut steel between the snake heads of each Caduceus and the snakes are entwined about each staff.

However, Irene Strieby has done some extensive research on this for us and she tells us that Carl Jung in his book, "Man and His Symbols", says that the wings of Mercury symbolize a divine force and therefore this button is not out of place with religious subjects. $1.00 and $3.50.

PLATE 31

PLATE 31

BUILDINGS & SCENES

1. SAIL BOAT SCENE. This button was found in Canada and is unusual as it has three distinctly different borders around the concave scene; two-piece pressed brass. $3.50.

2. CASTLE AND MILL IN THE MOONLIGHT. A concave, two-piece button of pressed brass with rope border. $1.50.

3. CASTLE WITH BRIDGE. Two-piece pressed brass. $1.25.

4. THE PRINCE RETURNS. The center design is of pewter on a brass background, tinted; a heart border with tin liner, copper tinted. $3.50.

5. AN ORIENTAL SCENE with ornamental, small bridge, spanning the pond. One-piece brass with pierced border. $3.50.

6. ANCIENT RUINS WITH STATUARY. The design is in high relief on the tinted brass background and the "chevron border" is in keeping with the design as this is one of the borders used in decoration by the ancient Greeks and Romans. $4.00.

7. Called "THE WEE HOOSE 'MANG THE HEATHER". The design of the house is on a darkened brass background and the Scotch Thistle design which forms part of the border is pierced and attached to the turn-under rim. $3.75.

8. THE RAT AND THE WINDMILL. the rat can be seen in the foreground at the left, also clearly pictured is a fenced enclosure, house and flying birds. Scarce. $8.00.

9. A two-piece pressed brass DUTCH WINDMILL with good detail. $1.00.

10. WINDMILL AND DWELLING, two-piece pressed brass, tinted. $1.50.

11. Another WINDMILL of different design, two-piece pressed brass. $1.00.

12. White and yellow metal showing a scene with WINDMILL, pond, bridge and ducks. $2.50.

13. This is said to be an ITALIAN VILLA outside Rome. Waterfall and bridge in foreground add interest; two-piece pressed brass. $3.00.

14. CASTLE. Two-piece brass with fine detail. $2.50.

15. Castle tower, MILL with mill wheel, bridge over running water and foliage make up the scene; two-piece brass; said to have originated in Poland. $1.75.

16. CASTLE WITH CLOUDS IN SKY. Stamped brass, metal rim and back. $2.00.

17. Called MEDIEVAL VILLAGE. Two-piece stamped brass, tinted. $3.00.

18. ALPINE CABIN, mountains seen in the distance. Two-piece pressed brass with plain brass rim; not often found in this large size. $6.50.

19. TYROLEAN SCENE, church steeple can be seen in distance. Stamped brass, nice detail. $3.00.

PLATE 32

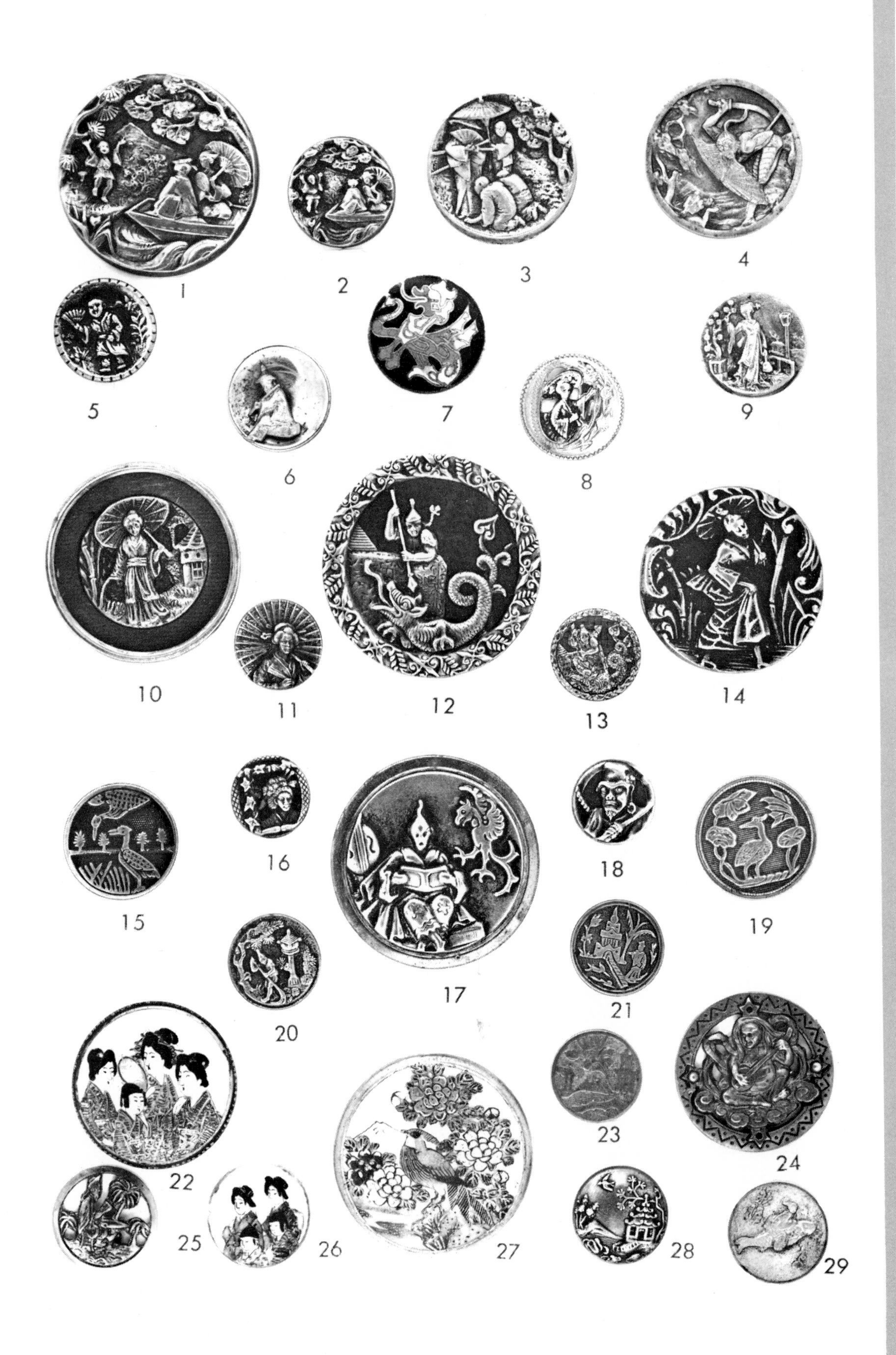

PLATE 32

ORIENTALS

Many picture buttons are decorated with oriental figures and designs. Some represent characters of light operas, such as The Mikado. Some of our loveliest buttons; enamels, ivories, Satsumas and those made of Cinnabar have originated in the Orient.

Satsuma ware was first made in the province of Satsuma in Japan during the 15th century. It is a ceramic ware characterized by a crackle glaze and is completely hand decorated. Satsuma buttons have been exported since the 1870's. All are lovely but the earlier ones are much finer.

Early Satsuma buttons can be recognized in several ways. The backs were quite flat with two holes to sew through that required a curved needle, while the later ones have a protruding shank. All have similar designs; flowers, native to Japan, Fujiyama, scenes with thatched houses, waterfalls and people. All have gold outlining but on the earlier ones, it is encrusted while on recent buttons, thin lines are used. The entire back of older ones was often covered with the same color as the border. This is not true of later ones. Many have backmarks but this is of no great significance as a backmark could be easily added before exporting. The more important consideration is the quality of the decoration.

1.&2. Called ORIENTAL THEATER. Two ladies are seated in a box watching a man performing on a stage. In Japan, men often played all parts in the so-called, "No Plays", using masks of females when they portrayed women. They believed that their art could be shown better through gestures and poses than by facial expressions. The No Plays were performed out doors and this possibly represents one being enacted. Two-piece with much detail. The same design can be found in black glass, lusters and opaque glass. $4.50 and $1.25.

3. THE MIKADO, entering the garden with his attendants. The Mikado is an opera by Gilbert and Sullivan. The same construction as 1 and 2. $2.25.

4. Oriental designs often represent something grotesque or violent and this is a good example. Two-piece stamped brass. $2.50.

5. KO-KO with fan (The Lord High Executioner in The Mikado). Two-piece stamped brass, concave. $1.00.

6. CHINAMAN WITH UMBRELLA. A concave white metal button with figure holding an umbrella. $1.00.

7. To the Oriental, the dragon has always been a symbol of power, divinity and sovereignty; we find it much used in Oriental decoration. This is a Champleve enamel in color on silver, background enameled black. $3.50.

8. PITTI-SING, a character in The Mikado. One-piece, pressed brass with silver tint, kimono tinted pink. $1.00.

9. MME. CHRYSANTHEME from the opera by the same name. One-piece pressed brass. $1.00.

10. YUM-YUM, also from The Mikado. Two-piece pressed brass. $3.00.

11. KATISHA. Her parasol forms the background of the slightly concave brass button. $.75.

12. CHINESE DRAGON SLAYER. A pierced brass design, attached to an ornamental border. A basket weave background. $4.50.

13. The small size of No. 12. $1.00.

14. PITTI-SING, a sister of Yum-Yum. A pierced brass design over a dark background. These buttons illustrating "The Mikado" were made about 1885, when the opera was first popular. $3.50.

15. A typical ORIENTAL DESIGN. Two-piece brass with design in low relief. $.75.

16. GEISHA GIRL, looking from window, framed by ivy. Two-piece pressed brass, showing head in high relief against darkened background. $1.00.

17. Called, "THE THRILLER". The man, apparently Chinese, looks frightened by what he is reading but there was probably some other inspiration for the design. Brass with tin collet. $4.00.

18. Called, "TIMUR". The face is well defined but grim. Two-piece pressed brass. $1.25.

19. ORIENTAL BIRD with foliage. One-piece pressed brass. $.75.

20. ORIENTAL SWEEPING GARDEN PATH. Two-piece pressed brass, tinted. $1.00.

21. ORIENTAL SCENE. Two-piece pressed brass with design in low relief. $.50.

22. SATSUMA with polychrome painting and gold encrustation. $25.00.

23. WILLOW PATTERN. One-piece pressed brass with familiar scene that has been used to decorate dishes (usually blue and white) for so many years. It illustrates a Chinese love story and is backmarked with Chinese characters. $2.00.

24. ORIENTAL PLAYING MANDOLIN. A one-piece pierced brass design, attached to the sawtooth border by four five point stars. $2.25.

25. One-piece pierced brass. AN ORIENTAL with background of palms. $1.00.

26. A SATSUMA with polychrome painting equal to the best in portrait painting. $12.00.

27. This SATSUMA, polychrome painted, has a Japanese pheasant and chrysanthemums in the foreground and illustrates well, the type of gold encrustation which was used on the older Satsumas. Mt. Fujiyama can be seen in the distance outlined against the crackle glaze background. Both 26 and 27 have a backmark which is a red cross inside a circle. $12.00 and $20.00.

28. PAGODA and bird in a small scene on a two-piece concave button. $.75.

29. KINKO, we are told, was a musician of the Japanese Court who died by drowning. Legend says that he returned from the sea, riding on a carp. One-piece, concave brass, silvered. $1.00.

PLATE 33

PLATE 33

SPORTS & PASTIMES

1. THE HUNT. The riders are in high relief in the foreground. The windmill, decorated with a cut steel star, and the trees are in low relief which gives dimension to the picture. The border of this one-piece brass button is formed by a curved riding crop, the handle of which is a hoof. This rare specimen is owned by Prudence Crawford. Value, $18.00.

2. Called, "WASHINGTON, THE HUNTSMAN". The design is of white metal with a brass border and back which is marked, "T.W. & W". Also from the collection of Prudence Crawford. $30.00.

3. A FABLE button called, "THE FISH AND THE SHEPHERD WHO PLAYED ON A CLARINET", Story found in LaFontaine. This is an exact reproduction of Dore's illustration. Two-piece metal. $6.50.

4. Called THE SWISS HUNTER, pierced brass with silver finish on tinted background, brass rim. $8.00.

5. THE KILL, pierced brass over darkened background, brass rim. $6.50.

6. TRAINING THE DOG. A convex, pierced design over a brass background. A tinted tin border frames this and the collet is of brass. $3.50.

7. BICYCLE GIRL in bloomer costume. White metal design attached to a scalloped steel liner, over a composition background. Twisted rope border of brass. $18.00.

8. WILD BOAR AND HUNTING DOGS. One - piece brass set in cut steel rim. $4.00.

9. A black, pressed horn button with excellently molded design of a rider clinging to an overhanging branch as his mount runs away in apparent fright. This button is not identified but it has been suggested that the design might have been intended to represent Ichabod Crane after he sees the "Headless Horseman". $8.50.

10. Called "UNION PACIFIC", this button shows with fine detail, a train on a trestle. It has a pierced shell with darkened background and a leaf design in the border. $4.50.

11. INDIAN RIDER, brass design on purple tinted brass background. $3.50.

12. THE LIGHT CAVALRYMAN, from a painting by Gerleault (1791-1824). A very high raised design on pebbled brass "T.W. & W". $12.50.

13. This button was loaned by Mrs. Louis Miles. It is called, "GRITTER", an Icelander who, according to the story, lived as an outlaw. He was supposed to be the strongest man who ever lived in Iceland. He overcame the huge ghost, named Gam, a troll, a giant, a witch and fierce robbers. Through no fault of his own, he was pursued by ill fortune. This was taken from "Hero Tales from Many Lands". The original story is "The Gritter Saga" by Allen French. The picture in the book is almost identical except for a slight difference in footwear. Note the animal skin used for a covering, with head, showing ears, drawn over Gritter's own head. A primitive shield is held in one hand and a dagger in the other. All brass, with a dark tint, cut-out design and oak leaf border. $25.00.

14. LADY POLING FLAT BOTTOMED BOAT. A nice design, pierced with background forming sky, enclosed in a pierced border over a steel liner. This specimen is tinted dark blue. $3.50.

PLATE 34

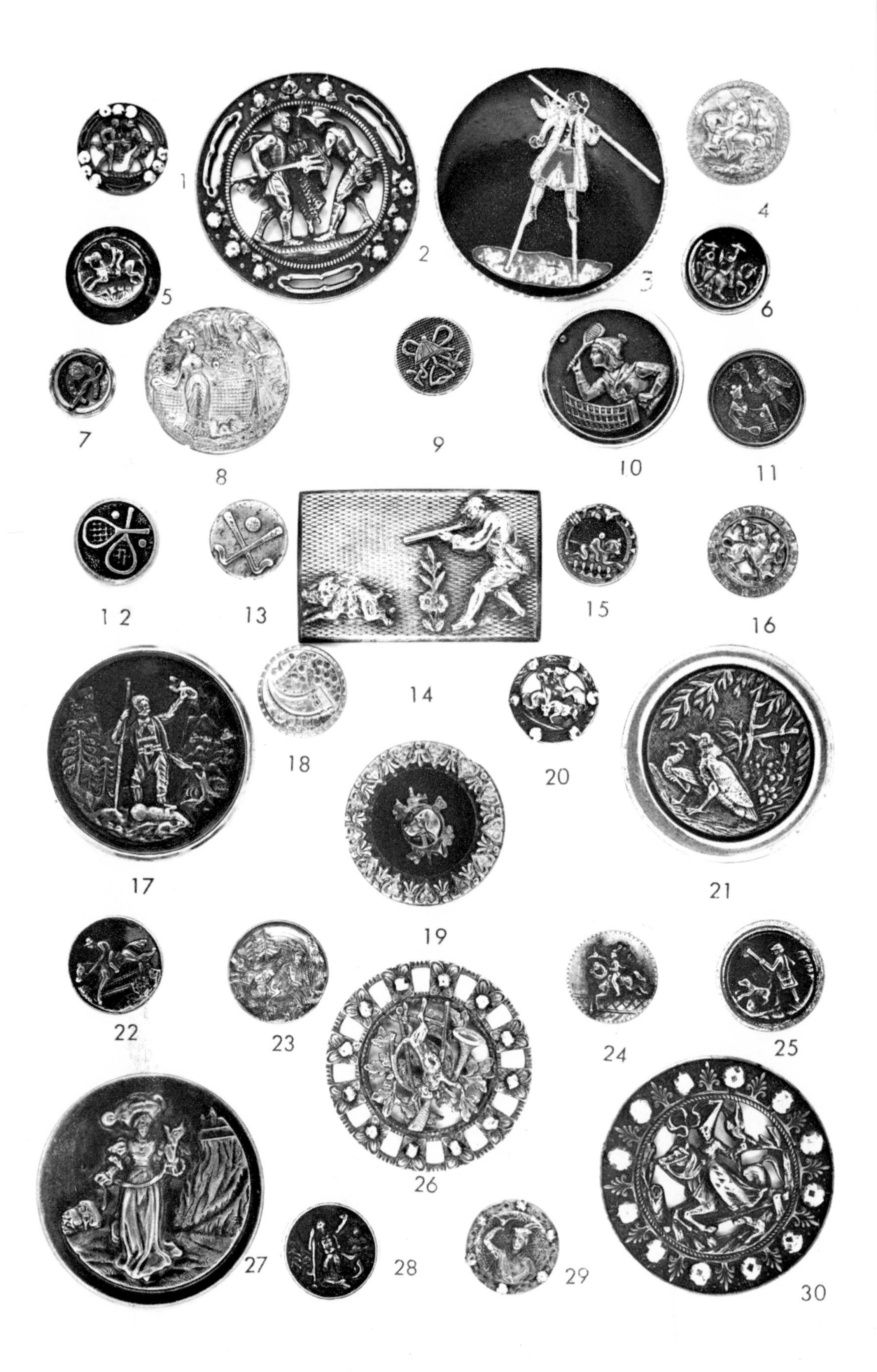
1
2
3
4
5
6
7
8
9
10
11
12
13
14
15
16
17
18
19
20
21
22
23
24
25
26
27
28
29
30

PLATE 34

SPORTS

1. and 2. THE GLADIATORS, professional fighters of ancient Rome who contended in the arena with either men or animals, using nets, shields and a trident - shaped weapon. All of this equipment can be seen in the design which is of pierced brass, with cut steel trim, exceptionally well made. Small, $2.00; Large, $15.00.

3. RETRIEVER. This fine button, owned by Edith Rodway, is of Champleve enamel with polychrome shades of blue, wine, green, orange and cream on a black background. The boy's hair is brown. Walking on stilts, is a sport, in itself, enjoyed by children but this button illustrates the sport of hunting, also. In swampy areas, such as those of the lower Mississippi, boys on stilts have been used by bird hunters to retrieve game and this is apparently what this youth has been doing. $32.50.

4. READY FOR THE JOUST. Jousting was another ancient sport in which two knights on horseback engaged in combat. The lance, or pike used as a weapon can be seen on this small, one-piece brass button. $1.50.

5. JOCKEY ON HORSEBACK, standing in stirrups, two-piece brass. $1.25.

6. HUNTING HORNS, two-piece brass. $1.00.

7. JOCKEY CAP, whip and horseshoe, a cut out design mounted on a two-part, pressed brass button. $.75.

8. BADMINTON. The costumes worn for active sport by Victorian ladies seem amusing today. Stamped brass, women in relief. $2.50.

9. JOCKEY'S EQUIPMENT, cap, crop and stirrup, two - piece tin. $.75.

10. PLAYING TENNIS, stamped brass with design in relief. $2.00.

11. TENNIS PLAYERS, two-piece brass with cut out design. $1.00.

12. TENNIS RACQUETS AND BALLS. Pressed brass. $.75.

13. GOLF CLUBS AND BALLS. Pressed brass. $.50.

14. An oblong shape, HUNTER, AIMING AT WILD BOAR, from Edith Rodway's collection of buttons which illustrate sports. Pressed brass. $6.50.

15. STEEPLECHASE. The horse is about to take a hurdle. Two-piece pierced brass with border formed by hunting crop, having a hoof as a handle. $1.25.

16. JOUSTING, similar to No. 4 but having a pierced design and border of nail heads. $1.00.

17. THE KILL. An Alpine hunter with a slain deer at his feet. A pierced brass design, mounted on darkened brass background with a tin rim. $6.50.

18. POWDER HORN, brass in high relief on hammered brass background. This is very scarce and could be classed with "Objects", as could Nos. 7, 9, 12 and 13. $1.00.

19. Head of HOUND, inside hunting horn. Brass design on dark brass background with heart border. $2.00.

20. THE PICADOR, inciting the bull to fight. One-piece silvered brass, cut-out design in relief, border set with cut steels. $1.75.

21. GAME BIRDS. Brass in relief with wide tinned border. Quite plentiful. $1.50.

22. STEEPLECHASE. Two-piece cut out design, applied to slightly concave brass background. $.75.

23. HUNTING DOGS with hunter in background, reeds and pine trees well defined. The silver and copper tints on this two-piece brass button are unusual. $1.00.

24. FALCON HUNTER. One-piece concave brass with cut out design applied. $1.50.

25. HUNTER AND DOG. Two-piece brass with tin rim. $1.00.

26. A cut out background of oak leaves is centered by a HANGING RABBIT, hunting horn and gun, attached to a pierced border set with cut steels. One-piece brass. $6.50.

27. MARY TUDOR WITH FALCON. (See Plate 36). Two-piece pressed brass. A scarce design. $12.00.

28. The small size of No. 17. $1.00.

29. A fine design of a FALCON HUNTER whose breast plate shows a Fleur-de-Lis and, though unidentified, he is doubtless a French nobleman. One-piece pressed brass with cut steel trimmed border. Rare. $1.25.

30. FALCON HUNTRESS of the Renaissance Period as indicated by her costume. Pierced brass, the wide border set with faceted steels. $15.00.

PLATE 35

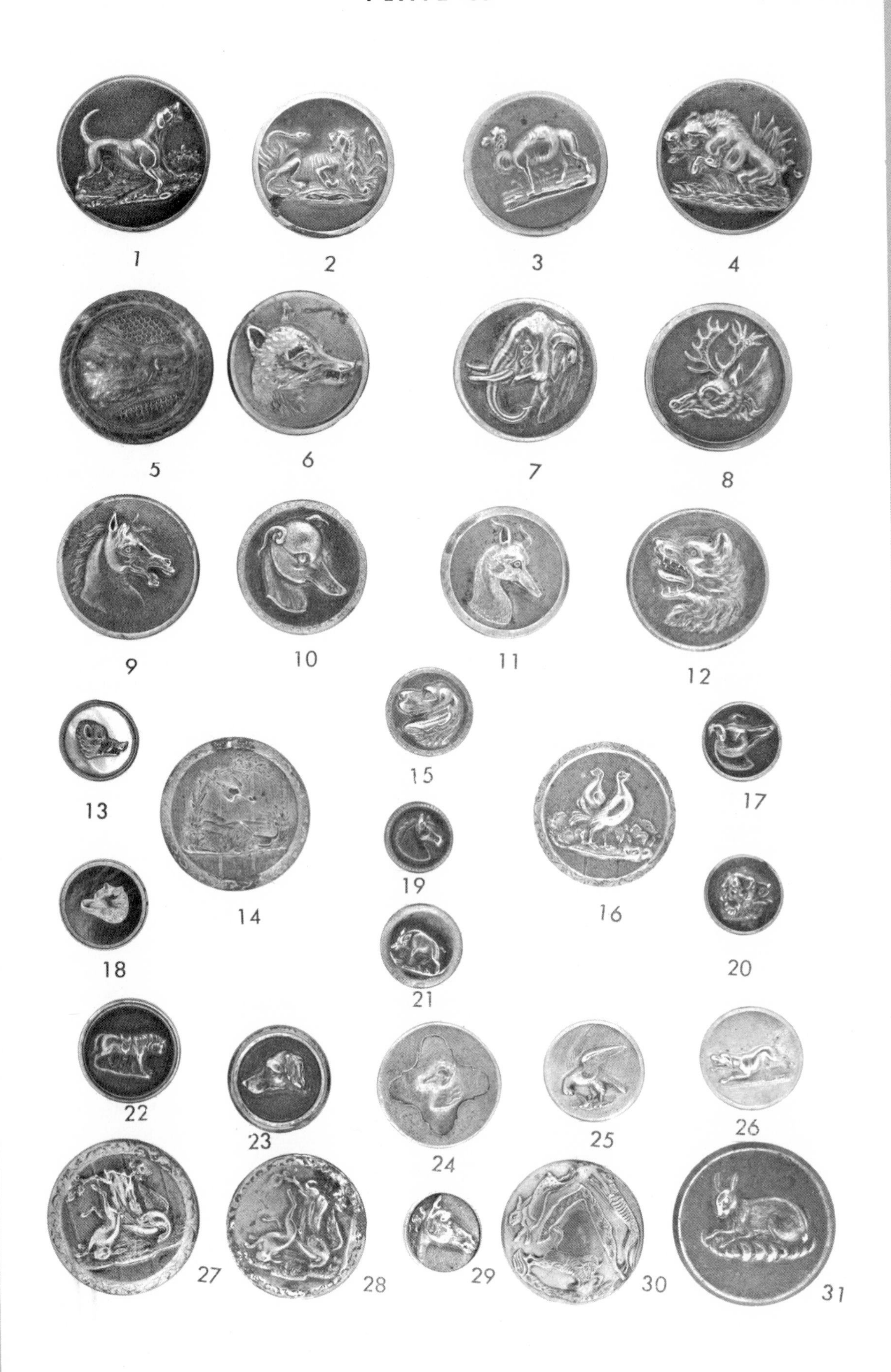
1
2
3
4
5
6
7
8
9
10
11
12
13
14
15
16
17
18
19
20
21
22
23
24
25
26
27
28
29
30
31

PLATE 35

SPORTS & SPORTING

Sporting Buttons were made to be worn on hunting costumes. Some are the size suitable for coats and some are smaller, for vests or coat sleeves. They were made in different materials but the greatest number are of brass. They are decorated with pictures of animals, either the animals used in pursuit or the game animals themselves. Most Sporting Buttons were made in sets, and it is interesting to try to assemble complete sets. This is not difficult as the border designs are the same for each button in a set and the makers name will be found on the back. The animals on these buttons are very well represented. Making the dies from which these sets of buttons were struck, required great artistic skill.

We have tried to show you as many examples from different sets as possible on this Plate.

1. HUNTING DOG, brass with stippled background. Back marked, "Extra Rich Treble Stand". $2.50.
2. TIGER AND SNAKE from Indian area. "Wadhams Co. Superior". This is an American firm. $2.50.
3. DROMEDARY. From the same set as No. 2. Back marked the same. $3.00.
4. WILD BOAR. "Treble Stand. Extra Rich" Same set as No. 1. $2.50.
5. White metal with WILD BOAR HEAD. "Sporting Designs". $2.50.
6. FOX. Same back marking as No. 1, but a slightly smaller size and with a different shank, therefore not from the same set. $2.50.
7. ELEPHANT'S HEAD. "Scovill Mfg. Co., Waterbury". $5.00.
8. ELK HEAD. This button has an applied rim. Others of the same set should have this same rim. Back mark the same as No. 1. $2.50.
9. HORSE'S HEAD. Same back mark as No. 1. $2.50.
10. HEAD OF HUNTING DOG. "Extra Quality Sporting". This button has a chased border. $2.50.
11. DOG'S HEAD. "Warranted Best Quality." $2.50.
12. HEAD OF WOLF. Same back mark as No. 1. $2.50.
13. This is the vest size. A brass WILD BOAR'S HEAD on pearl. Brass rim, tin back and no back mark. $.75.
14. GAME BIRDS, stamped on a paneled background. "Superior Quality Extra Rich". $2.50.
15. DOG'S HEAD. "Extra Sporting". $.75.
16. GAME BIRDS, from the same set as No. 14. Same back mark. $2.50.
17. DOG'S HEAD. "Extra Quality". $.75.
18. Brass HEAD on pearl, brass rim and back. Marked, "Superfin Paris". $.75.
19. HORSE'S HEAD, two-piece with brass back. "T.W. & W. Paris". $1.00.
20. DOG'S HEAD, Brass back, marked, "Extra Qualtiy". $.75.
21. WILD BOAR. "Superfin Paris". $.75.
22. HORSE WITH SADDLE, brass back, applied rim. "Superfin Paris". $2.00.
23. DOG'S HEAD in high relief, applied rim. No back mark. $.75.
24. This head is framed by a pierced, etched brass piece which is turned over the brass back. "Hayden & Hodson Extra". $2.00.
25. AN EAGLE in high relief, brass back. "Extra Treble Stand." $2.00.
26. HUNTING DOG, IN PURSUIT. "Extra Treble Stand". $1.00.
27. HANGING GAME. Same background, border and back mark as 14 and 16. $3.50.
28. The same design as 27 but a different background and border. Back marked, "Hayden & Hodson Extra". $3.50.
29. HEAD OF HORSE, $1.00.
30. BUFFALO, HOUND AND HARE, convex brass, turned over tin back. No back mark. $2.50.
31. RABBIT. "Extra Rich Treble Stand". $3.50.

Extra Rich, Treble, Superior, etc. refer to the gilding of the buttons. Treble would mean that the button had been dipped three times in the gilt solution. A few grains of gold were put in the solution to produce a goldlike finish.

PLATE 36

PLATE 36

LOVERS & COUPLES

Many of the great lovers of story, drama and opera have been represented on buttons. On Plate No. 36 we show you a few.

1. The identity of these two people can be easily guessed; PRISCILLA AND JOHN ALDEN, whose courtship and love story is told by Longfellow in, "The Courtship of Miles Standish". Two-piece stamped brass. $4.50.

2. Called ORIENTAL WEDDING and by some ORIENTAL GREETING. The latter seems suitable. One-piece pierced brass with riveted, steel, crescent moon. $6.50.

3. Small size of No. 2. $1.25.

4. Stamped yellow and white metal, two-piece. Called PAUL AND VIRGINIA, characters from a French story by Bernardin de St. Pierre, published in 1788. It is a tragic love story, typical of that era, which was made into plays and operas. In this picture Paul and Virginia are running in the rain, holding a covering over their heads. There are several slightly different buttons showing these two lovers but each shows the same pose. They were identified from an old toile (piece of fabric) which tells this story. $3.50.

5. MAUD MULLER (Maud Muller on a summer day/raked the meadow sweet with hay) — by John Greenleaf Whittier. One-piece pressed brass in relief. $2.00.

6. AN ORIENTAL COUPLE. One-piece, low relief. $1.25.

7. SPRING TIME, from a painting by Pierre Auguste Cot (1837-1883) who painted many idealistic portraits (N.B.B., May, 1947). $1.25.

8. The small size of No. 4. $1.25.

9. and 10. MARY TUDOR, sister of Henry VIII, a prinicpal character in, "When Knighthood was in Flower" by Edwin Gaskoden. She is mentioned as releasing her hawk and setting out to meet Brandon with whom she eloped. Large size No. 9, $8.00. Small size No. 10, $2.00. Brass, pierced border with steel mirror liner, figure in high relief over darkened background.

11. This button has been called by various names but it is quite obviously a companion to Mary Tudor and therefore must be BRANDON. Construction the same as No. 9. $8.00.

12. and 13. WOODLAND VOWS. Stamped brass, two-piece, bronze finish. Each $4.00.

14. LOVE'S SERVICE, a copy of a painting by this name which hangs in the Public Library at Woburn, Mass., painted by Siegert. This was identified by the Bay State Button Society for Couse and Maple, as noted in Button Classics. Two-piece, pressed brass excellent detail. $12.00.

15. CARMEN AND TOREADORE, stamped brass, two - piece, tinted. This button was cheaply reproduced in the 1940's in copper, not as clearly defined as this original with a heavy shank. The original, formerly selling for $12.50, now brings $8.00 and the reproduction $4.00.

16. Goethe's FAREWELL TO FREDERIQUE. This button was called "Washington's Farewell to Marion" for a long time but was positively identified by Alice Helgestad (N.B.B., March, 1949) from an exact print shown in "L'Illustration" for 1932. The print was from a painting by W. Friedrich, a German artist, and titled, "Goethe and Frederique Brien at the Gate of the Presbytery at Sessenheim". This interlude of Geothe's was the inspiration for his Marquerite and Faust. Two-piece stamped brass, tinted. $12.00. This is another button that was reproduced. The reproduction has a heavy white metal loop shank and a tin back. $4.00.

17. Two LOVERS WITH A BIRDCAGE, two-piece pressed brass, with nice detail, it is reminiscent of Boucher and Vanloo's 18th century miniatures on ivory and metal. This is one of the few all-brass buttons back-marked, "Eingetr Muster and W.L.R." $12.00.

PLATE 37

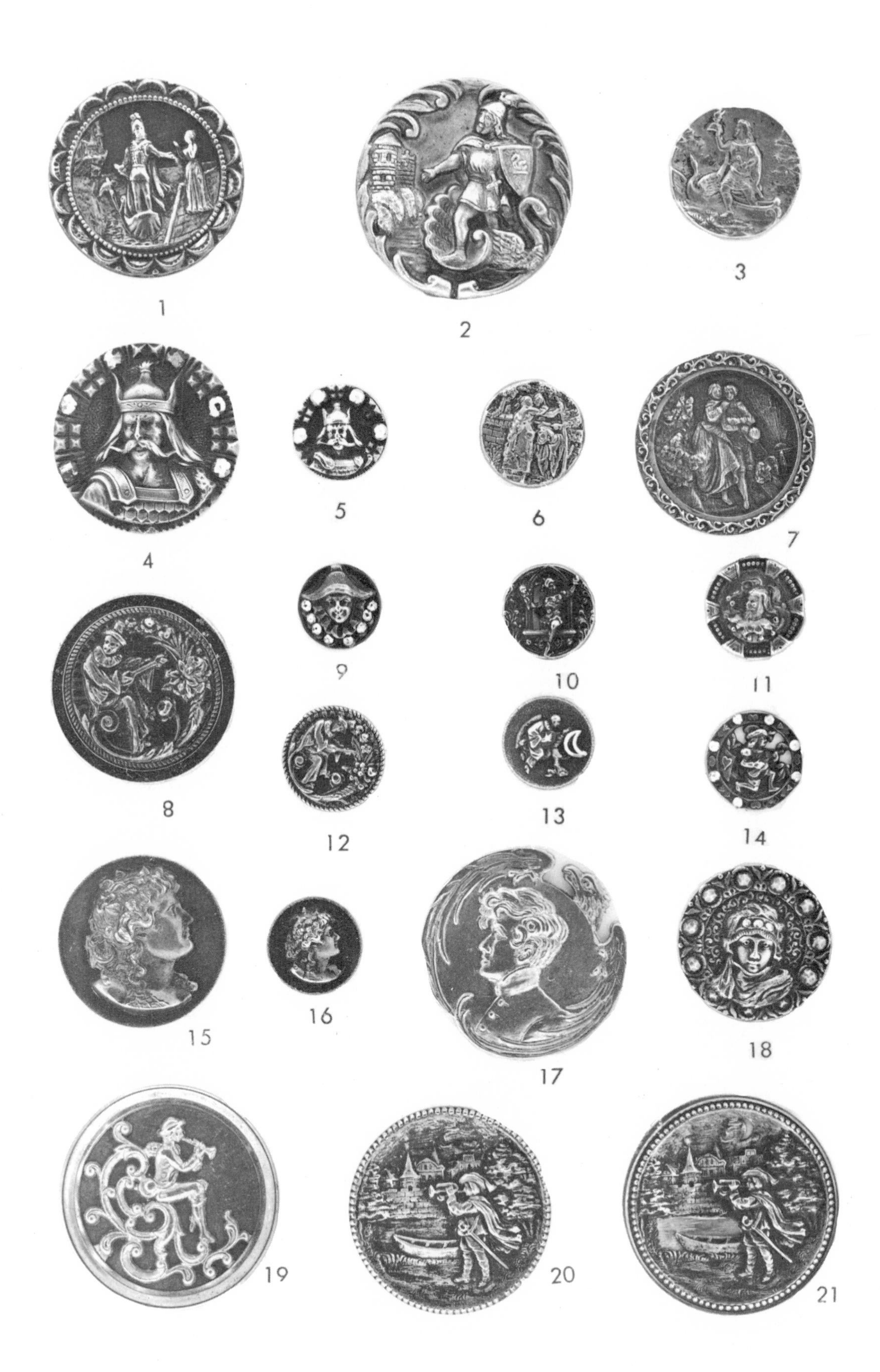

PLATE 37

THEATRE & OPERA

1. LOHENGRIN'S FAREWELL TO ELSA from the opera by Richard Wagner. In this picture the dove of the Grail is is about to draw the boat and Lohengrin away from the shore. A pierced design over darkened background; scalloped, pierced border shows steel liner underneath. $3.50.

2. THE ARRIVAL OF LOHENGRIN in swan boat. A swan also on his shield as he was known as the Swan Knight; two-piece brass, the picture having no rim. $6.50.

3. This medium sized button also illustrates THE ARRIVAL OF LOHENGRIN. Two-piece pressed brass, seldom found. $4.00.

4. This button has been called both "King Harold" and "WODEN" and the helmet does appear to be the Viking type but we have placed this representation here to show the marked resemblance to the beardless head of Lohengrin as shown on the first button, and we suggest that possibly this was intended to represent Lohengrin. The head is in extremely high relief, in one-piece brass with cut steel border. The same head is also found in black glass, black horn, and a steel cup with the head mounted on a wood background. $8.00.

5. The same head as No. 4 in the small size. $1.50.

6. IMMO AND HILDEGARDE, characters in, "The Wren's Nest" by Gustav Freytag; two-piece brass. $1.50.

7. LUCY ASHTON AND EDGAR, characters from "The Bride of Lammermoor" by Sir Walter Scott. Many plays and operas have been inspired by this book, the best known being, "Lucia di Lammermoor". A two-piece pressed brass button; also found in ivoroid with brass rim. $6.50.

8. CANIO, the clown in the opera "Pagliacci"; brass with a tinned rim, present value $3.00.

9. HARLEQUIN, a comic character; head is in very high relief, one-piece brass with cut steel trim. $1.50.

10. and 11. RIGOLETTO from the opera by Verdi, based on the drama, Le Roi s'Amuse by Victor Hugo. Rigoletto was the jester of the Duke of Mantua. In No. 10 he is coming through a window in one of his antics to amuse the court. He holds the mock scepter with carved fool's head which he usually carried. One-piece brass, pierced. $1.50.

11. Head of RIGOLETTO, superimposed on separate background, with ornate border. $1.25.

12. Another CANIO, the small size of No. 8, without tin rim. $1.00.

13. SCARAMOUCH, a stock character in 17th century Italian farce; stamped brass with cut steel crescent moon. $1.50.

14. CYRANO DE BERGERAC, as seen in the third act of the play by the same name, where he plays the "Theorbo" and sings to Roxanne. A pierced brass button with a border which is decorated with hearts and cut steels. Cyrano's large aquiline nose, which is one of his identifying characteristics, can be seen, even on this small button. $1.75.

15. and 16. SARAH BERNHARDT, one of the most famous of all actresses. One-piece, all brass buttons, head in very high relief. Medium, $4.00. Small, $2.00. Also can be found in black pressed horn.

17. LITTLE EAGLET, as played by "The Divine Sarah" in the play, L'Aiglon by Edmond Rostand, presented first about 1900. Little Eaglet was the Duke of Reichstadt, son of Napoleon and Marie Louise, and Bernhardt's portrayal of him was considered most remarkable, as she was 56 years old. A very fine, one-piece button with eagle and buttons on the costume tinted gold, and the rest silvered. $8.00.

18. Sarah Bernhardt as THEODORA, in the play written by Sardou and first produced December 26, 1884. Theodora was a Byzantium Empress and the scenes are at the time of the decline of the Roman Empire. A fine, one-piece brass button, pressed in very high relief, with cut steel border. $4.50.

19. PETER PAN, as played by Maud Adams. Pierced pewter design on darkened brass background with brass rim and tinned liner. $3.50.

20. and 21. THE TRUMPETER OF SACKINGEN, from a poem by von Scheffel on which several operas were based. No. 20 is a two-piece pressed brass button, value $6.50.

21. This representation is pierced brass over a tinned background, which shows through the cut out portions, making a silver moon and lake. A tinned rim also. $8.00.

PLATE 38

PLATE 38

PEOPLE

1. FRENCH SAILORS. One-piece brass with cut steels on wheel; rope border. Value, $8.00.

2. AUDUBON. A pewter figure in 18th century costume with bird on tinted background. Value, $3.00.

3. LANDSKNECHT, an early German soldier. One-piece silvered brass. Value, $6.50.

4. HENRY OF NEVARRE. One-piece pierced brass. Value, $3.50.

5. AENEAS, TROJAN PRINCE. Pierced brass; one-piece. Value, $2.75.

6. CHARLEMAGNE. Brass design over tinted background and steel mirror liner. Value, $4.00.

7. MARS, God of war. Silvered brass with shield of cut steel. Value, $3.50.

8. The same as No. 7 in the small size. Value, $1.00.

9. POSTUMUS, Roman emperor 259-267, ruled in Gaul and Britain and died in battle. This is a coin type button, silvered brass. Value, $2.50.

10. VERRAZZANO. He sailed up the Hudson River for a distance in 1524, long before Henry Hudson. Value, $5.50.

11. ROLAND. A two-piece pressed brass button. $4.00.

12. The same as No. 11 in the small size. Value, $1.00.

13. HENRY OF NEVARRE; brass, the head set in a frame with fleur-de-lis border. Value, $3.50.

14. CHARLES THE FIFTH OF SPAIN AND GERMANY. Pressed brass, pierced, showing darkened background. Value, $4.00.

15. ANDREA DEL SARTOS, known as "Andrea the tailor's son" - boy artist who lived in Italy, became famous as a fresco painter. Value, $3.50.

16. Another representation of ANDREA DEL SARTOS. Value, $3.50.

17. HECTOR; brass head and rim with heart border and darkened background. Value, $3.00.

PLATE 39

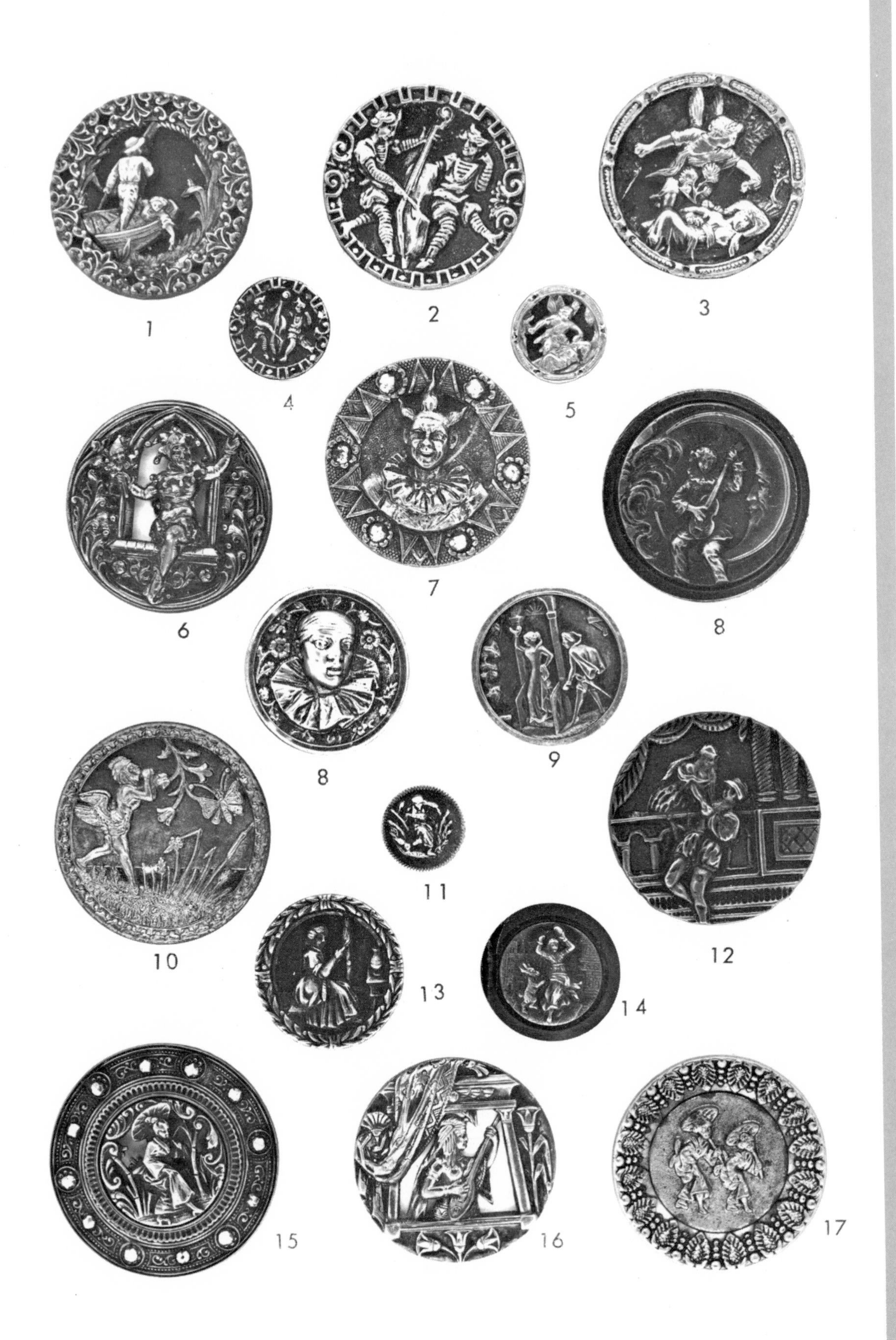

PLATE 39

MUSICAL & SHAKESPEAREAN

When an opera or play became popular during the nineteenth century, the characters were often portrayed on buttons. A few such are illustrated here.

1. This button has been identified (B.C., Page 247) as ARTHUR BONNICASTLE AND MILLIE BRADFORD, characters in a novel by J.G. Holland (1819-1881) who was at one time editor of Scribners' magazine and who wrote a number of sentimental novels that were widely read during his life time. A two-piece, pierced brass button with darkened background and decorative border. $8.00.

2. Called, "THE MINNESINGERS", (German poets and musicians who flourished about 1150-1350). Two-piece pressed brass. $6.50.

3. OBERON AND TITANIA, characters in "Midsummer Night's Dream" by Shakespeare, a comedy in five Acts. The pierced brass design, attached to rim, has a darkened, concave background. $8.00.

4. The small size of No. 2. $2.00.

5. The small size of No. 3. $2.00.

6. RIGOLETTO, the jester in Verdi's opera by the same name. The plot was taken from Victor Hugo's drama of intrigue, treachery, and revenge at the court of Francois I of France, and the first performance was in Venice, March 11, 1851. One-piece pressed brass, the design pierced to show Rigoletto stepping through an open window. $6.50.

7. PAGLIACCI, from the short opera by Ruggiero Leoncavallo, first produced in Milan in 1892. Pagliacci was the name given to the mimes and comedians, who were strolling players of 16th century Italy. Leoncavallo once wrote that in Montalto, the town of his boyhood and locale of the opera, an actor killed his wife after the performance. The composer's father was the judge at the trial. The episode made such a deep impression that Leoncavallo later immortalized it in Pagliacci. The clown is in high relief on a pebbled brass background, circled by a wide border, set with cut steels. $12.00.

8. SCARAMOUCH, a stock character in 17th century Italian farce. Scaramouch was beaten by Harlequin for his boasting and cowardice. This button has a steel cup foundation with a brass center on which the figure sits in high relief on a crescent moon. Scarce. $8.00.

8a. CANIO, who plays the part of Punchinelle in the role of Nedda's deceived husband in the opera "Pagliacci" (Nedda is Columbine in the play). This brass head is in very high relief and the brass background has a pattern of scattered flowers; tin rim. $2.50.

9. MACBETH AND LADY MACBETH from Shakespeare's "Macbeth", a tragedy in 5 Acts. This is a scarce button of stamped brass in high relief; two-piece. $5.50.

10. ARIEL from Shakespeare's "The Tempest", a comedy in 4 Acts. Ariel is a merry little sprite. The design of white metal is attached to the rim and behind the cat tails and grasses is a steel mirror, representing water; brass rim. $4.50.

11. OPHELIA, daughter of Polonius in Shakespeare's "Hamlet". White metal design on flat white metal background. $1.25.

12. ROMEO AND JULIET, the tragedy by Shakespeare was set to music in the opera by Charles Gounod (first performance in 1867.) This button supposedly illustrates the famous balcony scene; two-piece pierced brass. $18.00.

13. MARGUERITE, character in Charles Gounod's "Faust". At the beginning of Act Four, Marguerite is seen seated at her spinning wheel as the curtain rises. She is taunted by girl's voices from outside and then sings "The Spinning Wheel Song", which voices her love and longing for Faust. Pierced brass design with brass, laurel wreath border, steel liner and darkened background. $5.00.

14. ESMERALDA, the dancing gypsy-girl in Victor Hugo's, "Notre Dame de Paris" which was made into the opera "Esmeralda", by Dargonizsky and first performed in 1847. This is an escutcheon type, pressed brass design, set on a wood background. $10.00.

15. YUM-YUM from the Mikado. The pierced design is an escutcheon type; held within the border by a band of brass at the back, which is soldered to the outer rim and contains the loop shank; the border is set with cut steels. $6.50.

16. CLEOPATRA, a beautiful, pierced brass button decorated with lotus flowers and other Egyptian designs. Shakespeare's "Anthony and Cleopatra" tells the tragedy of the beautiful Egyptian Queen. $8.00.

17. PEEP-BO AND PETTI-SING from the Mikado. Figures are in relief in the brass center design. A brass pine cone border and steel liner. $3.00.

PLATE 40

PLATE 40

HEADDRESSES

1. AN ORIENTAL HAT, adorning a grim but impressive countenance. One-piece pressed brass. Rare. $2.50.

2. "KATINKA", (D.F.B.). This is a sixteenth century costume. Two-piece, stamped brass, pierced to show a tin liner. $1.00.

3. ARSINOE (wife of one of the Ptolemys). Her cap-like headdress partially covers long curls. Head in high relief on slightly convex background. Two-piece, gold tinted brass. $2.50. Also found in black, pressed horn.

4. Called, "VICTORIAN GIRL WITH LARGE HAT" by Nicholls. Pressed brass. $.75.

5. DE SOTO, wearing helmet. Hernando De Soto was a stern, harsh Spaniard, who came to America in search of gold and a direct waterway to the Pacific. He died after years of hardship, and was buried in the Mississippi River, which he had discovered instead of riches. Two-piece pressed brass with pressed pewter head applied. A similar button, trimmed with cut steels can be found. Value for this, $4.50.

6. MARGUERITE, from "Faust". A large hat and cap-shaped net form her headdress. One-piece pressed brass, pierced to show profile. This can also be found with cut steel trim. $3.50 - $5.00.

7. TURBANED LADY, unidentified but shown for the interesting head covering and hair-do. $1.00.

8. CLOWN HAT. Pressed, one-piece brass with good detail. The cut steels exactly fit the plaits in the neck frill. $1.50.

9. QUEEN ESTHER (Biblical). Silver, stamped in one piece. Not hallmarked. $2.00.

10. THEODORA as interpreted by Sarah Bernhardt. This is a Byzantine headdress, ornamented with jewels. One piece pressed brass, cut steel border. $4.00.

11. FANNY DAVENPORT with high-crowned and flower-trimmed hat and parasol. Fanny acted with especial success in "Fedora", "Cleopatra" and other plays. One piece pierced brass design, attached to rim and mounted over tin. $3.00.

12. WINKEN, BLYNKEN AND NOD, characters in a children's poem by Eugene Fields. They seem to be wearing dunce caps. The pierced design is mounted in a tin rim over a tin background with polka-dot design. Ornamental brass border. Not common. $4.50.

13. INDIAN PRINCESS, LALLA ROOKH, who was the subject of a poem by Thomas Moore. The headdress is of draped cloth, ornamented by coins and a dragonfly. Two-piece stamped brass with a palm leaf border. $4.50.

14. UNIDENTIFIED HEAD with draped cloth headdress. Head in very high relief mounted on silver tinted copper. $6.00.

15. Called, "GOVERNOR WINTHROP". The hat and costume are the same type as worn by him and this title has been in use for some time. We have seen this button in five different sizes and sometimes made of hard rubber. $6.00.

16. RIGOLETTO with his "cap and bells" from the opera, based on a novel by Victor Hugo in which, called Triboulet, he is the jester of Francis I. Rim and design of pressed brass. $4.00.

17. SIR WALTER RALEIGH in a courtier's costume with plumed hat, of the late 14th century. One-piece pressed brass, head in very high relief. Border set with cut steels. Fine. $12.00.

18. This headdress is formed by sprays of wheat and is a seasonal head, representing FALL. The button, with superimposed head, is made of hard rubber, possibly with some gutta percha added. $6.00.

19. Victorian CHILD'S HEAD. The straw hat is tied beneath the chin in a style used in the early 1900's. The hat is trimmed with wheat and is probably from another Seasonal Set, this one representing Fall. We have seen the same button with flower-trimmed hat which might represent Spring. Stamped brass. $3.50.

PLATE 41

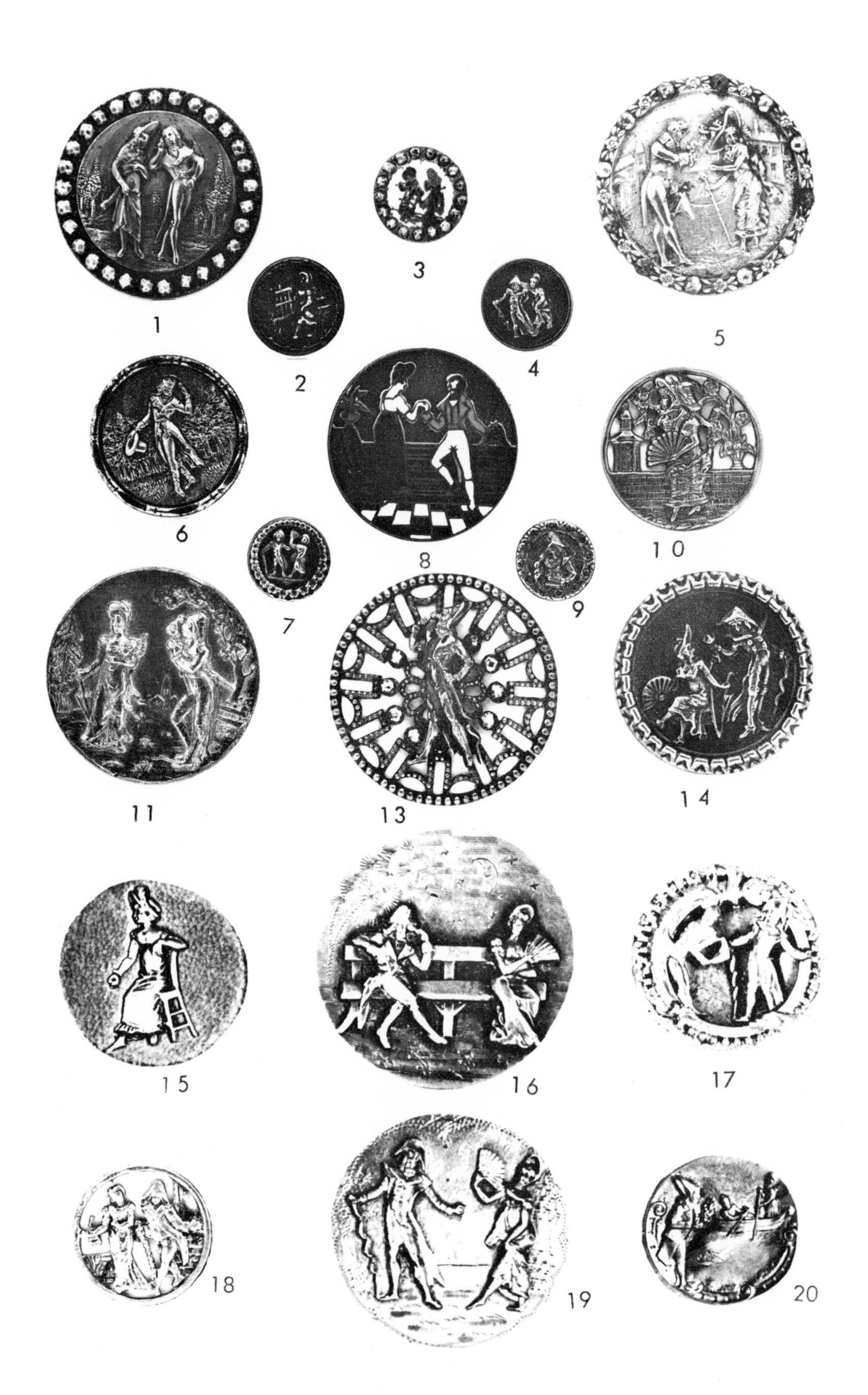

PLATE 41

FRENCH FOPS

Immediatley following the French Revolution, a class of people congregated in Paris who affected a certain type of dress and came to be known as "Fops."

The men usually are pictured in long-tailed, cut away coats, ruffled shirts, tight pants with long hose, tricorn or top hats and accessories such as canes, monocles and boutonniers.

The Ladies wore Poke bonnets, scarves, and long straight dresses which usually had the "Empire" waist line. They carried fans, parasols, and other small frumperies.

Their manners were exaggeratedly formal and overly "nice" and it is from the dress and manners of Fops that we get the meaning of "foppish" as used today.

The period in which Fops ("Incroyable and Merveilleuse" - (unbelievable and marvelous) flourished is called the Directorate, (1795-99). The buttons on which they appear are not plentiful but they are very desirable as they illustrate so well the fashions of that particular era.

1. INCROYABLE AND MERVEILLEUSE, posturing, trees in the background. One-piece brass, gilded with cut steel border. $12.00.

2. MERVEILLEUSE opening gate. Pierced pewter with brass collet. $1.00.

3. Enameled FOPS with cut steel border. $10.00.

4. Two FOPS posing with cane and fan on a dark basket weave background, brass collet. $1.50.

5. INCROYABLE presenting a bouquet, in a grand manner, to Merveilleuse. Tuilleries in the background. One-piece brass, gilded border with cut steels. $12.00.

6. THE PRINCE OF DANDIES, doffing his hat, standing on a path with a row of trees in the background. Brass, in splendid detail with steel collet. $5.00.

7. A similar pose to No. 4 but with a recessed background, darkened and lined. Patterned border. $1.25.

8. A scene from the comedy, "Mme Sans Gene", a satire on the life of Napoleon and Josephine (B.C. page 51). Metal stamped for champleve' work. Polychrome painting. $12.00.

9. This is called "THE TOWN CRIER" and is not a Fop although a cocked hat is worn and the dress seems similar. Brass with ornamental border. $1.50.

10. FROU-FROU. This is not a Fop, although dressed somewhat similar. Frou-Frou was the chief character in a comedy in 5 acts of 1869. One-piece brass with pierced background. $3.00.

11. INCROYABLE AND MERVEILLEUSE with church in the background. She is posing with parasol and bouquet, he with cane and monocle. One-piece brass, gilded. $8.00.

13. INCROYABLE posing with the monocle and cane. Brass figure applied to a pierced background which resembles a spider's web and is decorated with cut steel. Border and background are beaded. $8.00.

14. MERVEILLEUSE seated with open fan and Incroyable is presenting a rose. Brass figures in relief on a darkened background. Wide, ornamented collet. $7.50.

15. MERVEILLEUSE posed in straight backed chair. One-piece brass. $4.00.

16. INCROYABLE AND MERVEILLEUSE seated on bench, indifferent to each other and no doubt wisely, as the background shows a half moon and stars, as well as a tree which indicate a moonlight encounter. Brass figures applied to a flat, engraved background. $12.00.

17. Both brass figures here are men and one has doffed his hat. Darkened background, elaborately decorated collet. $6.50.

18. One-piece pierced brass. MERVEILLEUSE has her fan folded and carries a purse. $3.00.

19. INCROYABLE AND MERVEILLEUSE posing, each with pointed toe as though ready for the dance. Brass with engraved background. $8.00.

20. A MAN GREETING TWO LADIES IN A BOAT. One-piece stamped brass. Probably not a Fop but the costume is similar. $3.50.

PLATE 42

PLATE 42

CATS

Cat buttons are scarce and consequently expensive, but cat lovers are legion and the search for cat buttons goes on and on.

We first hear of the cat historically in Egypt, where she was protected and considered sacred. This was doubtless due to the cat's instinctive efficiency in destroying rodents which consumed the grain and food supply in that country. With the advent of Christianity, the cat naturally lost the exalted position of a deity and she even became associated with the devil and witchcraft in the minds of men. So eventually, she was a symbol of both good and evil, with the black cat especially designated as a sign of witchery and bad luck.

The grace and beauty, the lovable and perverse characteristics of the cat, have had great appeal through the centuries and we find her used repeatedly in both art and literature and, subsequently, by button designers. The cats shown in the two following Plates are from the collection of Mary Miller.

1. PLAYFUL KITTENS, one in the basket and one outside on its back; pierced brass with grass and flowers forming part of the design, over a pearl background. $6.50. $6.50.
2. KITTENS IN A BASKET. Pressed brass design with a pierced crescent border which shows polished steel underneath. $15.00.
3. BRIGHT EYES. A cat head with green glass eyes and bow under chin. Glass, modern. $2.00.
4. WISTFUL CAT. Brass on dark background with brass rim. $8.50.
5. The same as No. 1 in a small size. $3.00.
6. CAT CHORUS. A dog is leading two cats in singing. Two-piece brass. $3.00.
7. Called SCARED CAT. (N). Cats love to play in paper bags and this seems to be what this one is doing. Brass head with steel background. $5.00.
8. CAT IN BASKET. All brass, concave, with cat's head applied. $3.00.
9. CAT HEAD with bow on milk glass background, framed in brass border. $6.50.
10. BLACK GLASS CAT HEAD, with blue luster, medium size. $5.00.
11. IN DANGER. Cat reaching over wall for rabbit. Pressed brass, tin collet. $12.00.
12. SERENADE. Two cats, one playing a mandolin. Pewter. $4.00.
13. Called by some "LITTLE SLEEPER", by other "DICK WHITTINGTON". Two - piece pressed brass, design in relief. Scarce. $18.00.
14. A girl in a clown costume, playing stringed instrument, accompanied by cat. Brass cut out design in one-piece with the border, over a darkened background. $2.00.
15. LIFE OF A SPARROW. An exact copy of an illustration in an old book of children's stories. This story called, "The Life of a Sparrow," by Himself. A pewter design over tinted metal background with brass collet. $12.00.
16. CAT AND THE MOON. A black cat shown in front of a full moon; the rest of the background is green and the picture is under celluloid with a tin rim. $3.00.
17. VICTORIAN GIRL playing with cat and ball. Pressed brass in low relief. $4.50.
18. TWO CATS IN WOODEN SHOE. One-piece pierced metal with cat tails and foliage for background. $5.00.
19. This design is of cut-out brass over red silk and illustrates the Nursery Rhyme, "Pussy Cat, Pussy Cat, Where Have You Been?". $6.50.

PLATE 43

PLATE 43

CATS

1. THE CAT AND THE LOOKING GLASS, a pierced brass design showing an open window. The mirror is of steel. $35.00. This is also classed with fables.

2. KITTY AND THE LIZARD, from LaFontaine's Fable. One-piece pierced brass decorated with cut steels. $18.00.

3. PUSS IN BOOTS from the Nursery Tale by this name. In this design puss is holding up a rat, which in reality is a wicked ogre whom the cat has caught by cleverly persuading him to change himself to this form. Very rare. $35.00.

4. This must be a CIRCUS CAT as he seems to be revolving in a hoop or ring. Pierced brass. $3.00.

5. CONTENTED CAT sits inside a decorated brass border with head outside. Probably an Ashlee. $5.00.

6. PLAYFUL WHITE KITTY. This is a modern button but very charming. White, painted on black glass. $2.50.

7. MEOW, another painted in natural colors, which is most attractive. $6.50.

8. Four grotesque WILDCAT HEADS at each corner of a square, enclosing a round purple and white opaque disk. A flower and leaf form rises from the center of each side of the square and is attached at the top, to the brass border. $4.50.

9. RELUCTANT CAT WITH BIG BOW, posing with a bored expression. An interesting shape with eight points, enclosing an oval, resembling a rug, on which the cat sits. $5.00.

10. KITTEN CAPERS, at midnight, I should say. Pressed brass with design in relief, tin collet. $6.50.

11. CAT IN NEEDLEPOINT SLIPPER, two-piece pressed brass, splendid detail on raised design and paneled wall of background. $5.00.

12. THROUGH THE MOUSE HOLE. The mouse can be seen at one side, one-piece brass. $6.50.

13. CIRCUS CAT (N) plunging through hoop with paper center, one-piece brass. $6.50.

14. KITTEN QUADS. A concave brass button with brass cats and steel shoes which look like wooden-shoes. Very Scarce. $27.50.

15. A square button with decorative frame enclosing a PERSIAN CAT HEAD. $6.50.

PLATE 44

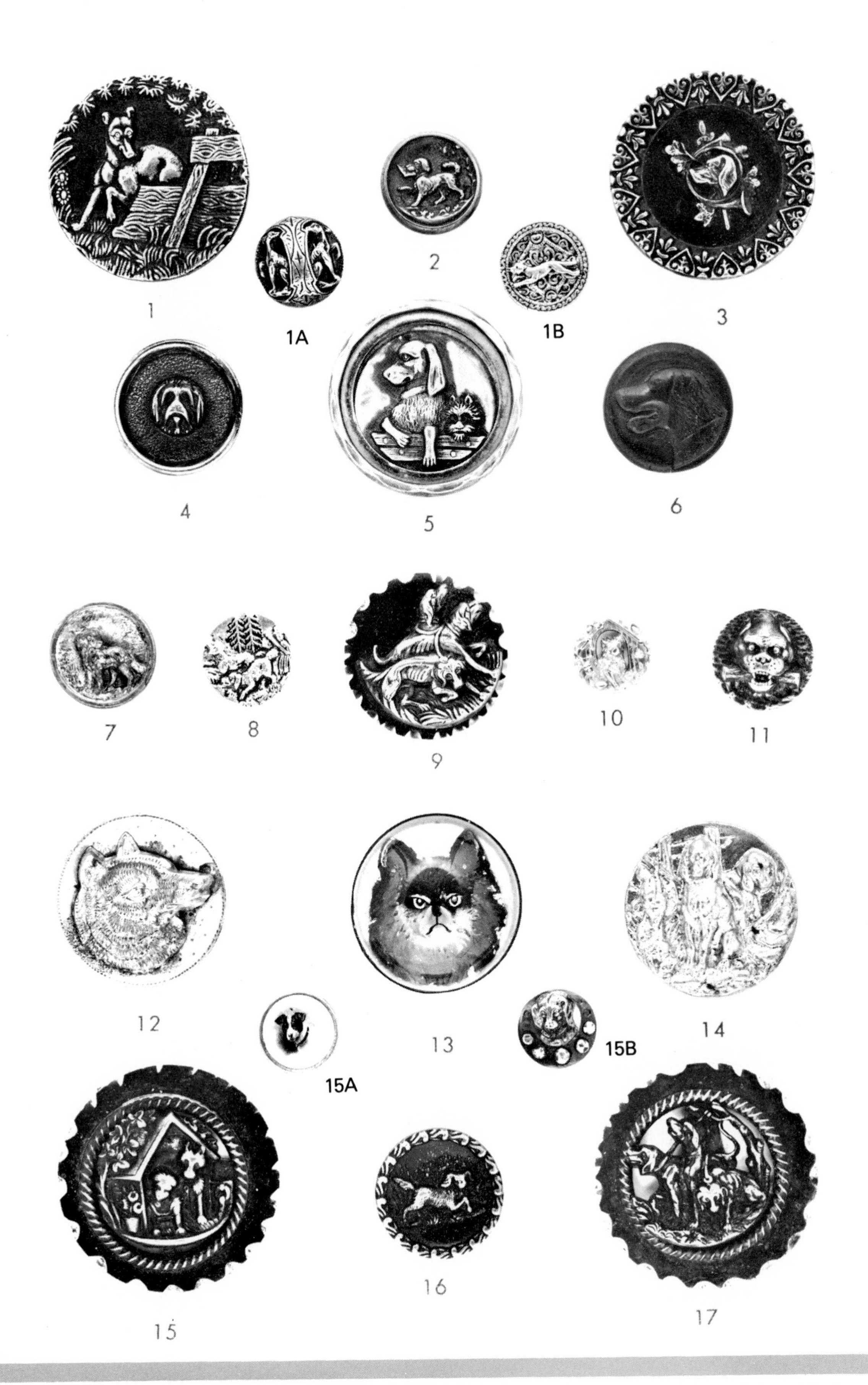

PLATE 44

DOGS

Man's best friend, the dog, assumes varied poses as he appears to us on buttons that can be found by the dog conscious collector.

1. WHIPPET. Brass. Design in low relief. $3.50.

1a GREYHOUNDS with tokens of the chase, heavy convex brass. $.75.

1b RUNNING DOG, possibly whippet. Brass. $.75.

2. LETTER CARRIER. Brass, dog in relief. $1.00.

3. DOG HEAD IN HUNTING HORN. Brass with heart border. $3.00.

4. SHAGGY DOG HEAD, brass in high relief. $1.25.

5. DIGNITY AND IMPUDENCE, from the painting by Landseer. Brass, steel collet. $8.00.

6. DOG HEAD of brown composition, low relief, common. $.75.

7. Silvered copper dog in very high relief. Paris back mark. $1.50.

8. DOGS HUNTING, pine trees and man in background. Made of tin with design in low relief. $.50.

9. HOUNDS OF ST. HUBERT. The dogs are an escutcheon, fastened to the loop shank and the background is steel. $2.25.

10. SMALL DOG IN DOG HOUSE. Pierced brass. $.75.

11. FEROCIOUS BULLDOG, retrieving stick in water. Dog in very high relief. Back - marked, "T.W. &. W." $2.00.

12. HUSKY, head in very high relief on a one-piece, brass background. $1.50.

13. Probably a POMERANIAN. A very high domed glass top has the head shape pressed inside and painted in natural colors, mounted in a brass cup-shaped back with brass loop shank. $7.50.

13a A Lithograph of a TERRIER HEAD; a waist-coat button under celluloid, brass with gilt rim. $2.50.

13b ST. BERNARD, life-saving dog of the Alps, barrel can be seen around neck. This comes in a large size and in various styles. This design is pierced and has cut steel trim underneath the head. $1.75.

14. AFTER THE HUNT. This shows hunting dogs and game in very high relief. Pressed brass, one-piece, back-marked, "Eingeter Muster, W.L.R." $2.00.

15. IN THE DOG HOUSE. The child, dog and dog house are of brass, fastened by a pin shank to a scalloped steel rim. $4.50.

16. RUNAWAY DOG. Pressed brass. $1.75.

17. HOUNDS OF ST. HUBERT. Same construction as No. 15. $4.50.

St. Hubert lived in the Ardennes, a famous hunting forest. The well known legend about him represents his conversion as having been brought about while he was hunting on Good Friday, when a stag bearing between his antlers a cross or crucifix surrounded with rays of light appeared to him. He is the patron of of hunters, and is also invoked in cases of hydrophobia. His feast is celebrated on November 3. (Encyclopedia Britannica).

PLATE 45

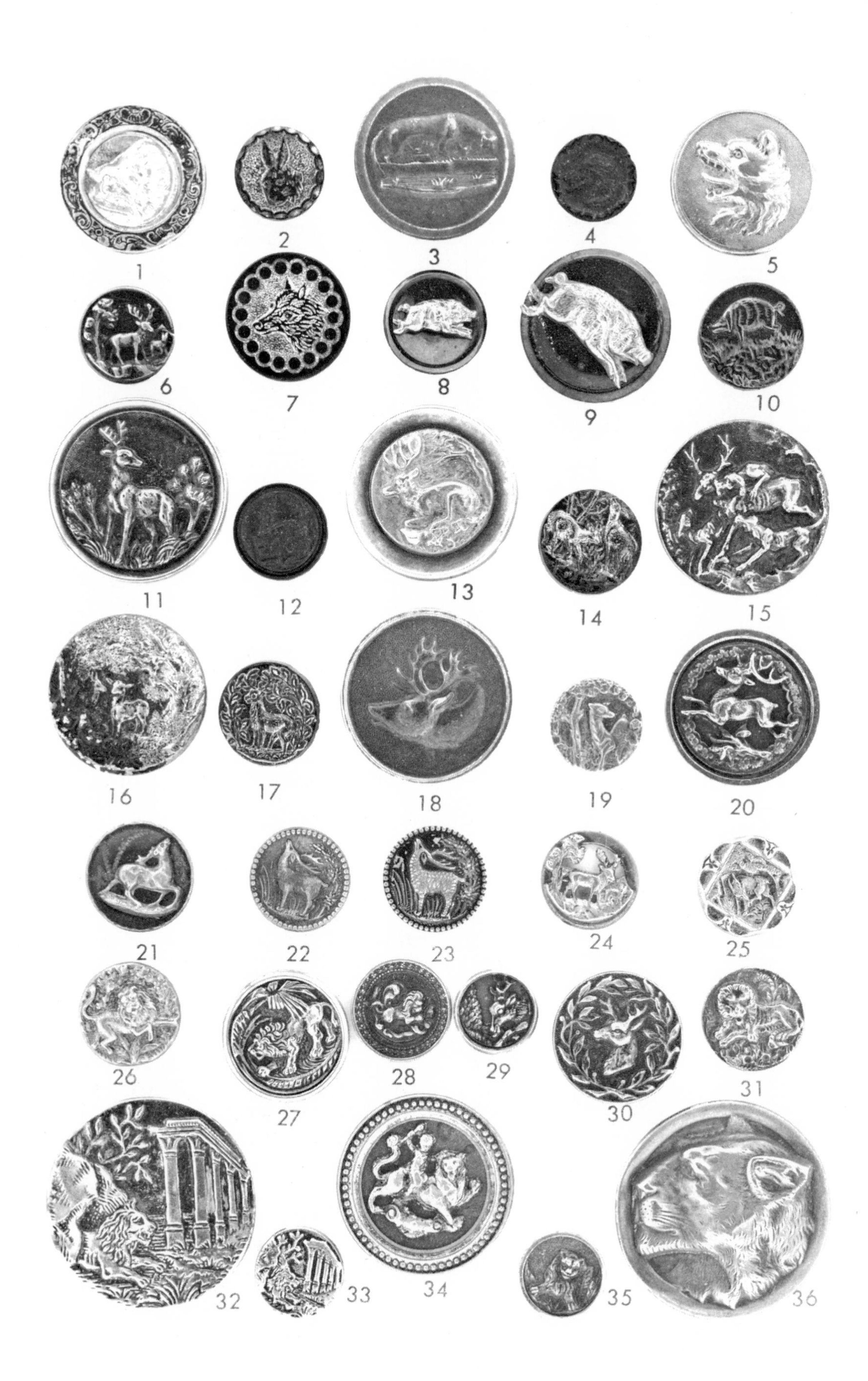
1
2
3
4
5
6
7
8
9
10
11
12
13
14
15
16
17
18
19
20
21
22
23
24
25
26
27
28
29
30
31
32
33
34
35
36

PLATE 45

WILD ANIMALS

This Plate shows wild animals, mostly deer. To these could be added the elephant, camel, squirrel, giraffe, mountain goat, polar bear, monkey, etc. Examples of these other mammals, as well as domestic animals can be found elsewhere in this book.

1. WILD BOAR'S HEAD. This beast has been a favorite of the chase since earliest times due to its great strength, speed and ferocity when at bay. It is now extinct in the British Isles but is still hunted in other parts of Europe. The boar head has always been considered a special food delicacy. This button is a German hunting coat button, all brass, in two parts , with head in very high relief. $2.50.
2. RABBIT HEAD, black glass, the head outlined in gold. Background of gold with scalloped border. $2.00.
3. PUMA, one of the largest animals of the cat family. It is called "couguar" by the French and "panther" by U.S. hunters. This button is made of "britannia", a metal alloy composed chiefly of tin. It is one of a set of hunting coat buttons, each of which pictures a different animal. Sometimes when found they have a coating of black enamel. Although they do not show the skilled craftsmanship of some sporting buttons, the animals illustrated are unusual and a set is very desirable. $2.50.
4. WOLF HEAD, a cameo-like head with dull finish and a bright scroll border, backmarked with the patent date 1880. $1.50.
5. WOLF HEAD, a well made hunting coat button of heavy brass. Single buttons of this type are valued from $2.50 - $4.00, while complete sets bring a higher price.
6. ANTLERED STAG and doe, pierced brass with background tinted pink. $1.00.
7. FOX HEAD, of bright black glass, outlined in silver with silver luster background. $2.00.
8. and 9. RUNNING PIG. A silvered pig, escutcheon type, on a concave brass background which has a bright wine colored tint. Small $1.25; medium $3.00.
10. WILD PIG, iridescent lustered black glass, cameo type design. $2.00.
11. STAG ALERT, two-piece pressed brass. $2.00.
12. DEER, jumping fence, dull finish, cameo type, black glass design with border in a bright finish. $1.00.
13. DEER, RESTING, two-piece brass, design in high relief. $1.75.
14. BUCK AND DOE, iridescent black glass, cameo type design. $2.00.
15. STAG AT BAY, two-piece brass, high relief. $2.75.
16. DOE AND SPIKE-HORNED buck, one-piece pressed brass with tinting of red and gold. $2.25.
17. STAG, gold lustered black glass, cameo type design. $1.00.
18. MOOSE HEAD, a hunting coat button of britannia metal (See No. 3) with head in high relief and with a brass rim. $2.50.
19. DOE, two-piece brass, well designed. $.75.
20. STAG, LEAPING, a steel cup background with pierced design set in cup. $2.50.
21. STAG, in high relief on concave background of Japanned brass. $1.25.
22. ELK, on a one-piece concave brass background. $1.00.
23. ELK, the same design as No. 22 but on a flat one-piece background. $1.00.
24. STAG AND DOE, of pierced brass. $.75.
25. WOUNDED STAG, two-piece silvered brass, pressed design set in a square center. $1.25.
26. LION IN JUNGLE, brass, two-piece, tinted. $1.00.
27. LION AT BAY under palm, pressed brass, tin rim. $1.75.
28. LION, pouncing on serpent, two-piece brass. $1.00.
29. STAG, DRINKING, two-piece brass, design in relief on tinted background, tin rim. $.75.
30. STAG HEAD IN WREATH, two-piece pressed brass, tinted. $1.50.
31. LION AND PREY, white metal, one-piece. $.75.
32. LION IN TEMPLE RUINS. Said to be the ruins at Palmira, a famous city of the East, known among the Arabs as Tadmar and mentioned in II Chron., VIII, 4. Solomon is said to have built, "Tadmar in the wilderness". A two-piece tinned zinc button, tinted to accent detail. $4.00.
33. The small size of No. 32. $1.00.
34. PAN, THE LION TAMER, from a Thorwaldsen design. A pewter design on a wood background, brass rim. $3.50.
35. LION AND FOLIAGE of tinted brass on tinted tin background, tin rim. $.75.
36. LIONESS, one-piece pressed brass, head in very high relief. Scarce. $6.50.

PLATE 46

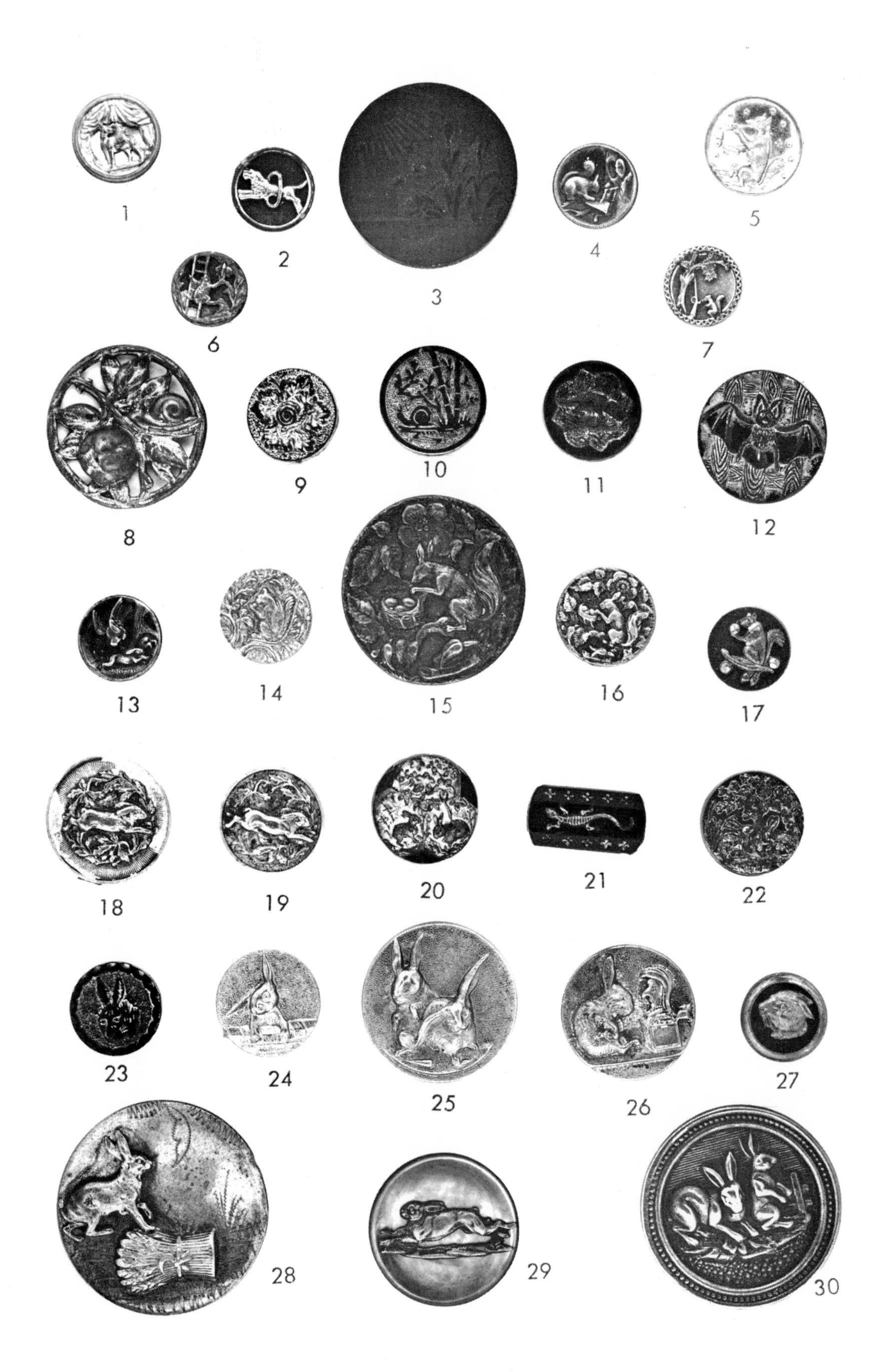
1
2
3
4
5
6
7
8
9
10
11
12
13
14
15
16
17
18
19
20
21
22
23
24
25
26
27
28
29
30

PLATE 46

ANIMAL LIFE

This plate consists chiefly of small mammals with a few amphibians, reptiles and mollusks included. Some may be classed with Fables, and some of the rabbit buttons are likewise Sporting Buttons; that is, buttons which were made originally to be worn on hunting costumes.

1. GREYHOUND on curtained stage. Brass in relief over a tin background. $2.00.

2. CIRCUS POODLE jumping through a hoop. Two-piece pressed brass, with tin collet. $2.00.

3. THE SUN AND THE FROGS, a Fable Button, illustration in "Fables of Fontaine", by Parquet and Emy. Made of black plastic horn with frog, cat tails, birds and sun in low relief. $6.50.

4. SQUIRREL'S POSTOFFICE (N). One - piece pressed brass, design in relief. $2.00.

5. REYNARD AND HIS PIPE from "Reynard the Fox" by Goethe, the design taken from a picture by Kaulbach whose pictures first appeared in 1846. Reynard is blowing pipe dreams to impress his audience with his importance. Two-piece, copper-tinted brass, the design in relief. $4.00.

6. FROG ON A LADDER, catching a butterfly. Pierced brass design. $2.00.

7. CURIOUS SQUIRREL. (N), inspecting gun which is propped against a tree. Pierced brass. Nice detail for such a small button. $2.00.

8. SNAIL on a branch of a fruit tree, a one-piece button with pierced design. Silvered brass. $2.50.

9. SNAIL ON A LEAF. Black glass, gold lustered background. $1.00.

10. SNAIL UNDER BAMBOO. Black glass, gold lustered background. $3.00.

11. PLATYPUS, a small, duck-billed, egg laying, water mammal of Australia. Black glass. $2.00.

12. BAT. Black glass, parti-lustered with gold. $2.50.

13. HAWK'S PREY; the rabbits are running to safety in a hollow tree. The design is cut out of brass with rim turned under, on a pink-tinted background. (This button is used to illustrate the fable, "The Sparrow and the Hare" but the bird is definitely a hawk.) $2.00.

14. SQUIRREL EATING NUT, sitting on limb of tree, one-piece pressed white metal. $1.25.

15. This is called ROBBER SQUIRREL by Nicholls but it seems to fit the fable of the DISCONTENTED SQUIRREL who shared a tree with a nightingale and is discontented because he cannot fly like the bird. He sets out on a long journey, has many horrible experiences, and eventually is dropped from the claws of an eagle into his own home tree. "Ah," says he, "My dear, native home. If I am ever tempted to leave you may I undergo a second time all the miseries and dangers from which I have now so wonderfully escaped." (Calif. Brief, Feb. 1960). Pressed brass, pierced design having a purplish brown tint. $6.50.

16. The same as No. 15, in small size. $2.00.

17. SQUIRREL eating nut. White metal. $1.00.

18. RUNNING RABBIT, on wreath of oak leaves, rayed background, silvered brass, medium size. $2.75.

19. The same as No. 18, gilt finished brass, small size. $1.25.

20. Lustered black glass RABBITS under a tree. $2.50.

21. LIZARD, an intaglio design, gold lustered on black glass. $1.00.

22. TWO RABBITS under flowers and foliage, in relief on a multilustered black glass button. $2.50.

23. A black glass RABBIT head, background gold lustered, face gold outlined, scalloped border. $2.00.

24. RABBIT looking over wall with one ear lopped. Two-piece silvered brass, pebbled background. (T.W. & W.) backmark. $4.00.

25. TWO RABBITS, one with ear lopped, similar to 24, silvered brass, pebbled background. (T.W. & W.) $8.00.

26. RABBIT AND JACK-IN-THE-BOX. One-piece, design in high relief on pebbled background. (T.W. & W.) $5.00.

27. Brass HEAD OF A RABBIT on velvet background. Rare. $2.50.

28. RABBIT AND SHEAF OF WHEAT. A one-piece deeply concave button with halfmoon and vegetation engraved, rabbit and grain applied. $10.00.

29. A brass RABBIT running, applied to a concave smoked pearl. $3.00.

30. RABBITS AT FENCE. Two-piece pressed brass, rabbits in relief. $8.00.

PLATE 47

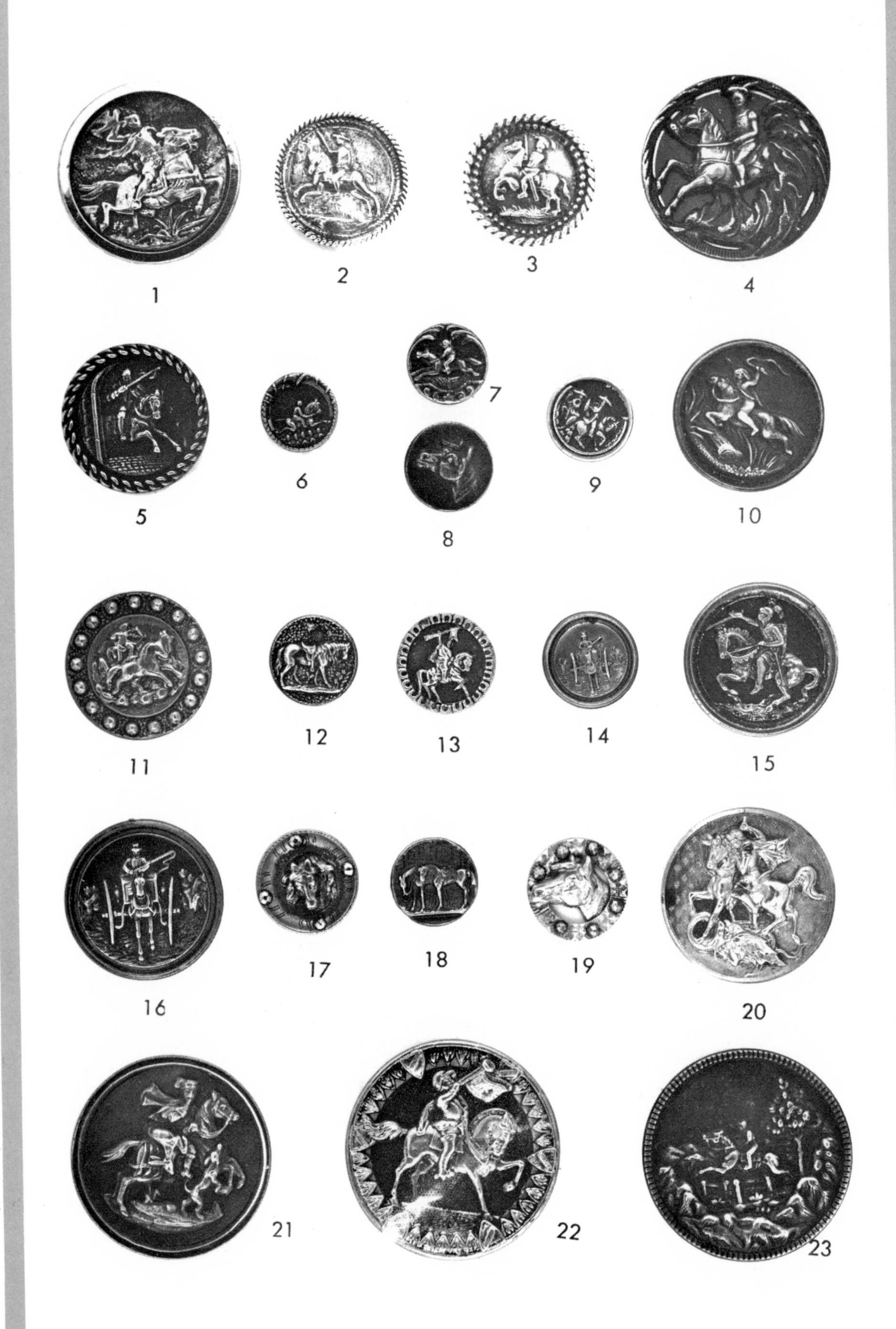

PLATE 47

HORSES

1. FALCON HUNTER, two - piece pressed brass, picture in low relief, tin rim. $3.50.

2. HORSE AND TRAINER, hall marked silver with rope border. $15.00.

3. HORSE WITH SOLDIER ON PARADE. The man has a plumed hat, sword raised and scabbard at side. Hall marked silver with twisted rope border. $12.50.

4. CHARLES V of Spain and Germany (1500 - 1558). The pierced design is attached to the leaf border which widens at one side, curving over the steel liner and forming part of the design. $5.00.

5. IVANHOE, an armored knight setting forth with accouterments of the joust, two-piece pressed brass with chain border. $6.00.

6. STEEPLECHASE. Two-piece brass, a riding crop with hoof handle forms the collet. $1.00.

7. A small figure on horseback, two-piece pressed brass. $1.00.

8. Brass HORSE'S HEAD on flat steel back. $.75.

9. HUNTING HORNS, two riders bearing horns, two-piece pressed brass. $1.50.

10. Called INDIAN RIDER, two-piece pressed brass. $2.75.

11. CHARIOTEER. This is evidently an early battle scene as the charioteer has bow and arrow drawn; pressed brass in low relief. $1.75.

12. A HUNTING HORSE, wearing an English saddle. This is a Sporting Button and quite scarce. The same design is found on larger buttons of this type. Two-piece brass. $1.00.

13. A MOUNTED RIDER, wearing chained armor and spiked helmet. This has been called "Headless Horseman" but the head can be seen, tilted to one side and is clearly visible in the larger button that is sometimes found with the same design. Two-piece brass, figure in relief, horseshoe border. $1.00.

14. ENGLISH DOG CART with horse and driver, two-piece pressed brass. $2.00.

15. ARMORED KNIGHT directing battle. Two - piece pressed brass, tinted black. $2.75.

16. TWO-WHEELED CART with driver, pressed brass, two-piece, scarce. $8.00.

17. HORSE'S HEAD in concave center of one-piece brass button with cut steel trim. $1.50.

18. SADDLED HORSES, WAITING. Two-piece pressed brass, nice detail. $2.00.

19. HORSE'S HEAD, in two parts, the head brazed to the rim which is decorated with cut steels. $1.50.

20. DRAGONSLAYER, one-piece pressed brass, design in relief. $4.00.

21. HUNTSMAN AND DOG, a steel cup with a wood background for the cut out picture which is applied. Good acton detail is shown. This button can be classified in three ways and is of three materials. $6.50.

22. THE HERALD, a pierced brass design, mounted on a tinted brass background and attached to the ornamental border. $6.50.

23. STEEPLECHASE, picture and rim of one - piece brass in low relief, quite plentiful. $3.50.

PLATE 48

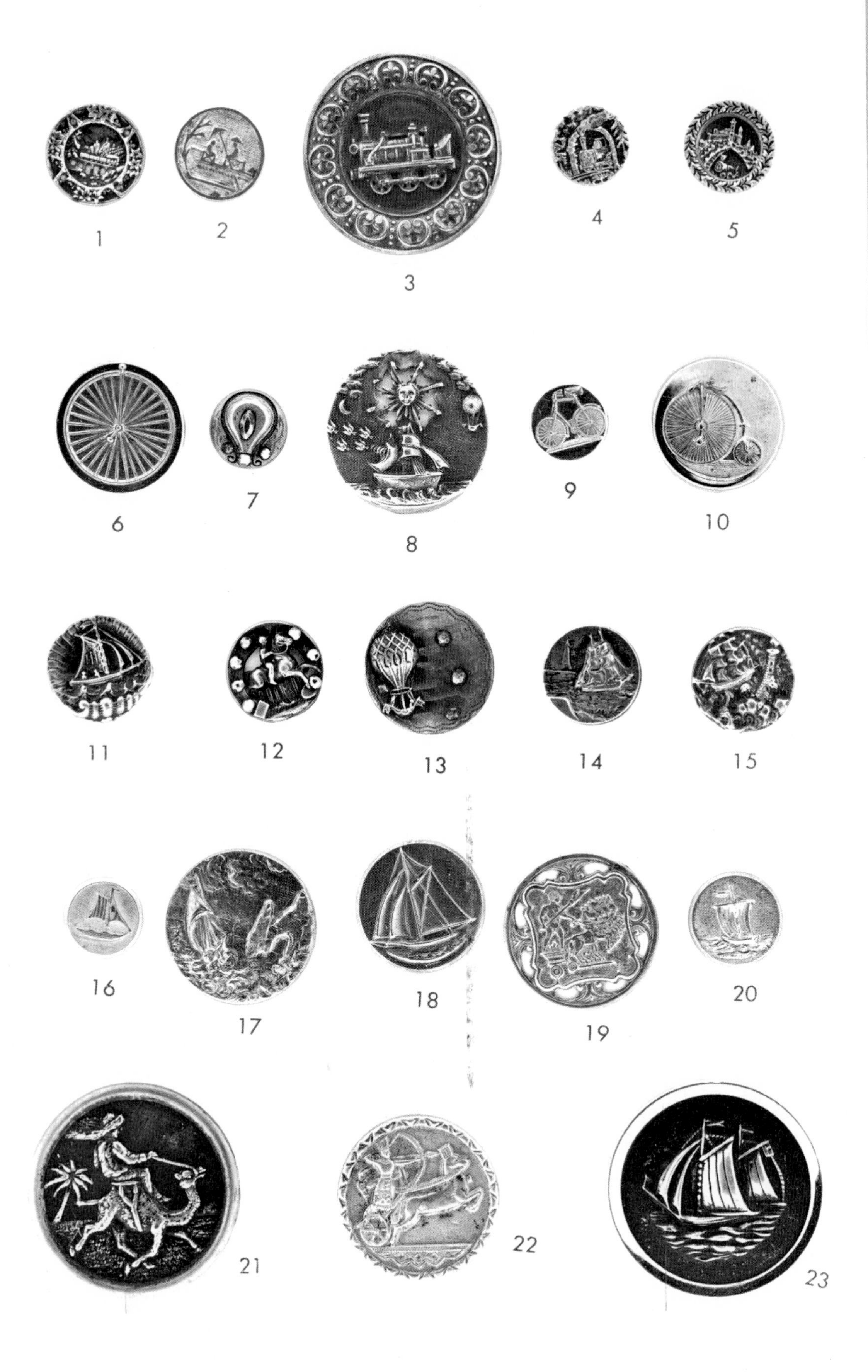

PLATE 48

TRANSPORTATION

If interested in this category, the buttons we have illustrated can be found quite easily and horses, automobiles, airplanes, stage coaches etc. added. Vehicles are found on a variety of materials and the search is rewarding, the mounting always interesting and effective. An entire card of boats with each identified also makes a special display.

1. Called UNION PACIFIC. Shows a train upon a trestle. $1.25.
2. TWO FIGURES IN A BOAT. Brass in low relief. $1.00.
3. An early steam R.R. ENGINE. Quite unusual. Brass mounted on flat brass background with wide, ornamental border. $12.50.
4. A TRAIN, with steam engine, coming out of a tunnel. Tinned zinc. $1.50.
5. Another TRAIN emerging from a tunnel, a city above. Brass with leaf border. $.75.
6. UNICYCLE. Brass, backmarked, "Horstman Bros. and Co. Phila." Undoubtedly made to be worn by a member of a bicycle club. $2.50.
7. A conventionalized BALLOON. Brass with cut steel trim. $.75.
8. This interesting button shows a CARAVEL and a BALLOON and is also enhanced by a sun which is apparently rising and a crescent moon that has not yet disappeared. Birds, clouds, waves, sun's face, and rays of sun are well defined. A one-piece brass button, pierced between rays of sun. Scarce. $15.00. The large size, $25.00.
9. TWO WHEELER. White metal with darkened background. $1.50.
10. HIGH WHEELER. Gilded brass, backmarked, "Scovill Mfg. Co." Probably another button made for a bicycling club. $2.50.
11. Not so easy to find is this "CUTTER" inside a concave brass sea shell. $1.00.

For History of the Bicycle see J.B., Aug., 1962. (British)

12. STEEPLECHASE. One-piece, pierced brass with a horseshoe set with cut steels, forming a border. $1.50.
13. Concave brass with repousse design of BALLOON. Three cut steels. $3.00.
14. THREE MASTED SHIP, lighthouse in the background. One-piece tinted brass. $2.00.
15. Although near a lighthouse, this three-masted sailing vessel is in trouble ON THE ROCKS. One-piece pressed brass. $1.50.
16. A very small one-piece pressed brass SAIL BOAT. $.75.
17. SHIPWRECK. One-piece, yellow and white tinted metal. $1.75.
18. A SAIL BOAT. One-piece brass. $1.25.
19. The means of transportation here is an early one: AN ANCIENT CHARIOT, with four horses and driver. The design is in a square center with outer portion pierced. One-piece brass. $1.75.
20. A SLOOP (one-masted vessel). One-piece brass. $1.00.
21. SHIP OF THE DESERT. Design of white metal on brass background, brass rim. $4.50.
22. ASSYRIAN CHARIOT, carrying bowman. Assyrians are said to have been the first to use horses in warfare. Pressed brass in low relief. $2.50.
23. This SCHOONER carries an American flag, and resembles the racing yacht "America" which won a race in 1851 around the Isle of Wight, against a large fleet of British yachts. A brass boat in high relief on a black tinted brass background, tin rim. $2.50.

PLATE 49

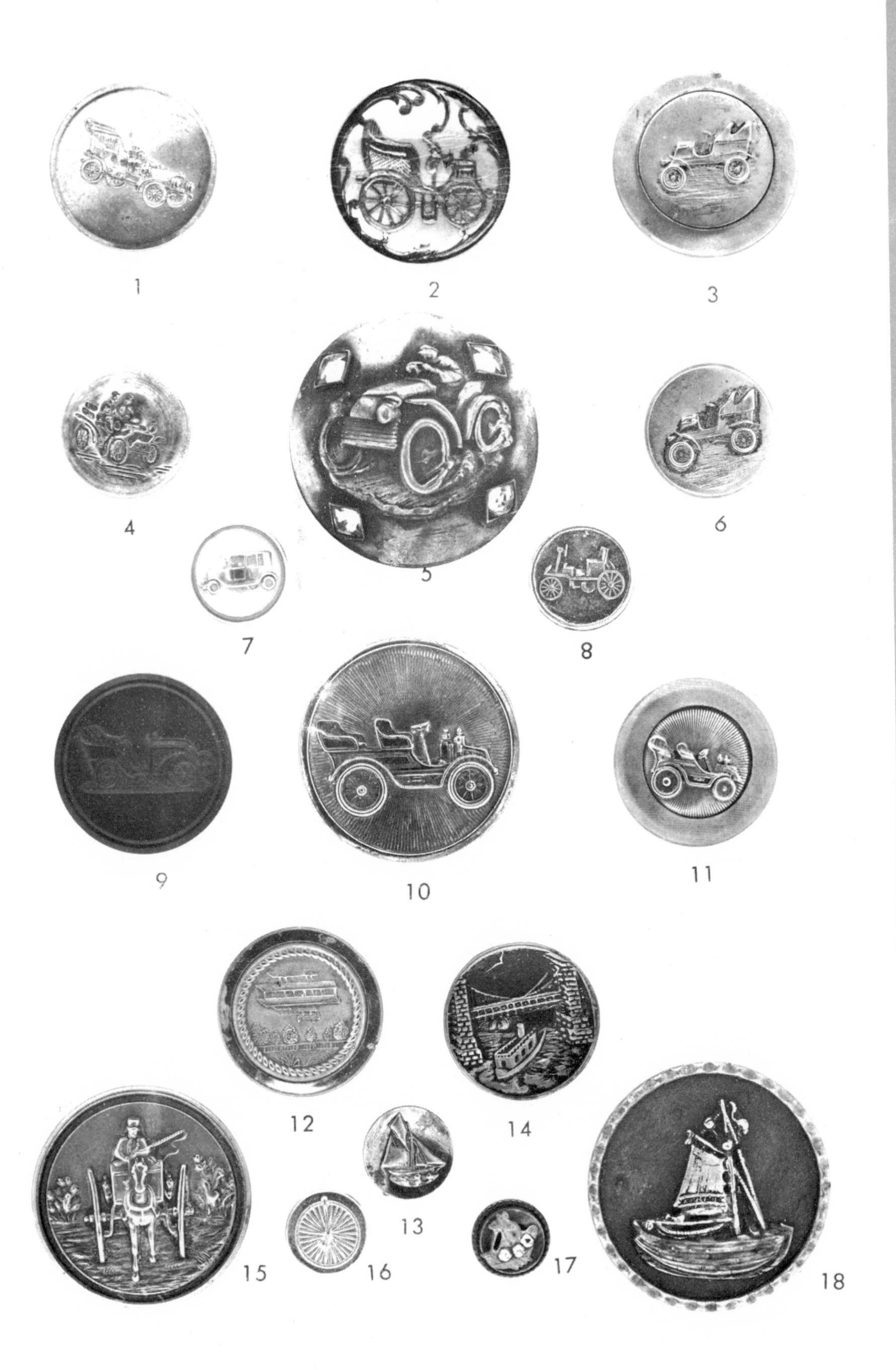

PLATE 49

TRANSPORTATION

Credit is given to Krebs, who designed the Panhard car in 1894, for the first gasoline automobile but the motor car is not the product of a single man's invention; neither was the achievement accomplished within a single century. Many of the earliest automobiles, very much resembling the horseless carriages that they were expected to replace, were made in Europe. Likewise, many of the buttons with automobile designs, came from Europe. Because of this and although we have spent much time in research, we hesitate to positively identify any of the motor vehicles shown here.

Henry Ford completed his first successful horseless-carriage in 1896 and it is safe to say that no automobile buttons were designed before 1894, either in Europe or in the United States. The period in which they were made was undoubtedly the 1900's. Many collectors believe that they were made to be worn on linen "dusters". Anyway, it is interesting to see how many different types can be found and great fun to try to identify them.

1. This one is of stamped brass with white metal back. The design is in very fine detail, even showing the tool box on the fender, which was standard equipment in case one had to "get out and get under". $4.50.
2. This one, which is of pierced brass with an attached border, prettily designed and a pearl background, seems to be an early electric type. $15.00.
3. One-piece brass, the model thought to be European. $4.50.
4. Two-piece, with the design impressed on the brass face. This car has two passengers and we would like to believe that it is the 1906 Cadillac. $5.00.
5. This large brass button, ornamented with four glass stones is known as "Barney Oldfield". It can be seen that this is a racing car, certainly. The history of Motor Racing is an interesting one. The speed of racing cars of today is quite different from that recorded in 1906, when a Renault won the first Grand Prix event at 63 m.p.h. $27.50.
6. The same automobile model as No. 3, a smaller, two-piece brass button. $4.50.
7. This has a silvered face and is back-marked, "Stokes & Sons". It looks to us like a Ford Model "A" Tudor Sedan of 1929. $4.50.
8. One-piece, silvered; one of the very earliest types. $6.00.
9. This is of pressed horn, dyed black, very rare and in nice detail. $8.00.
10. A large, silvered, one-piece button with rayed background. $3.50.
11. Brass with an automobile which is similar to No. 10. $3.50.
12. The Wright Brothers made their first successful flight in the air at Kitty Hawk, N.C., in 1903. This button commemorates their flight and reproduces, quite accurately, their plane. Stamped brass, two-piece. $10.00.
13. A brass escutcheon, showing a sailboat, in a steel cup. $.75.
14. Called, "BROOKLYN BRIDGE". Two-piece, stamped brass. A ferryboat is passing under the bridge and a gull soars above it. Scarce. $3.00.
15. A scarce button of stamped brass, in relief, known as, "THE JAUNTING CART". $15.00.
16. A UNICYCLE, two-piece pressed brass. $.75.
17. A steel cup with a concave center of dark pearl which has a brass sailboat superimposed and trimmed with riveted cut steels. $1.00.
18. A brass BOAT with pewter sails and rig, on a wood background. White metal rim and back. Not often found. $7.50.

PLATE 50

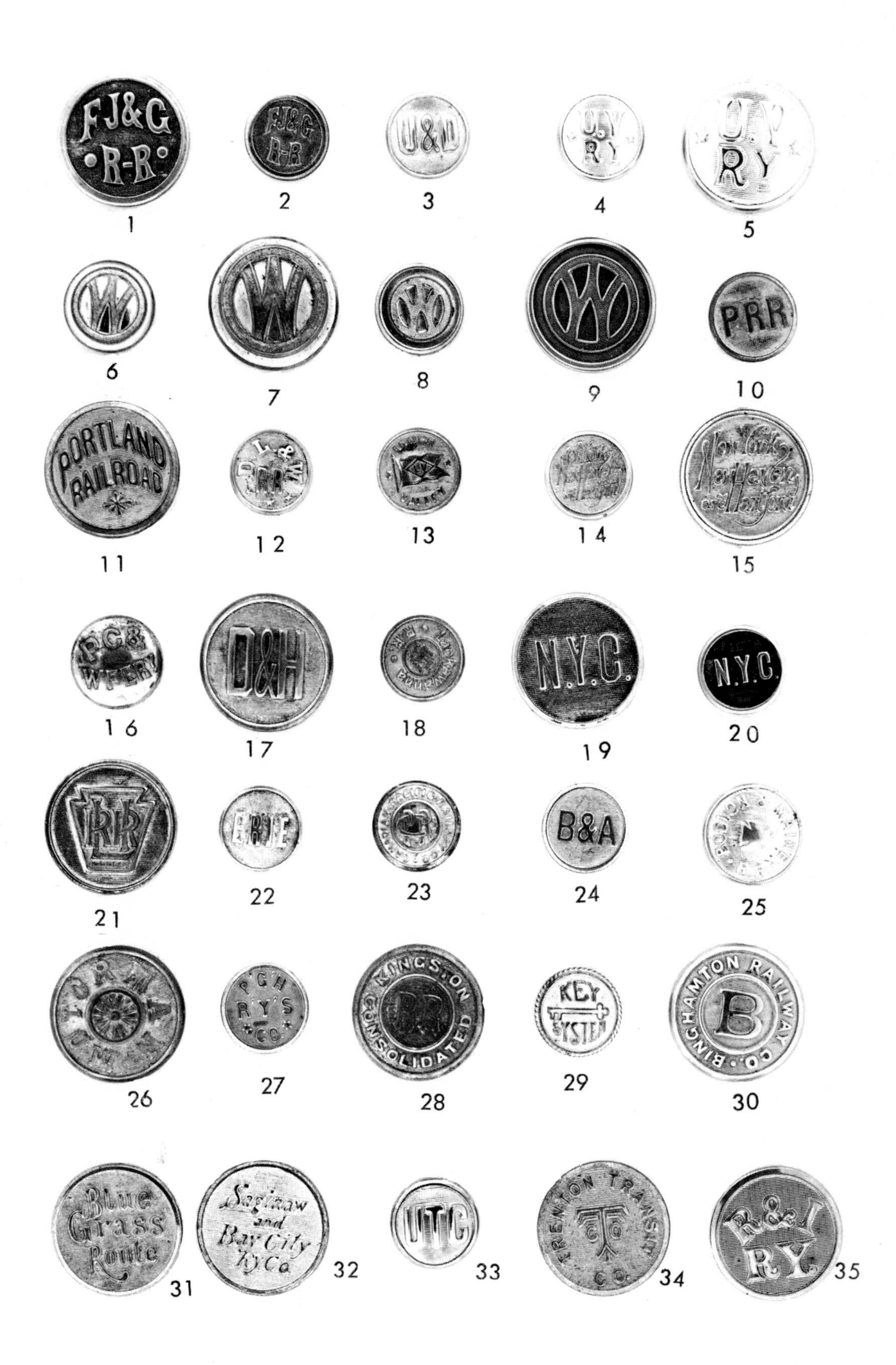

1 2 3 4 5 6 7 8 9 10 11 12 13 14 15 16 17 18 19 20 21 22 23 24 25 26 27 28 29 30 31 32 33 34 35

PLATE 50

RAIL TRANSPORTATION

By Donald Van Court

1. and 2. FONDA, JOHNSTOWN & GLOVERSVILLE Railroad was a steam road from 1870-1894 when it added local electric lines. It operated between Schenectady and Gloversville, N.Y. from 1903-1938, when busses took over. Buttons obsolete since 1960. Large, $3.50, Small $1.50.
3. ULSTER AND DELAWARE Railroad, a steam road, ran between Oneonta, N.Y. and Kingston Point from 1875-1932 when the N.Y. Central R.R. took over as its "Catskill Mountain Branch". Convex U & D buttons made in the early 1890's; flat after 1900. Buttons obsolete since 1932; Large $3.50; Small $1.50.
4. and 5. UNADILLA VALLEY RAILROAD, a little N.Y. State Line which grew by acquiring branches of larger railroads. The buttons were in use after 1895, when the dies were cut. The Railway became a Railroad in 1904. Large $4.00. Small $2.00.
6.-9. N.Y., ONTARIO & WESTERN Railway, the mythical "Old & Weary" which ran from Cornwall, N.Y. to Scranton, Pa. and Oswego, N.Y. between 1880 and 1953. Dies for the flat buttons were made in 1901; convex Nos. 6 & 7 about a decade later. Gold color common; silver rare; all obsolete. $3.50 and $1.50.
10. and 11. PORTLAND Railroad, the transit system of Portland, Maine. The experts in this field class it as a "rural trolly". Despite close similarity to Pa. R.R. designs, this pair of flat buttons have successive serial numbers in Waterbury's die number index. All known Pa. R.R. "PRR" buttons are convex. Large $2.50, Small $1.00.
12. and 18. DELAWARE, LACKAWANNA & WESTERN Railroad ran from Hoboken, N.J. to Buffalo, N.Y. No. 12 was not made till the 1870's; used until 1900 when No. 18 was made, as a convex style. No. 18, flat, appeared in 1949 and is in use today, even though the D.L. & W. merged with the Erie in 1960 to form the Erie Lackawanna R.R. No. 12, $2.00 & $1.00. No. 18, convex $2.00; Small, $.50.
13. LEHIGH VALLEY R.R. was a competitor of the D.L. & W., crossing it several times between Jersey City, N.J. and Buffalo, N.Y. Passenger service ran between 1855 and the 1960's. This button was used from the 1880's until the late 1920's when a flat style with flag and no name came into use. Large $2.00; Small $1.00; No name $.50 and $.25.
14. and 15. NEW HAVEN & HARTFORD R.R. formed from many smaller lines, began passenger service in 1872 and still runs today. This design first used in 1896 is still worn. Large $1.00; Small $.50.
16. POUGHKEEPSIE CITY AND WAPPINGERS FALLS ELECTRIC Railway took over an old horse car line dating back to 1871. It served the named cities between 1895 and 1917 when "Electric" was dropped from its title. The last trolleys ran in 1935. Small $1.00.
17. DELAWARE & HUDSON CO. for better than 100 years D & H meant Railroad and Canal, interchangeably. In 1899 the extra C for canal disappeared from steam locomotive tenders. This button, first made in the 1880's, is still seen. Large $1.00; Small $.50.
18. See No. 12.
19. and 20. N.Y. CENTRAL R.R., the second of that name, was formed in 1914, although this button might date back to 1896. The original N.Y.C. was formed in 1853 and lasted until 1869, when it became the N.Y. Central & Hudson River R.R. The N.Y.C. & H.R., in turn became part of the "new" N.Y.C. Buttons still in use. $.50 and $.25.
21. LONG ISLAND Railroad, one of the nation's oldest, was incorporated in 1834. In 1966, it became part of the Metropolitan Commuter Transportation Agency of the State of New York. This button was used from 1920-1950, when the L.I.R.R. was part of the Pa. R.R. family. Large $1.00.
22. ERIE. Depending upon the exact date when this convex button was made, it could be from the N.Y. Lake Erie & Western R.R. as made for them by Scovill in 1882 or from the Erie R.R. of 1898. Although the Erie R.R. and D.L. & W. R.R. merged in 1960, flat Erie buttons are still in daily use. Convex Scovill, Large $2.00; Small $1.00. Flat $.50 and $.25.
23. CANADIAN PACIFIC Railway, one of Canada's two trans-continental lines began its passenger service in 1886. $.50 and $.25.
24. BOSTON AND ALBANY R.R. is now part of the N.Y. Central R.R. These buttons were worn between 1907 and 1950 when N.Y.C. came into use. $2.00 and $.75.
25. BOSTON AND MAINE R.R. began carrying passengers in 1836. This convex button worn first in 1895 is still in use. $.50 and $.25.
26. MOTORMAN around counterweighted wheel; this was used widely by traction lines, too small to have their own buttons; rarely used today. $1.50 and $.75.
27. PITTSBURGH Railways, the traction system of Pittsburgh, Pa., used this as the cuff and cap button between 1902 and recent years when it was taken over by Pittsburgh's Port Authority. The coat button has the name written in full. $.50 and $.25.
28. KINGSTON CONSOLIDATED R.R. connected uptown Kingston with the summer terminal of the U. & D. R.R. at Kingston Point. Obsolete. Large $2.50.
29. KEY SYSTEM CARS served the Oakland-Berkley, California area between 1903 and 1959. At the end, its trains ran across the Golden Gate Bridge. Obsolete. $2.50 and $1.00.
30. BINGHAMTON Railway Co., 1901-1929. This is the first button used by this 30 mile trolley system. Obsolete. $3.50 and $1.00.
31. KENTUCKY TRACTION & TERMINAL CO., the "Blue Grass Route", centered around Lexington, Ky. An 89 mile system, abandoned in 1934. $3.00.
32. SAGINAW AND BAY CITY Railway, a Michigan interurban, 1903-1921. Obsolete. $3.00.
33. There were various companies where these could have been used, probably a Traction Co. of Albany, N.Y. $.25.
34. TRENTON TRANSIT CO., Trenton, N.J. 1929 until recently. $1.00.
35. R. & I. RY. Northwestern Illinois, 1902-1931. $2.50.

PLATE 51

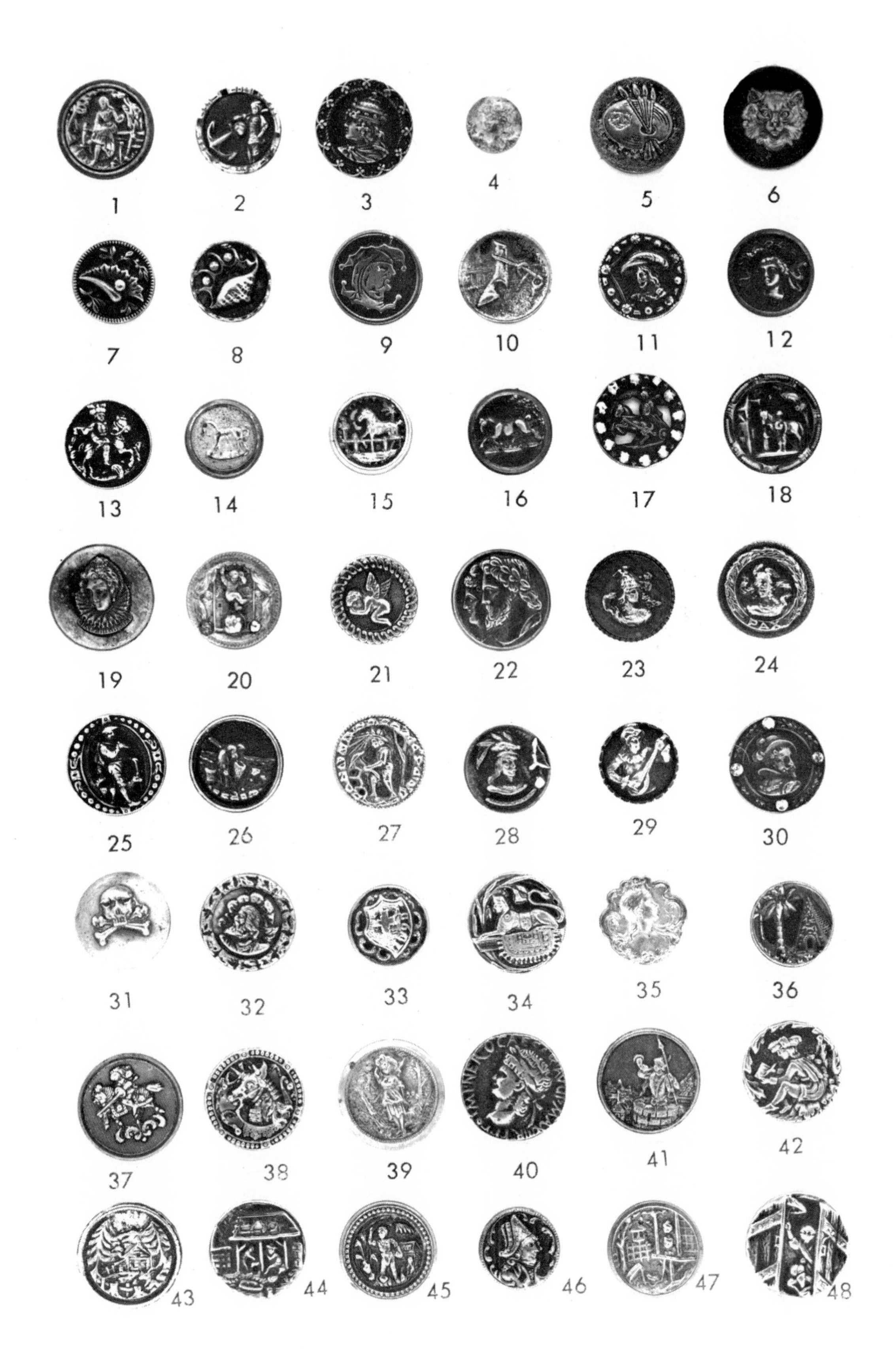
1
2
3
4
5
6
7
8
9
10
11
12
13
14
15
16
17
18
19
20
21
22
23
PAX
24
25
26
27
28
29
30
31
32
33
34
35
36
37
38
39
40
41
42
43
44
45
46
47
48

PLATE 51

MISCELLANEOUS METAL PICTORIALS SMALL SIZE

1. HOLY FAIR, this title given by Nicholls, from a poem by Burns. Pressed brass, tin rim. $1.50.
2. ANCHOR AND SAILOR, a steel cup with brass design and one cut steel. $1.50.
3. THEODORA, one-piece brass with applied brass head. $1.50.
4. SEASONAL HEAD, shown here for comparative size; it is a diminutive size, any button from this size, 3/8 inch, up to 1/4 inch is classed as "small". $.75.
5. CAT HEAD ON PALETTE, two-piece brass, Paris back-mark. $1.50.
6. CAT HEAD, a brass escutcheon in high relief, on flat steel. $2.00.
7. and 8. Rare SEA SHELL designs, two-piece pressed brass, shells in high relief. $1.50 ea.
9. CLOWN HEAD, either smiling or frowning, according to which way one holds the button (two faces). $1.75.
10. TETHERED HORSE'S LEG, two-piece pressed brass. $1.75.
11. CHARLES I, one-piece pressed brass in high relief. $.75.
12. LORD BYRON, two-piece tinted brass with velvet background, which is cut out forming hat, collar etc. $1.50.
13. JOHN GILPIN (See J.B. September, '60), a hard white metal design on flat steel back. $1.00.
14. SADDLE HORSE, a quasi-uniform button, two-piece gilded copper, probably made for a riding club. $2.00.
15. A COB IN PASTURE. Cobs were high-stepping horses that were usually given "bobbed" tails; a two-piece brass button with pewter design. $2.00.
16. UNHARNESSED COB RUNNING, a quasi-uniform button, two-piece brass. $2.00.
17. ACHILLES IN CHARIOT. This resembles a marble relief which shows Achilles, dragging the body of Hector. One-piece pierced brass, cut steel border. $1.25.
18. AT THE INN; two-piece pierced brass, showing darkened background. $2.00.
10. QUEEN ELIZABETH. One-piece concave brass with applied head. $1.00.
20. CHILDREN'S CIRCUS. One-piece pressed brass, concave cut steel trim. $1.00.
21. CHERUB, Two-piece brass, pierced rim with liner. $2.00.
22. JUPITER AND HERA. Two-piece pressed brass. $1.25.
23. BELLUM. A brass head, mounted on a wood background in a steel cup. $1.50.
24. PAX. One-piece, silvered brass. $1.50.
25. WOODMAN SPARE THAT TREE, two-piece pressed brass. $1.25.
26. CLAM DIGGER, two-piece pressed brass. $1.50.
27. THE BERGMANN'S LIED (N), two-piece pressed brass. $1.25.
28. CAPTAIN JOHN SMITH; concave brass, applied head with cut steel trim. $2.00.
29. MINSTREL WITH LUTE. A fine brass design in high relief in steel cup. $1.50.
30. SIR WALTER RALEIGH. One-piece brass in high relief, cut steel trim. $1.50.
31. SKULL AND CROSS BONES. A rare uniform button of The Duke of Cambridge's Own Lancers, a unit of The Light Brigade. Full dome, burnished gilt, die struck. $2.00.
32. FREDERICK BARBAROSA. Two-piece brass, high relief. $1.00.
33. COMMEMORATIVE OF THE NORMAN INVASION, shield has cross, three stars and the date 1090. One-piece, convex brass. $1.75.
34. ANDROSPHINX; two-piece pierced brass over darkened background. $1.50.
35. THETIS, MOTHER OF ACHILLES, resembling the likeness of her by Benjamin West. One-piece silvered brass. $1.25.
36. PYRAMID AND PALMS, two-piece brass with velvet background. $1.25.
37. BAYARD, THE ARMOURED KNIGHT, said to have been the first knight to put armour on his horse. Tinted brass with pewter design. $1.25.
38. THE ARMOURED HORSE HEAD. One-piece pierced brass. $1.00.
39. BAREFOOT GIRL WITH BASKET OF FLOWERS, one-piece brass with applied brass rim. $1.00.
40. One-piece brass COIN HEAD. $1.25.
41. TRUMPETER OF CRACOW, tinted brass design over darkened background. $.50.
42. CELLINI, 16th Century Italian artist, goldsmith and engraver. Two-piece pierced brass. $1.50.
43. WESTWARD HO. The deer, cabin and pine trees caused this to be named after a rare, pressed glass pattern of the 1870's. Two-piece brass with a tin rim. $1.25.
44. LIVINGSTON IN AFRICA. Two-piece brass with much detail. $1.25.
45. NATIVE HOME LIFE, a jungle scene. Two-piece pressed brass. $1.00.
46. JOHN PAUL JONES. Two-piece pressed brass. $1.25.
47. TRAPPING A BIRD, two children in doorway, string attached to snare. Two-piece brass. $1.25.
48. ORIENTAL WITH PARASOL at open gate. Two-piece pressed brass. $1.00.

PLATE 52

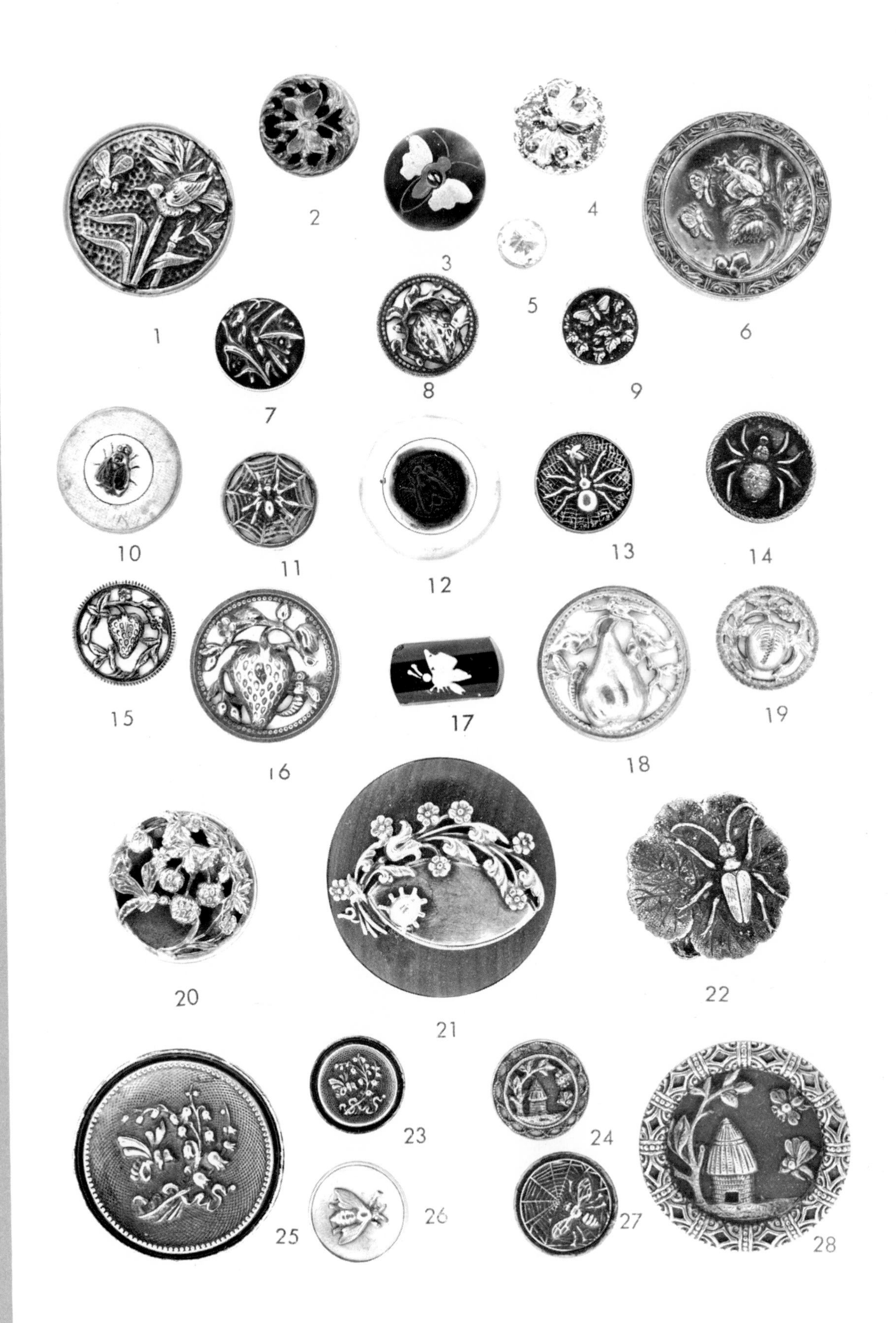

PLATE 52
ASSORTED INSECTS

Insects are defined as a class of small invertebrate animals, with three clearly defined body regions: head, thorax, and abdomen, with only three pairs of legs and usually with one or more pairs of wings. Entomologists have described more than 625,000 kinds of insects and it is estimated that well over 500 types have been used by button designers. Foremost, in popularity, was undoubtedly the butterfly and we find it used on buttons of different materials, many of which show its lovely colors. The insect classification affords the opportunity for varied collections. One may try to find as many different types in one material as may be assembled but it is fascinating to see how many of one type of insect, possibly a butterfly or bee, can be found in different materials.

1. DRAGONFLY with bird on bamboo. The dragonfly has a long slender body and two pairs of equal, narrow wings. The adult is very agile on the wing and has, probably, the best eyesight of all insects. The one shown here doesn't appear to be making use of his eyesight for he is dangerously close to the long bill of the bird. Two-piece pressed brass. Scarce. $2.50.
2. A lovely little BUTTERFLY. A pierced design in varigated tint over a background which has a much deeper tint. Brass. $.75.
3. A brown horn, sew-through button with BUTTERFLY inlaid in silver and gold colored metal. $2.00.
4. A one-piece silvered brass BUTTERFLY with blue cut steels decorating its wings. $.75.
5. A diminutive pressed brass BUTTERFLY with silvered background. $.75.
6. BEES AND ROSE. Two-piece pressed and tinted brass with leaf border. $1.75.
7. BUTTERFLY and flower. Two-piece brass $.50.
8. BEETLE on a nut. There is a type of fruit fly that attacks a walnut but this appears to be a beetle. Pierced brass, one-piece with the nut in high relief. $1.00.
9. BUTTERFLY on grapevine. Two-piece pressed brass. $.50.
10. HOUSEFLY. Milk glass center with molded design, painted black, set in silver tinted copper rim. This is an early Victorian jewel type button. $2.25.
11. SPIDER and web. One-piece pressed brass with spider in high relief. $.75.
12. HOUSEFLY. Black glass center with molded design, set in wide brass rim. Victorian jewel. $2.25.
13. SPIDER AND FLY. One-piece pressed brass with design of a spider web as background. $1.00.
14. A well designed SPIDER, set in a deeply concave brass button. The background is tinted black and accents the spider. The rim has a rope design and is untinted. $1.25.

15. and 16. Two similar one-piece brass buttons, showing an insect on a strawberry. Small, $.75; Medium, $1.25.

17. An oblong black glass button with white enameled BUTTERFLY; branch and leaves in fine gold outline. Scarce. $1.25.
18. Here we find the same insect as in No. 16, on a pear. There is a set of these buttons each showing a different type of fruit, all are one-piece pierced brass and the insect has been called a BEE. Flowers are seen in the designs, and since the flowers of these fruits are pollinated by bees, the insect is undoubtedly a bee attached to the fruit by the artist to give balance to his design. $1.50.
19. This fruit is a plum and, although the abdomen of the insect seems longer, we believe it is lengthened to balance the stem opposite, and is supposed to represent a BEE. $1.00.
20. Another BEE with a branch showing strawberries, flowers and leaves. A pierced brass design attached to the rim of a concave button. $1.25.
21. The flower spray and LADYBUG are gold colored metal, while the oval center is white metal. This design is mounted on a lovely convex wood background. $5.50.
22. Called, "BEETLE ON LEAF". It is also said to be a long-horned beetle on water lily leaves. Stamped brass with superimposed beetle. $1.75.

23. and 25. BUSY BEES with lily of the valley. Brass design applied to a concave brass background, with black - painted, tin rim. Small, $.50; Large, $1.75.

24. and 28. BEES AND BEEHIVES in high relief on a tinted brass background. The ornamental borders are pierced showing steel liners underneath. 24, small size is quite plentiful. $.50.

25. BUSY BEE see above. No. 23.
26. A BEE, mounted in a concave, two-piece brass button. $.75.
27. A BEE, on a spider web. Two-piece brass button with tin rim. $.75.
28. See No. 24. Value, $3.00.

PLATE 53

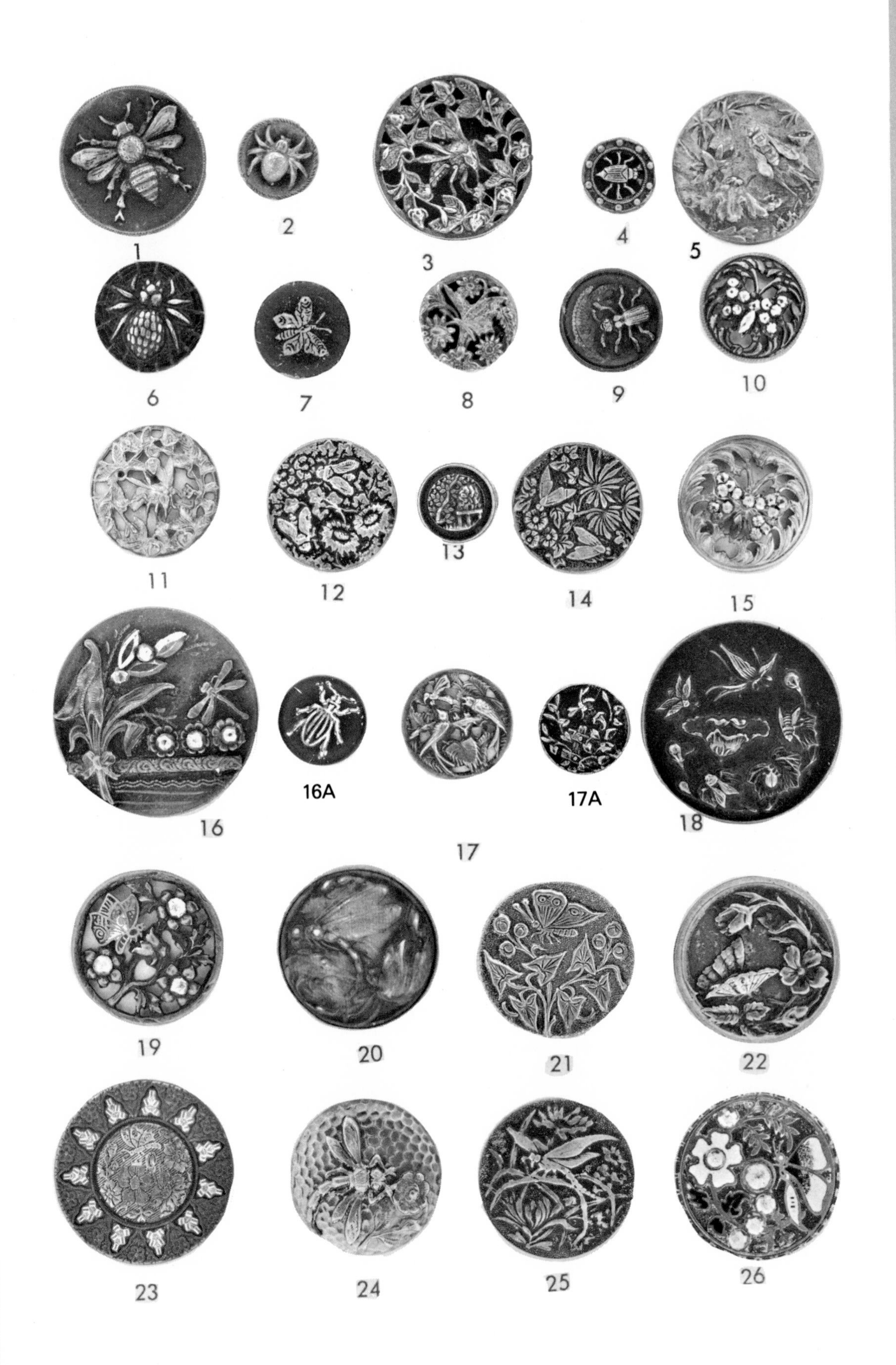

PLATE 53
ASSORTED INSECTS

1. A concave brass button with large BEE in high relief. $1.75.

2. A concave brass button, small size with SPIDER applied. $.75.

3. A pierced brass design showing a MOSQUITO on strawberry vines, attached to the rim and applied over a concave brass background, tinted. $1.75.

4. A BEETLE. Pierced brass over a tin liner, tinted red. $.75.

5. This button is a "Freak", but not "home-made". It is a tinted, pressed brass button with a FLY applied to a bird's back. The fly is nearly as large as the bird. The only explanation which occurs to us is that when "Insects" became popular, an over supply of bird buttons was converted to "Insects", by the maker. $2.50.

6. A one-piece pressed brass button, showing a spider's web and a SPIDER in high relief. $1.50.

7. A "True Tole" (decorated tin) button, black with silver BUTTERFLY. Tole ware buttons are becoming quite scarce. $1.00.

8. BUTTERFLY AND SUNFLOWERS, pierced brass design over a concave, tinted background. $.75.

9. Concave tinted and engraved brass button with applied brass BEETLE. $1.00.

10. One-piece, pierced brass BUTTERFLY in a delicate design. Cut steels encrust the body and wings of the insect. $1.25.

11. One-piece pierced brass, silvered, showing the same MOSQUITO design as No. 3. $1.75.

12. HOUSE FLIES ON FLOWERS. Two-piece pressed brass with darkened background. $1.50.

13. Small BEE HIVE. Two-piece brass with tin rim. $.75.

14. A companion button to No. 12, same construction, different foliage and flowers, slightly different insects but very similar composition. $1.50.

15. The same button as No. 10, in the medium size, shown to give the variation of price and size. $1.75.

16. A stamped and etched brass button with edge turned under; ribbon tied leaf bouquet with cut steel riveted flowers and DRAGON FLY. From the collection of Edith Rodway. Scarce. $6.50.

16a. A dull finished black glass, modified-ball button with intaglio design of BEETLE, outlined in silver. $1.00.

17. A one-piece pierced brass design, showing a DRAGON FLY hovering over a nest with two baby birds; mother and father bird greatly annoyed. $1.25.

17a. Morning Glories on fence with BEE above, two-piece brass with red tinted background. $.50.

18. Five insects: three BEES, a BEETLE and a BUTTERFLY are shown on this button. Two-piece pressed brass with darkened background. Very rare. $6.50.

19. One-piece pierced brass, flowers with cut steel centers, enameled (Champleve) BUTTERFLY. $2.75.

20. Ivoroid DRAGONFLY in a rimmed brass mounting. $6.50.

21. BUTTERFLY hovering over an Arrow-Head plant. Two-piece pressed tin; in good, shiny condition. $1.75.

22. BUTTERFLY AND WILD ROSE. Two-piece pressed brass with darkened background. $1.00.

23. A two-piece pressed brass button, still having its original tits of bronze, gold and silver; a tin liner shows through the pierced border which resembles a sun burst. The center disk shows flowers and a BUTTERFLY in low relief. $1.50.

24. Convex stamped brass, silvered, with superimposed DRAGONFLY. $2.00.

25. DRAGONFLY in natural surroundings; two-piece, stamped brass, darkened background. Paris backmark. $1.50.

26. A steel cup with brass center, over which is a pierced design of flowers and BUTTERFLY, fastened with ornamental cut steels; flower, leaves and butterfly are enameled. $8.00.

PLATE 54

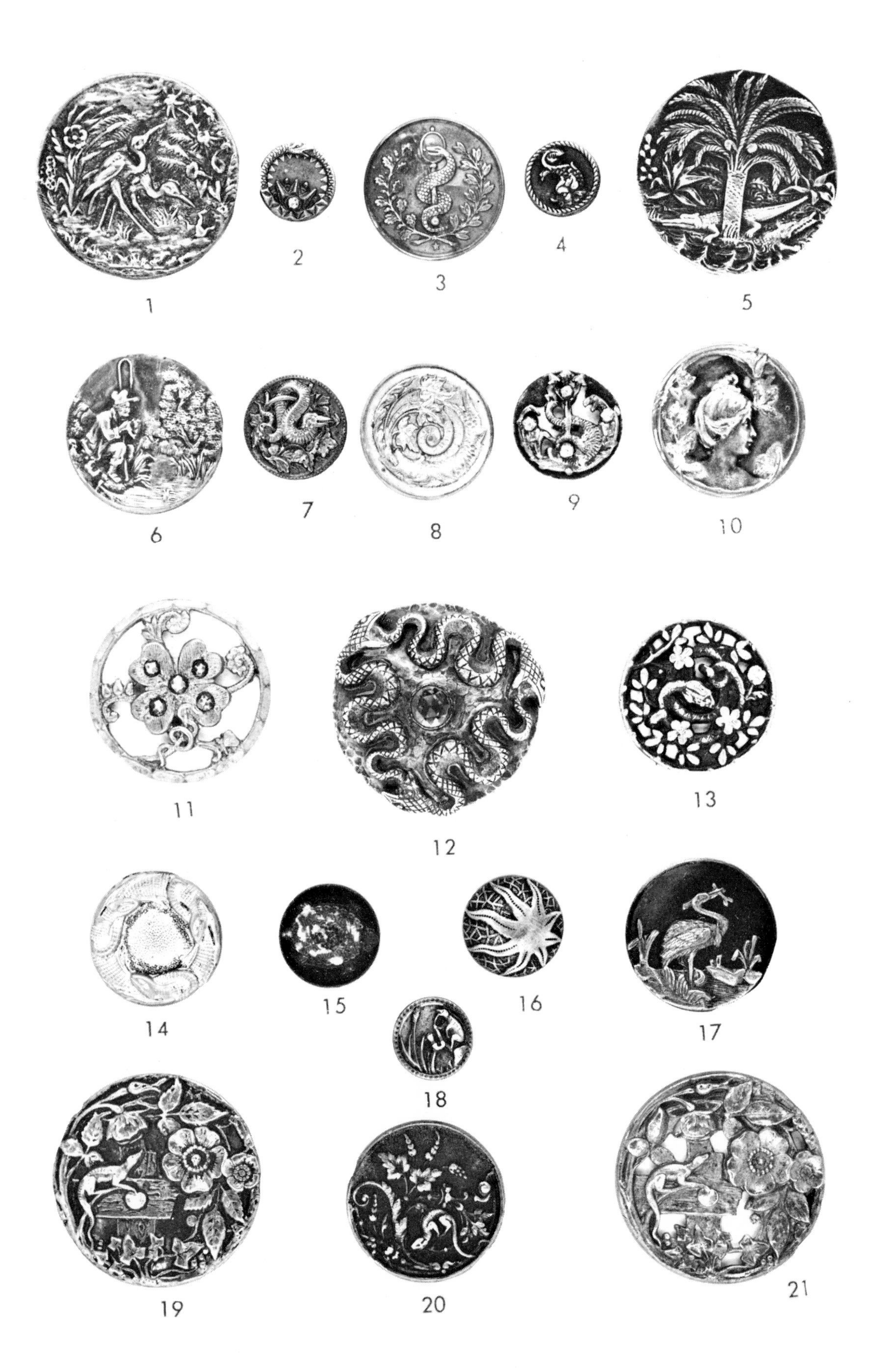

PLATE 54

REPTILES & AMPHIBIANS

The snake can be found on many buttons and during the Victorian Era it was also much used for different articles of jewelry. Designers were undoubtedly intrigued by the graceful curves of the snake's coiled body. Much symbolism is also attached to the serpent.

Frogs are not often found on buttons but the antics in which we find them engaged are fascinating.

1. Shows a pair of Cranes about to have a supper of frog's legs. The two-piece pressed brass button has a background design of flowers, foliage, and cat tails. $3.50.

2. A tinted brass button with a raised rim which is a COILED SNAKE with his tail in his mouth. In Egypt this symbolzies Eternity. $1.50.

3. SERPENT ENTWINED ABOUT A STAFF. The serpent has legendary healing powers and this design is used, with slight variations, in different branches of the army medical corps; two-piece pressed brass. $3.50.

4. A DOLPHIN; brass design applied to tinted brass background; rope border; two-piece. $1.00.

5. ALLIGATORS UNDER PALM TREE, two-piece stamped brass. Rare. $6.50.

6. THE LITTLE FISH AND THE FISHERMAN (see Fables). Two-piece pressed brass. $2.50.

7. SERPENT IN THE GARDEN. Two-piece pressed brass; not plentiful. $1.50.

8. A FISH AND SEA WEED form a curved design, stamped on a concave brass background; two-piece. $1.00.

9. DOLPHIN AND TRIDENT. Flat steel background with pierced brass design, cut steel trim. The trident is a three pronged fish spear. In mythology it was carried by Neptune and was a symbol of his power over the waves. $1.50.

10. ISIS. The asp, dedicated to her, is seen on her head; a lovely white metal button with gilded decoration. $2.50.

11. A SHAMROCK, decorated with cut steels, a snake coiled around the stem. Probably the designer had St. Patrick, the patron saint of Ireland, in mind as there is a legend that St. Patrick drove the snakes out of Ireland and the shamrock is, of course, the Irish symbol. A one-piece, pierced brass button. $3.50.

12. THREE SNAKES, swallowing each others' tails; white metal with snakes in high relief on a "hammered" background; green glass stone. $5.00.

13. COBRA, coiled amid flowering branches (N). Pierced white metal. $2.00.

14. THREE SALAMANDERS, entwined; silvered brass. $1.00.

15. A TURTLE in high relief on a red, painted background; composition. $1.00.

16. STAR FISH, convex brass, stamped. $1.00.

17. CRANE WITH FISH IN BILL; pierced brass design on concave, purple tinted background; two-piece. $1.50.

19. FROG WITH PIPE in cat-tails, two-piece with pierced design. $.75.

19. LIZARD ON THE FENCE, with ivy and flowers; pierced brass design with brass background. $2.50.

20. LIZARD in foliage and at the right, above the lizard, can be seen a snail; two-piece pressed brass. $2.00.

21. The same as No. 19, only this is a one-piece, pierced design. $3.50.

PLATE 55

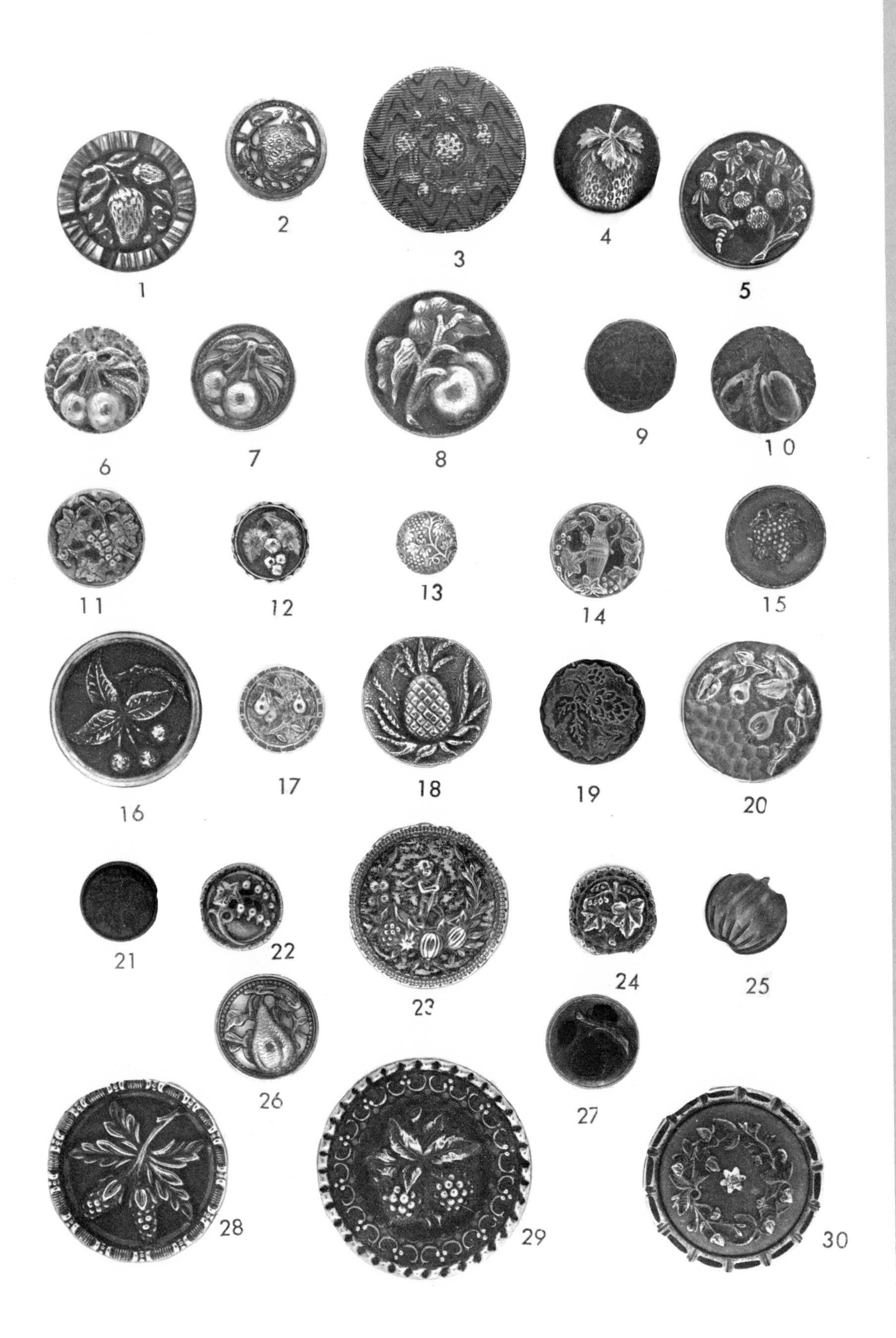

1
2
3
4
5
6
7
8
9
10
11
12
13
14
15
16
17
18
19
20
21
22
23
24
25
26
27
28
29
30

PLATE 55

FRUITS

The fruit buttons shown on this Plate, might be called Various and Assorted. Various is a term used by collectors to denote three different sizes: small, medium, and large. Assorted usually means, of different materials and having different designs.

1. A design of STRAWBERRIES, leaves and flowers, stamped from brass and superimposed on black pearl. $1.50.
2. One-piece pewter, pressed and pierced, showing STRAWBERRY and bee. $.75.
3. More STRAWBERRIES on a textured brass background, two-piece. $.75.
4. A large, tinted brass STRAWBERRY, in very high relief on a flat steel background, escutcheon type mounting. $2.00.
5. A pierced design, showing a bee and branch of STRAWBERRIES, leaves, and flowers, applied to a slightly concave background. $1.00.
6. CHERRIES, one-piece brass, fruit in high relief. $.75.
7. CHERRIES, the same design as No. 6, but in pierced brass. $.50.
8. Concave brass with APPLES of white metal, applied. $1.25.
9. Black glass CHERRIES, molded, with bright finish. $.50.
10. PLUMS, iridescent black glass, molded. $1.00.
11. A pierced brass design of GRAPES, applied over a concave, brass background. $.50.
12. A steel cup with center design of GRAPES. Brass leaves, cut steel grapes. $.75.
13. A brass ball with a pressed, all-over design of a GRAPE VINE. $.35.
14. A wine pitcher, bordered by a GRAPE VINE WREATH. A pierced brass design over a velvet background. This could also be classified with Pictorial Objects or Velvet Backgrounds. $1.00.
15. A two-piece pressed brass button, with a stem of GRAPES and leaves, tinted purple, on a concave brass background. $.50.
16. A pewter design of CHERRIES, stem and leaves, applied to a darkened brass background. Tinted brass rim. $.75.
17. Stem of FIGS. One-piece pressed brass, with gold tint. $.50.
18. One-piece brass with PINEAPPLE in high relief. Rare. $2.50.
19. Black glass, gold lustered, with design of BLACK-BERRIES and leaves, molded. $.75.
20. PEARS, two-piece brass, fruit in relief on hammered background. $1.00.
21. Black glass GOOSEBERRIES, dull finish, $.75.
22. CURRANTS. The pierced design and turned-under rim are in one piece; tinned liner and brass background. $.50.
23. A pierced brass design attached to brass rim shows Cupid as a gardener, with a harvest of MELONS and GRAPES; brass background with mottled, brown tint. $2.00.
24. CURRANTS and leaves; two-piece pressed brass. $.50.
25. A realistic, smoked pearl APPLE. Twentieth century. $.50.
26. One-piece pressed brass PEAR with insect. (medium size is shown with Insects.) This size, $.75.
27. A pierced design of brass, over a velvet background. The stem design is pressed in the face, while the velvet background forms the PEAR AND LEAVES. $.75.
28. Two-piece, stamped brass design of BLACKBERRIES, attached to rim, with tin liner and darkened background. $1.25.
29. Two-piece pressed brass with BERRY design in high relief. Pierced brass border, showing liner of shiny tin. $1.50.
30. A steel cup. The center design is a wreath of STRAWBERRIES, leaves, and flowers, circling a cut steel star, riveted. $2.50.

PLATE 56

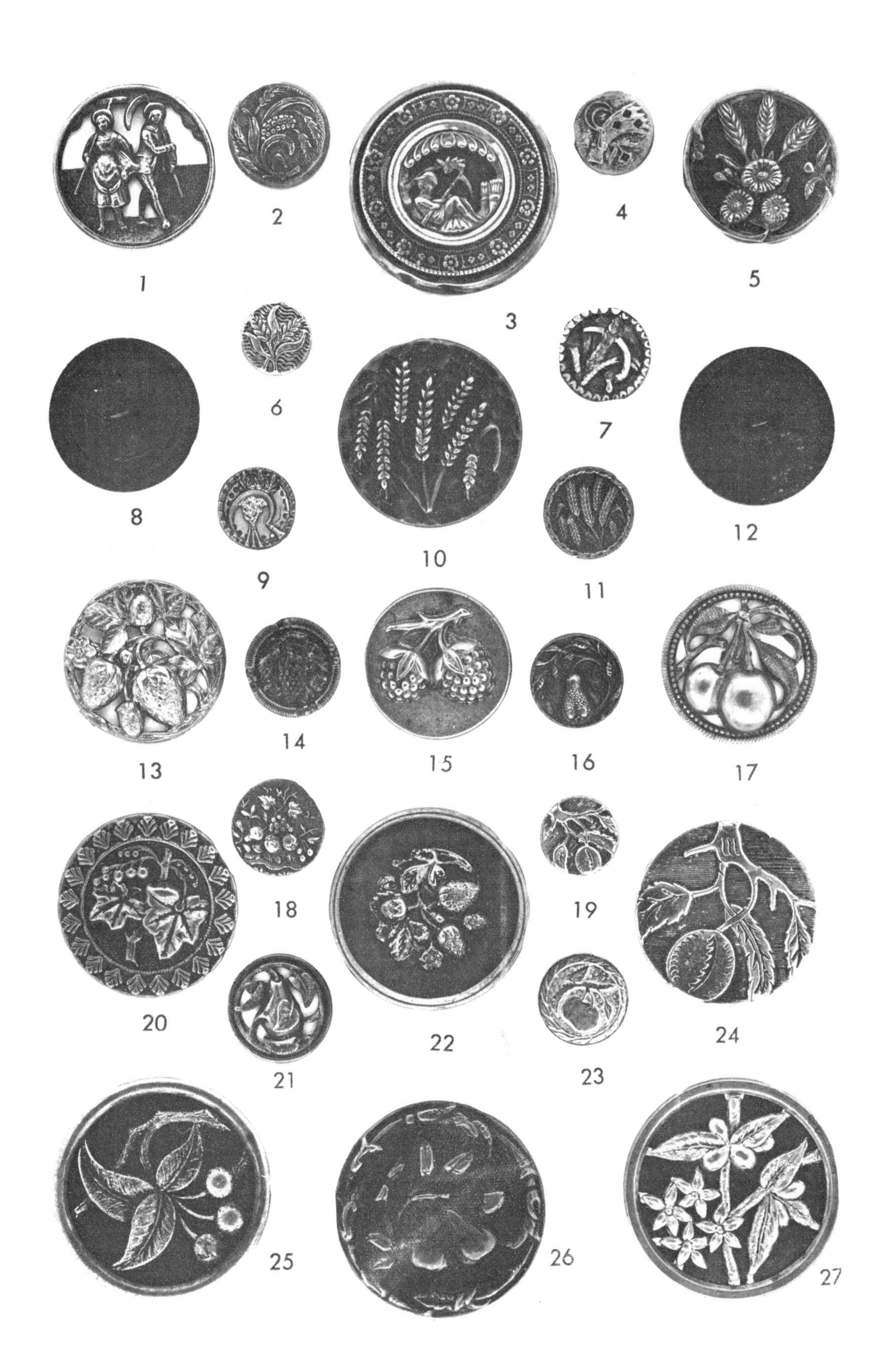

PLATE 56

GRAIN & FRUIT

These buttons come under the general classification of PLANT LIFE. Several show scythes and two picture people. These could also be included in an arrangement which pertained to HARVESTING or FALL.

1. Called, "THE REAPERS". One-piece brass. $2.00.
2. BARLEY, two-piece pressed brass, back-marked, "T.W. & W." $.75.
3. Another REAPER, the pierced brass design shows a man resting and holding his scythe with two sheathes of wheat stacked in front of him; design set in a tin frame, surrounded by pressed brass border. $2.75.
4. SICKLE AND SHEAF OF WHEAT, pierced brass over shiny tin liner. $.75.
5. WHEAT AND FLOWERS, pierced brass design over dark brown tinted brass background, stem border. $1.00.
6. Pressed tin; two stalks of WHEAT with leaves. $.50.
7. WHEAT AND SICKLE, one-piece pressed pewter. $.75.
8. Pressed horn, dyed black, two-hole sew-thru, SHEAF OF WHEAT. $2.00.
9. THREE STALKS OF WHEAT AND SICKLE, pierced brass over tin liner. $.50.
10. SEVEN STALKS OF WHEAT, in high relief on tinted brass background. $2.00.
11. The same design as No. 10, but attached to a pierced border. $.50.
12. Two-hole sew-thru of pressed horn, SICKLE AND GRAIN. $2.00.
13. STRAWBERRIES, leaves and flower; pierced brass, silvered. $1.00.
14. STRAWBERRY, molded black glass, lustered. $1.50.
15. BLACKBERRIES, two-piece brass, pressed, with berries in high relief. $1.00.
16. PEAR. Two-piece, concave, pear in high relief, blue tinted background.$.75.
17. One-piece, pierced brass CHERRIES, fruit in very high relief. $1.25.
18. Two-piece pressed brass with pink tinted background, the design shows a FRUIT PIECE of PEARS, APPLES, GRAPES, CHERRIES AND LEAVES. $.50.
19. PLUM, branch and leaves. Tinned zinc with pink tinted background,. two-piece. $.75.
20. CURRANT LEAVES AND CURRANTS, with stem. Pressed brass design, two-piece. $1.00.
21. One-piece pierced brass, PEAR and leaves, similar composition to No. 17. $.75.
22. STRAWBERRIES, STEM, LEAVES AND FLOWER, superimposed on a concave, brown tinted background, brass rim. $1.50.
23. Tinned zinc face, stamped face, two-piece design shows CHERRIES on a stem. $.50.
24. PLUM, the same design and construction as No. 19. $2.00.
25. CHERRIES, white metal design applied to darkened background, nickel rim. $1.00.
26. PEARS, two-piece, pressed brass, design in high relief on brown tinted background. $2.00.
27. Stem with ORANGE BLOSSOMS, leaves and fruit. Pewter design applied to a darkened brass background, brass collet. $1.25.

PLATE 57

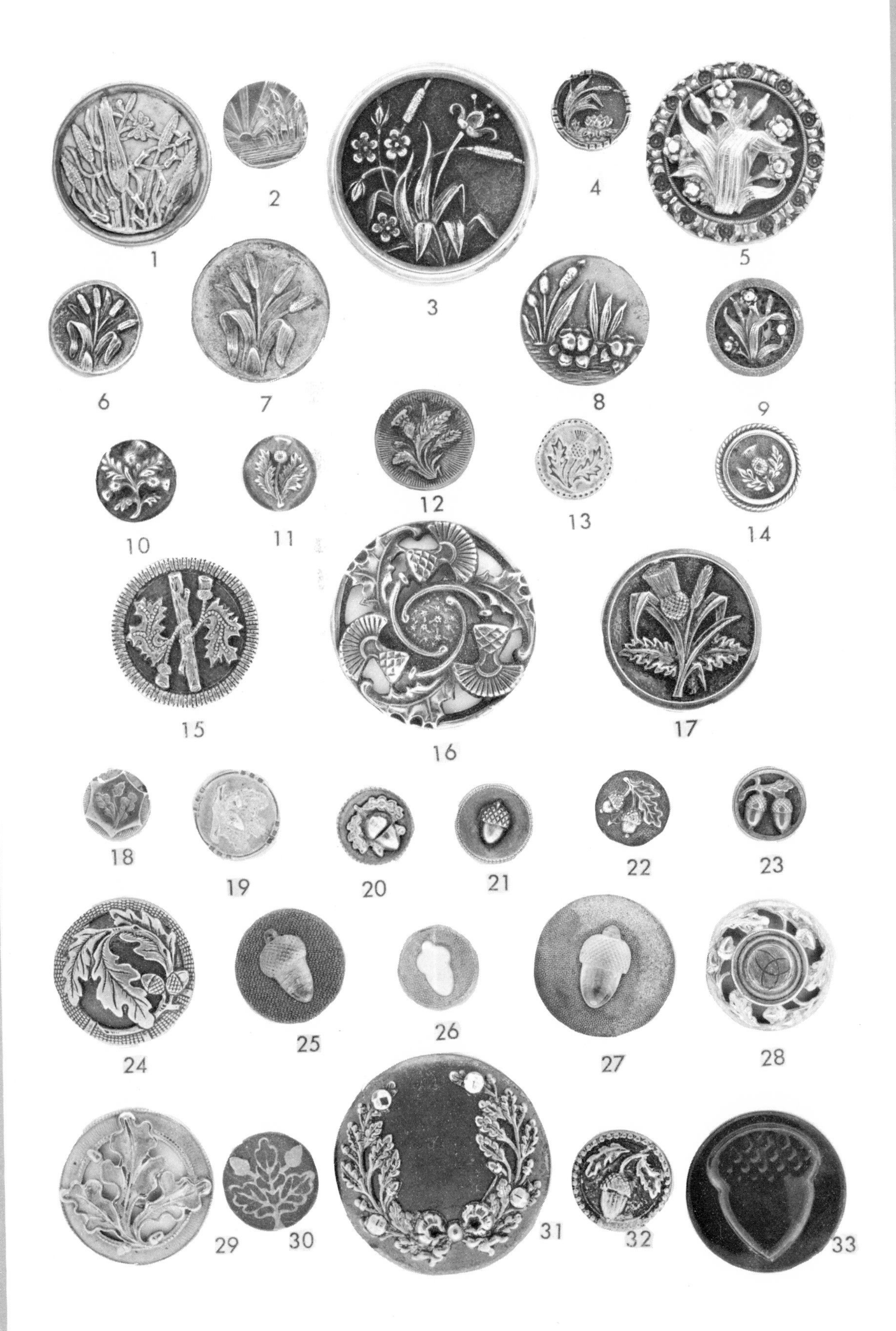
1
2
3
4
5
6
7
8
9
10
11
12
13
14
15
16
17
18
19
20
21
22
23
24
25
26
27
28
29
30
31
32
33

PLATE 57

PLANT DESIGNS

So many plant designs are shown on buttons that it is possible to assemble trays of one plant only, such as the cattails, acorns or thistles shown here. Thistles are the most difficult to find.

1. SEDGES with small butterfly. The design is of pierced pewter, over a metal background. Brass rim. $1.50.

2. CAT-TAILS AGAINST SUNRISE. A small two-piece brass button with stamped design. $.75.

3. CAT-TAILS AND WILDFLOWERS. A pierced pewter design over darkened background. Silvered rim. A very graceful design. $1.75.

4. CAT-TAILS AND WATER LILY. Stamped design, tinted green. $.50.

5. CAT-TAILS AND FLOWERS, with cut steel centers. The design is superimposed on a darkened metal background. The attractive border has flower heads that are similar to those in the center design. One-piece. $1.25.

6. and 7. Concave brass with design of CAT-TAILS applied to the center. Two sizes $.35 and $.75.

8. CAT-TAILS AND WATER LILIES. A highly convex, pressed brass button, two-piece. $1.00.

9. A design of CAT-TAILS AND FLOWERS, similar to No. 5 but applied over a "screen" background. These "screen backs" are quite scarce. $1.00.

10. Flat steel with brass escutcheon of THISTLE WITH THREE BLOSSOMS. $.75.

11. Flat brass with one THISTLE in relief. $.75.

12. Two-piece brass, slightly concave, with THISTLE AND WHEAT in relief. $.75.

13. Two-piece, gilded brass with one THISTLE. $.75.

14. Silvered THISTLE. A uniform type button with back-mark of "D. EVANS and CO.". $1.25.

15. A conventional design with THISTLES AND LEAVES applied over a darkened background. Two-piece. $1.00.

16. A conventional design of SCOTCH THISTLES. One-piece pierced brass. $1.50.

17. THISTLE AND WHEAT. A pierced brass design, applied to a concave brass background. Two-piece. $1.75.

18. through 23. comprises a row of small ACORN buttons, approximate value of each $1.00. No. 18 is an early gilt, engraved.

19. Gilded brass.

20. Concave brass with acorn of cut steel, applied.

21. Brass acorn applied to center of concave brass background. Two-piece.

22. Two acorns. Early silvered metal, backmarked "D. Evans & Co".

23. Two acorns, pierced brass, two-piece.

24. A two-piece brass button with pierced design of ACORNS AND OAK LEAVES, attached to border, over darkened background. $.75.

25. "Cloth covered", convex button with molded glass ACORN in the center. Early and scarce. $1.25.

26. A molded milk glass ACORN, on a brass background. $1.00. These little buttons can be found with clear and colored glass acorns also.

27. A medium sized brass button with clear glass ACORN. $1.00.

28. A 20th century pierced brass button with a border of ACORNS AND OAK LEAVES, painted in natural colors. $.75.

29. A pierced brass, one-piece button having center design of OAK LEAVES and TINY ACORNS. 20th century. $1.00.

30. A composition button with white metal ACORNS AND OAK LEAVES, inlaid. $1.25.

31. AN OAK LEAF AND ACORN WREATH, mounted on a convex, brass button with cut steels. $1.75.

32. Two-piece, pressed brass in high relief. $.75.

33. CELLULOID ACORN, circa 1910. $.75.

PLATE 58

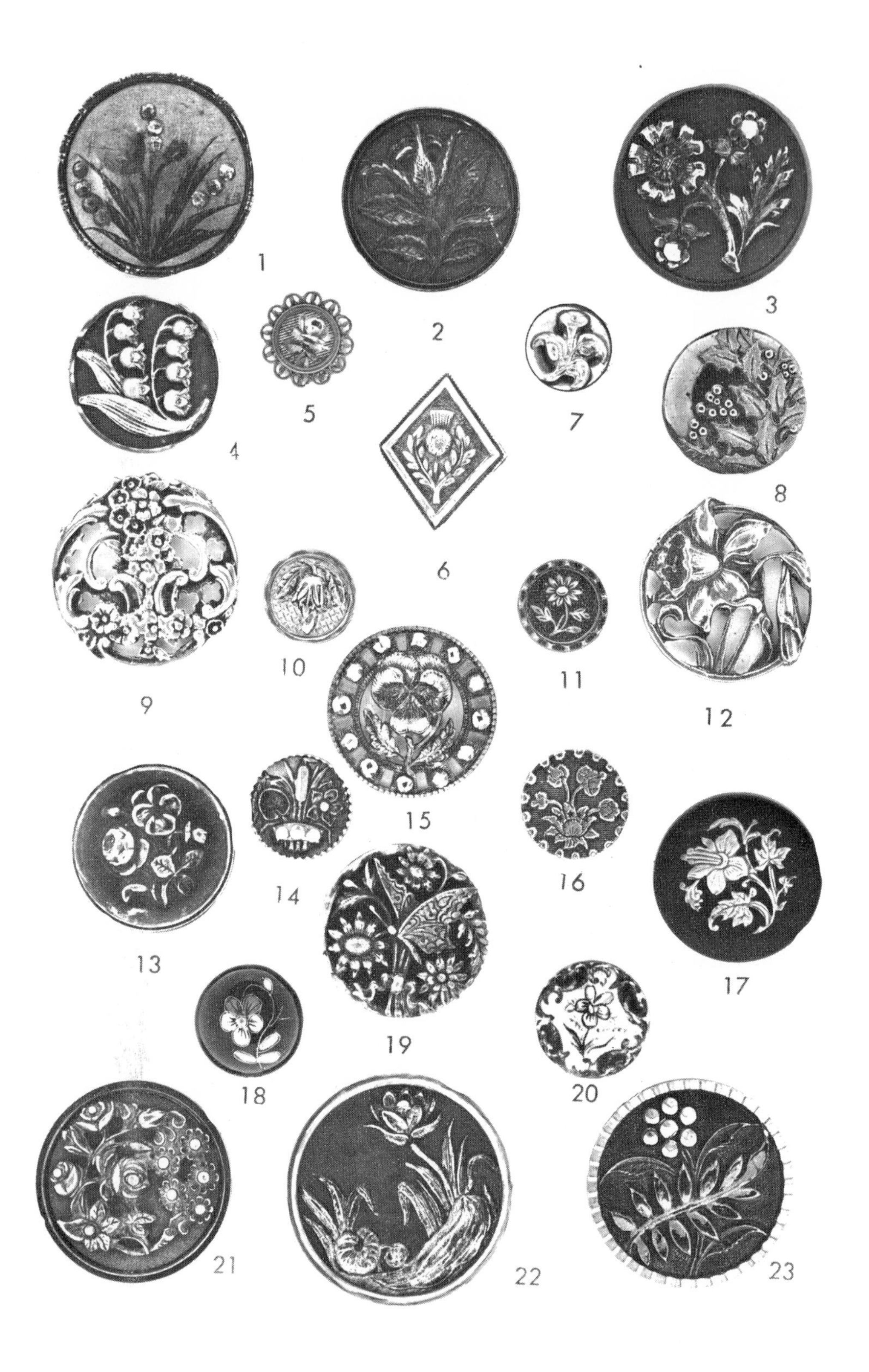

PLATE 58

FLOWERS

Flowers have always been an inspiration for any form of decorative art and their beauty and adaptability was not overlooked by button designers.

Although roses and pansies were favorite subjects, almost any flower or plant can be found illustrated in some manner on an antique button or stud. In fact, Mable Esten (see N.B.B. November, '64) has made a classification list of Plant Designs on Buttons which extends from lower plants, such as algae and fungi, to higher plants of the composite family, as the chrysanthemum.

A few lovely buttons, mostly from the Victorian Era are shown on the opposite page.

1. A TULIP, etched and painted on a tinted metal background, embellished with cut steels and set in a steel border. (lily family) $2.00.
2. A tinted metal MOSS ROSE BUD with foliage (Rose Family). $1.00.
3. A metal ORIENTAL POPPY, with cut steel trim, set in a saucer shaped wood background (composite family). $1.25.
4. LILY-OF-THE-VALLEY (lily family) pewter on brass. $1.00.
5. A RED ROSE with green leaves, paper under glass. Mounted in a brass border, cut out and scalloped. $1.25.
6. A THISTLE (composite family). This button is one worn on an authentic Scottish costume. The doublet and waistcoat of the Scottish costume always have these distinctive buttons, diamond shaped, and made either of silver or silver colored metal. They are made in one-piece and are decorated with Scottish patterns of different types. (N.B.B. September, '63). $2.00.
7. A brass MORNING GLORY in a steel cup. (convolvulus family). $.75.
8. HOLLY. A lustered black glass button. $1.25.
9. WILD ROSES in a basket with leaves and design of intricately pierced silver. $3.00.
10. AN ACORN (beech family) in high relief, made of hard white metal. $.50.
11. An ivoroid DAISY on a brass background with brass border. $.50.
12. A DAFFODIL, stamped and pierced silver. $4.00.
13. PANSY AND ROSE, brass in tinted brass saucer. $1.00.
14. CAT-TAIL (Monocot family) made of tinted pewter. $.50.
15. Lovely bronzed brass PANSY with pierced center and border, decorated with cut steels. $2.25.
16. POPPIES, made of white metal. $.50.
17. A HONEYSUCKLE, metal inlaid in Vegetable Ivory. $2.00.
18. A PANSY painted in blue, white and green and outlined in gold on black glass. $1.75.
19. A butterfly perched on a SUNFLOWER (composite family). The design and border are pierced brass, over a saucer shaped background which is tinted red. $1.00.
20. A VIOLET, enameled in white on a light blue background with a black scroll border that is enhanced by black enameling. $1.75.
21. ROSES AND FORGET-ME-NOTS, pewter on brass. $.75.
22. A WATER LILY and bud, pewter on brass with brass border. $1.50.
23. A tinted pewter button showing a DAISY and leaf. $1.50.

PLATE 59

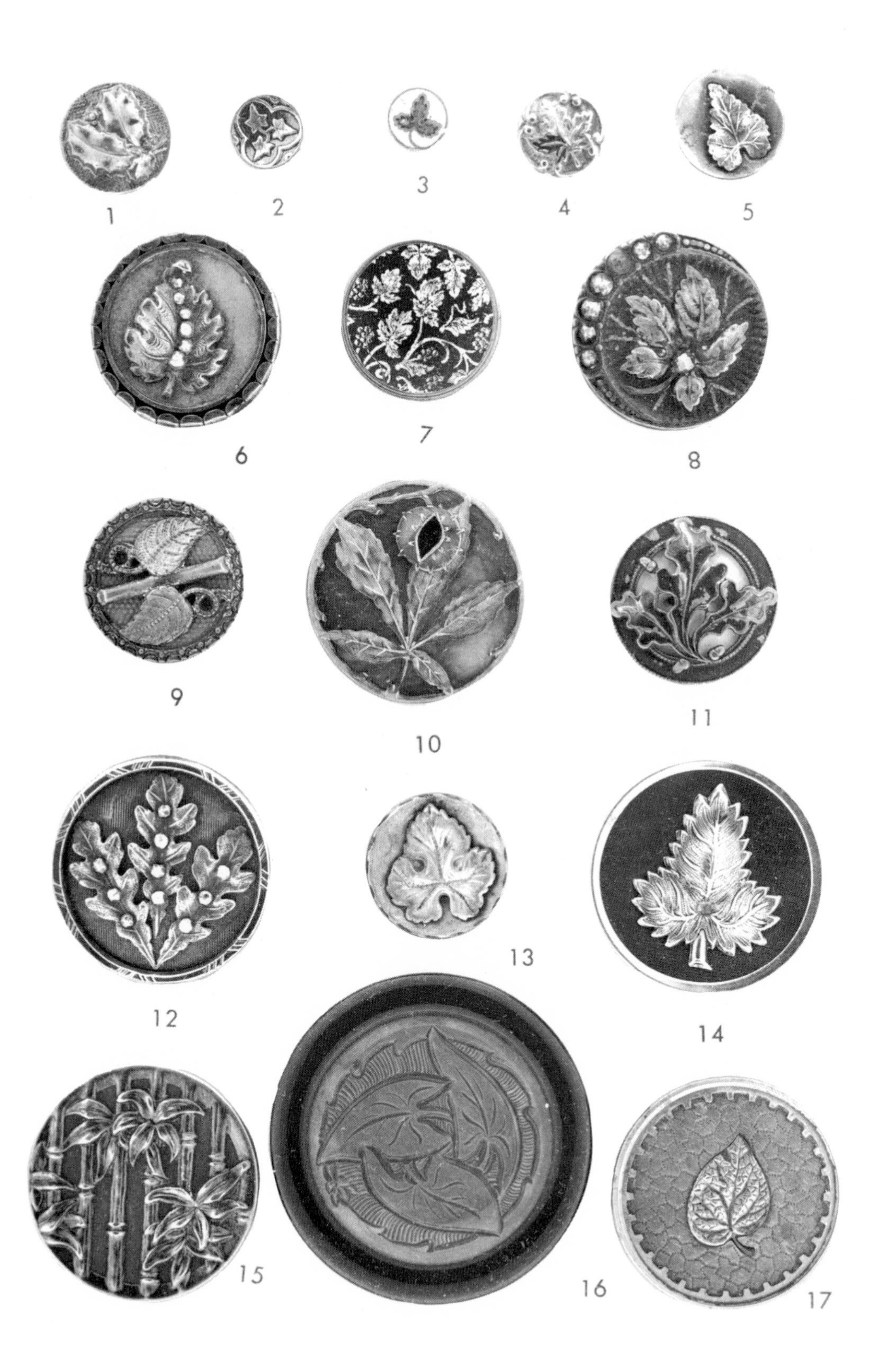

PLATE 59

LEAVES

It is possible to easily identify many leaf forms on buttons but often the designer's fancy achieves a pleasing effect but distorts the true identity of the leaf.

A thorough study of "Leaf Designs On Old Buttons" resulting in a Classified List has been made by Mable M. Esten and described with illustrations in N.B.B., November, 1966.

The buttons shown in this Plate are not difficult to find or identify and many more can be added.

1. HOLLY, (holly family), stamped brass with design in relief. $.75.
2. ENGLISH IVY (ginseng family). Tinned zinc with leaves in low relief. $.50.
3. An IVY LEAF, enameled in green on a white background with leaf outlined. Stem and rim in gilt. $.75.
4. MAPLE LEAF (maple family). This is enameled in autumnal colors with gilt outline and border. $.75.
5. GRAPE LEAF (vine family). A concave white metal button, darkened, with vine tendrils etched on each side of the leaf. $.50.
6. This is a brass leaf with cut steels ornamenting it, applied to a steel cup. it is an ACANTHUS LEAF (acanthus family). The acanthus leaf was much used in architectural decoration. $1.75.
7. A true tole, concave button with GRAPE VINES, leaves and small grapes. $1.25.
8. BUCKEYE (horse chestnut family), brass in relief on bronze tinted background with crescent border set with cut steels. $1.50.
9. PAPER BIRCH (hazel family), leaves and branch tinted in natural colors and attached to scalloped border. Brass background with contrasting tint outlined by a steel liner. $1.00.
10. HORSE CHESTNUT and leaf (horse-chestnut family). Nut, leaves and rim are cut from one piece of brass which turns over the back. Amber glass shows through the slit in the nut and the background is of smoked pearl. $12.50.
11. OAK LEAVES (beech family). One-piece pierced brass, leaves and rim are painted. Leaf veins, outline and acorns are gilt. $1.00.
12. More OAK LEAVES of brass, trimmed with cut steels and set in a steel cup. $2.25.
13. Another brass GRAPE LEAF in relief on concave cup-like brass button. One-piece. $.75.
14. FILBERT (N), white metal design in high relief on black tinted background which gives contrast. Tin rim. $2.00.
15. BAMBOO (grass family). The design is in one-piece with the turned-under rim of brass. The background and design have a purplish tint. $1.50.
16. ARROW HEAD (water-plantain family). Carved celluloid center. Dark rim, green. $2.00.
17. BEGONIA (begonia family), pressed brass raised slightly from a pebbled brass background with a brass rim and a saw-tooth steel liner. $2.00.

PLATE 60

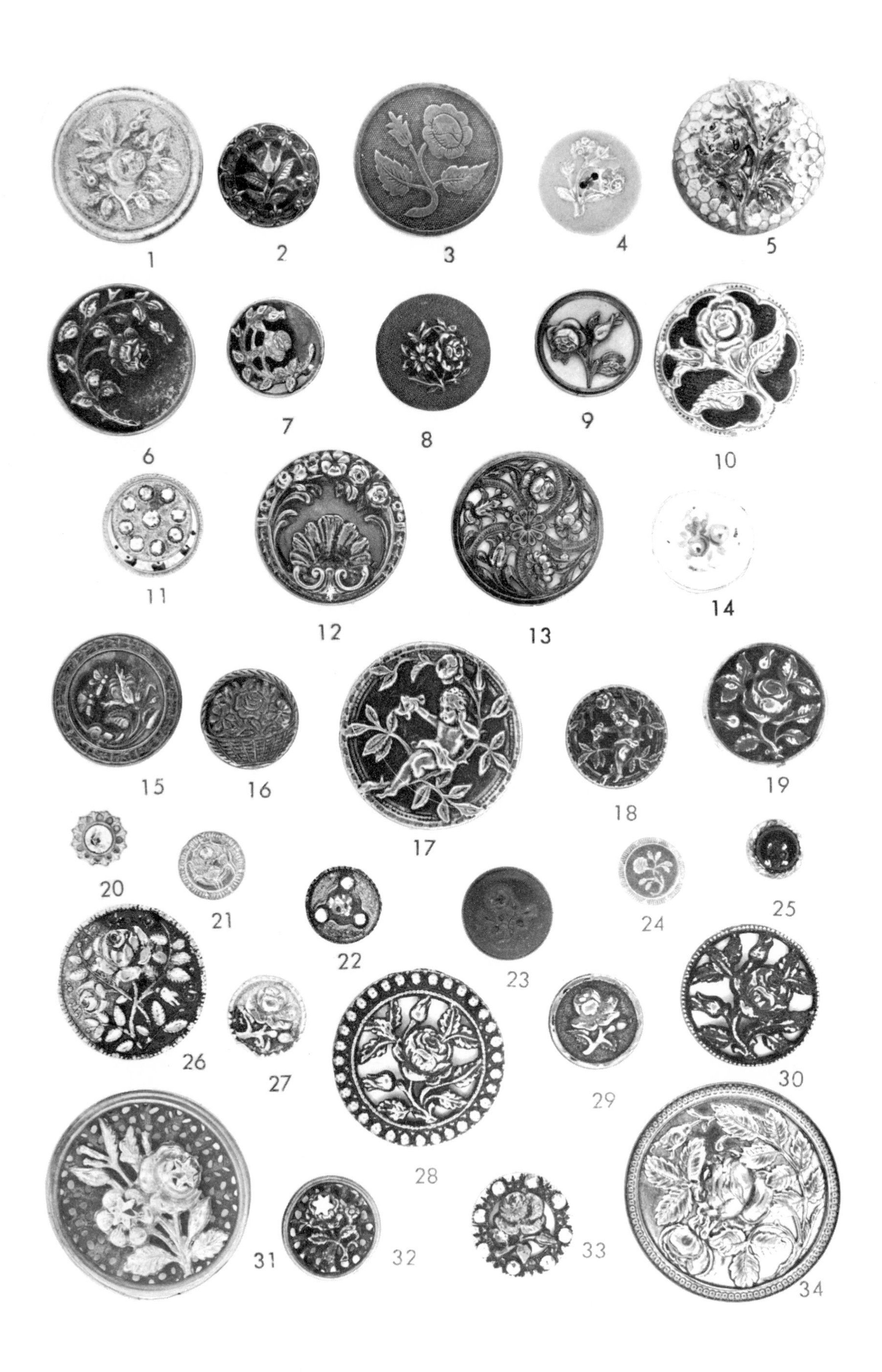

1
2
3
4
5
6
7
8
9
10
11
12
13
14
15
16
17
18
19
20
21
22
23
24
25
26
27
28
29
30
31
32
33
34

PLATE 60

ROSES

The rose is not only loved for its fragrance and beauty but for centuries it has been a symbol of love, romance and perfection. It has always been used in design but was especially popular during the Victorian Era when everything was lavishly decorated. It was freely used by button designers, both alone and in combination with other flowers. It is possible to find examples of buttons that are decorated with roses in nearly every material that was used. Those shown here are quite easily collected.

1. Two-piece brass with concave center. $.75.
2. MOSS ROSE, pierced brass, tinted blue over a blue velvet background, fleur-de-lis border. $.75.
3. One-piece brass, rose in low relief. $1.00.
4. Light grey composition, two-hole sew-thru, white metal rose spray inlaid. $1.00.
5. A silver tinted, highly convex, brass button with rose and buds in high relief, applied. $1.25.

6. and 7. A brass rose and bud with curved stem applied to a slightly concave brass button. This is one of the most common rose designs but it is quite lovely, especially when found in one of the many tints that are available. Medium size, $.50; small, $.25.

8. This nosegay is applied to a high, convex, mottled and tinted brass button. $.50.
9. Pierced brass design, attached to rim, over white celluloid background. $.75.
10. A pierced design in one-piece with the rim; tin with a brown velvet background. $1.50.
11. Gilded brass with cut steel trim and a white enameled crescent which has painted roses and leaves (red and green). $.75.
12. Two-piece; a pierced brass rococo design with celluloid background. $1.00.
13. One-piece pierced brass, five curving arms like those of a star fish radiate from the center and between each is a different flower head, one being a rose. $.75.
14. Hand painted pink rose with green leaves on white enamel center; stippled grey enameled border. $3.00.
15. Two-piece brass, concave center with moss rose and two butterflies. $1.00.
16. A threadback; the stamped brass face represents a basket of flowers, the most prominent being a rose; background tinted purple. $1.50.

17. and 18. This cherub, resting on a rose branch, may be intended for Cupid as both he and the rose are symbols of love but no wings are visible; a two-piece pierced brass design with brightly tinted blue metal background. Medium size, $2.50. Small size, $1.00.

19. Two-piece pierced brass over tinted background. $.75.
20. A diminutive brass button with pierced border and enameled center with hand-painted pink rose and green leaves on white. $1.00.
21. Two-piece brass, back-marked, "extra fein"; the center a rose. $.50.
22. A steel cup with chased metal center, the portion between the three cut steels is slightly recessed and painted with pink roses and green leaves. $1.00.
23. Goodyear Rubber, 1851; rose in relief. $.75.
24. One-piece gilt with rose spray. $.75.
25. Twin roses (pink with green leaves) in black glass set in brass rim; a jeweled waist-coat button. $1.25.
26. White metal, design in relief, background tinted in two colors. $1.00.
27. The same construction as No. 26 but higher and more convex. $.50.
28. A one-piece, pierced design with border which simulates cut steels, tinted pink. $1.00.
29. White metal, pressed design, one-piece, pink tint. $.25.
30. Pierced, tinted white metal, identical with No. 28 except for border. $.75.

31. and 32. One-piece brass with "screen backgrounds", rolled rim, floral decoration silvered and applied to concave background, star shaped cut steels in the center of each flower. 31, $3.50. 32, $.75.

33. One-piece pierced brass with cut steel border. $.75.
34. One-piece pressed brass with rose in very high relief. $1.00.

PLATE 61

PLATE 61

WOOD BACKGROUNDS

Wood has been used in different ways to make buttons but these illustrated here were created during the 19th century. A thin sheet of wood veneer is used as a background for the metal picture or design. The picture is usually applied but in some cases it is in one piece with the collet. The rim, itself, is often quite ornamental. (See N.B.B., March, '52.)

1. PAN RIDING A LION. The picture is of white metal, tinted brown to blend with the background; brass border also tinted. $3.50.

2. This is a Kate Greenaway design, called "TRUMPETER" from, "Pipe Thee High", the stamped brass design is attached to the border. $5.00.

3. BIRD ON FLOWER SPRAY; brass design is attached to the border. $2.00.

4. A Kate Greenaway design called, "AT THE WELL"; pierced brass with brass rim on a wood background. $3.50.

5. RAMPANT LION with Shield, over wood background and with brass rim. $2.00.

6. BRANDON; brass design attached to cut-out border which shows steel liner. $8.00.

7. POUCH of brass, tin collet. $3.50.

8. MOUNTAIN LION, tinted brass, tin collet. $4.00.

9. WARRIOR EQUIPMENT, brass design attached to rim on wood background. $3.00.

10. EGYPTIAN CAT. This design is attached to an elaborate border which incorporates a fleur-de-lis design. $5.50.

11. DOVE chained to perch, applied to background. Leaf border of brass. $4.00.

12. CORSELET, brass escutcheon on wood background. $3.50.

13. JUPITER AND MINERVA. $4.00.

14. DRAGON. $2.00.

15. FLOWER AND BUDS. Brass flowers have large cut steel centers. The wooden background has an elaborate brass border. $3.50.

PLATE 62

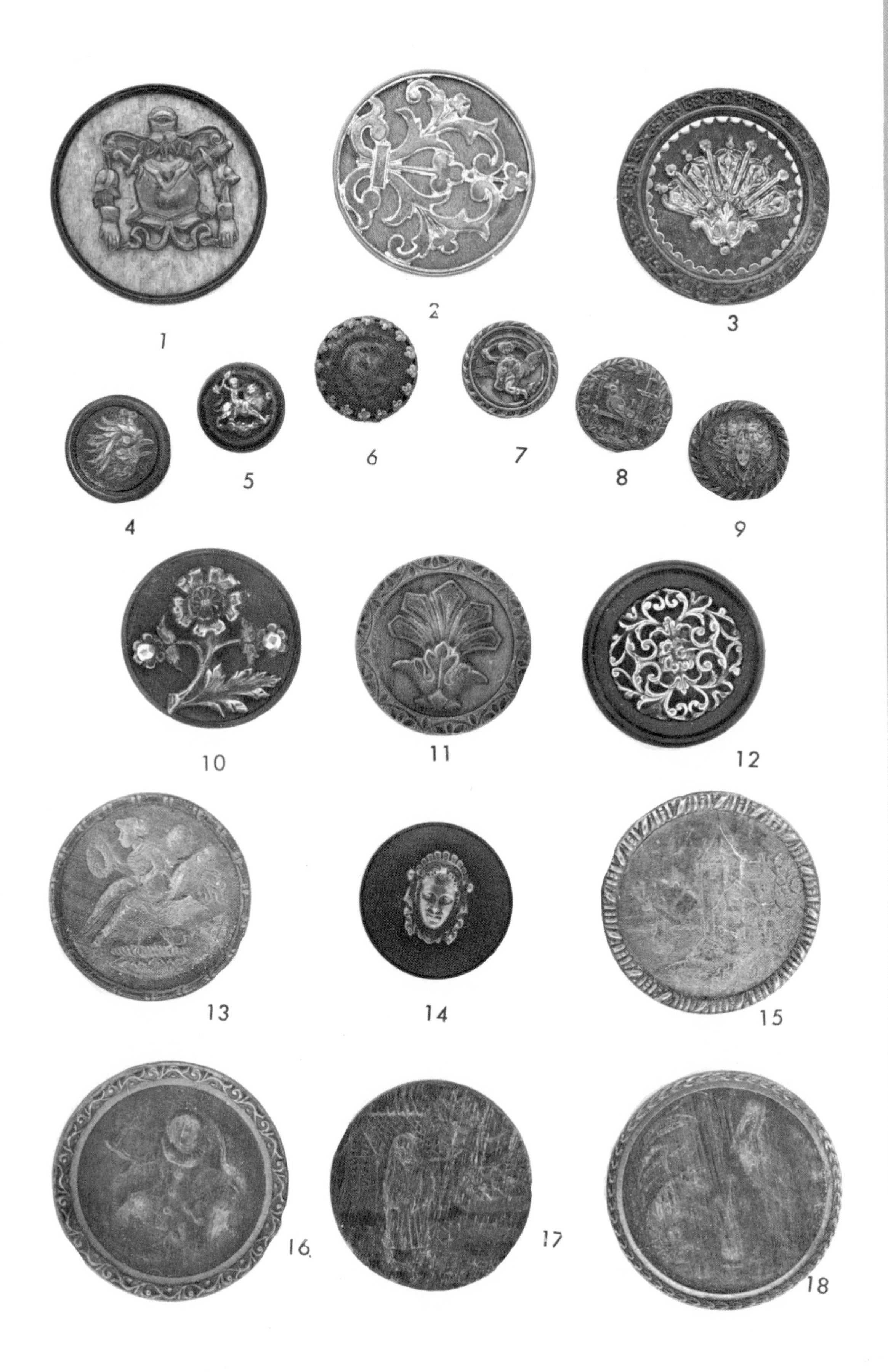

PLATE 62

BUTTONS OF WOOD

We have definite proof that wooden buttons were made during the last part of the eighteenth century, but those of the early 19th century show the same craftsmanship. The wooden picture buttons were made at about the same period, in the nineteenth century, as metal picture buttons. Many were made of pressed wood (pressed in a mold). Sometimes the material was wood that had been softened and made plastic, in other cases it was saw dust or similar bits of wood, held together by a binder. A fine article titled, "Wood Buttons Through The Centuries", by Margaret F. Kelso may be found in N.B.B. for March 1952. The above information is from this article.

1. ARMOR. A brass design, attached to the wood veneer background by means of pins. Darkened brass rim. $3.50.
2. A BRASS HINGE. A pierced design, attached to the brass border. Wood veneer background. $3.50.
3. A white metal FAN, applied to a wood veneer background which has a scalloped tin "liner" inside the rim. Pretty border of brass is tinted brown and fan was originally tinted. $3.50.
4. A brass disk with WILD COCK'S HEAD, set in a wooden button. The back of the button has a small disk with a center hole; the escutcheon type design on the face is attached to the shank which goes through this hole at the back. $1.50.
5. The same construction as No. 4 but a pierced brass design of "PAN TAMING A LION". $1.25.
6. Pressed wood. A brass rim with prongs holds the wooden portion which has a portrait of the artist RUEBENS. Metal back. $1.50.
7. GANYMEDE, son of Tros, King of Troy (Greek mythology). Because of his great beauty, according to legend, he was carried off by Zeus, in the shape of an eagle, to serve as a cup-bearer. The pierced brass design is attached to the brass border; steel "liner" and wood veneer background. $1.50.
8. HEN OF THE FENCE, a pierced brass design over wood veneer background. The design is in one piece with the rim which is turned over the metal back. $1.00.
9. MEDEA, great friend of Jason in Greek mythology. Tinted brass head, applied to a wood background, brass rim. $1.00.
10. This is a concave, wooden button with a FLORAL design, tinted and trimmed with cut steels. The design is an escutcheon type, attached through the button, to the shank which has a small brass plate. $3.50.
11. This is a wooden button mold, such as used as a foundation for a cloth or crocheted covering. The round side is at the back and face is covered with a thin wood veneer. The brass ornament is attached through a hole in the mold to the shank. Brass border applied separately. $2.00.
12. A concave, all-wood button with a WHITE METAL DESIGN applied. Two pins, attached to the design are pushed through the wood and clinched at the back. $2.00.
13. A pressed wood pictorial showing GANYMEDE seated on the eagle of Zeus. Thunder was Zeus' weapon. The eagle was his favorite bird and one often carried his thunderbolts. You can see these at the base of the picture. Brass rim and metal back. $10.00.
14. A concave all-wood button with brass escutcheon which is a HEAD. $2.00.
15. Pressed wood, showing a SCENE with castle, water, boat, cliffs etc. Brass back and border. $4.00.
16. The wood grain shows plainly on this button, indicating that it was not made of sawdust and glue. It is a pressed design of SCARAMOUCH, seated on a crescent moon. Scaramouch was a stock character in a 17th century Italian farce. Metal back, brass rim with running scroll design and steel "liner". Scarce. $10.00.
17. All wood, pressed design on face of button with fine detail, which shows AN ORIENTAL GENTLEMAN standing in front of a dwelling. This, unlike any other shown here, has two holes in a rounded back to sew through. $5.00.
18. THE FOX AND THE STORK, from Aesop's Fable; a pressed wood design which shows the grain in the wood; same construction as No. 16. Both buttons are extra large. $8.00.

PLATE 63

PLATE 63

BORDERS

Many button designs are greatly enhanced by the borders which encircle them. Often the border is related in some way to the center design, but on many, there appears to be no connection. In a study of borders made by Grace Moore (N.B.B. September, '64) she has divided these interesting frames into seven classes and named 31 different borders. On this Plate we have illustrated fifteen that we found especially attractive. Elsewhere in this book, you may note others, such as the lovely paste borders and the Angel Heads and Stars which form a frame for "The Madonna And Child".

1. SCREW HEAD BORDER. The center motif is a FIVE POINT STAR with fleur-de-lis finials. This is of pierced brass, showing a steel liner; a two-piece brass button with darkened background. $4.00.

2. BORDER OF RUNNING DOGS, with center design showing LIZARD AND SNAIL; one-piece brass. $3.00.

3. A LEAF BORDER for a pewter bird, applied to a wooden background. A tin inner rim compliments the color of the bird; the pressed leaves of the border decoration are brass. $3.50.

4. IVY LEAF BORDER for "MORNING GLORIES", a lovely button, given this name by Mrs. Ray McBride. The picture was found on the cover of a book by Louisa May Alcott, published in 1872, and called, "Morning Glories and Other Stories" (See J.B., February, '64). A cut-out brass design on a wood background. $4.50.

5. HEART BORDER. It is possible to find twenty different buttons with this border. The center of this is a brass head, not positively identified, but sometimes called, "Isabella"; on a slightly concave background of darkened brass with a bright tin rim inside the border. $3.00.

6. A wide FLOWER AND LEAF BORDER of pierced brass which harmonizes well with the floral design of brass in the center. The pebbled background is of darkened brass. $2.00.

7. "TAURUS THE BULL" BORDER. This button probably has no connection with the Zodiac. It is a one-piece brass button which was brought from Europe by the late Joseph A. Stawski and its true identity is unknown. Combats and spectacles with bulls were common in Ancient Thessaly and Imperial Rome. The first Roman amphitheatre built for this sport was called Statilus Taurus. The figure in the center design looks like an athlete of this ancient era and we believe the button might well be named Taurus. $8.50.

8. HELMET BORDER surrounds four more helmets which form the center design. The material is 19th century pewter and because of its softness, many have been destroyed through use and are not common. $2.50.

9. CROSS IN OVAL BORDER; a hard, white metal button, in one piece, centered with a brass Mercury Head. $2.50.

10. BORDER OF CIRCLES, RECTANGLES AND FLOWER HEADS; a one-piece, pressed brass button with griffin applied to a steel disk and centered against a rayed brass background. Flowerheads form a five-point star. Evidently moon (the round steel disk) and star are represented. $2.50.

11. BIRD AND FLOWER SPRAY BORDER, of pierced brass, decorated with cut steels. The center design is a brass MASK with pierced steel trim, attached to a basket-weave, brass background. $4.00.

12. DIAMONDS, a rolled brass border with steel liner under the cut-out diamonds; the brass floral spray, a chrysanthemum, is applied to a wood background. $2.50.

13. LEAF BORDER of brass, framing a brass head of BELLUM in very high relief on a darkened brass background. Rare. $5.00.

14. LEAVES AND STEMS, alternated with crosses inside ovals, form this intricate brass border. The center design of THE DOVE OF PEACE is of pierced brass, attached to the border, over a wood background. $4.00.

15. TURNED CORNERS, sometimes called Handkerchief Corners. These rims are very ornate and the buttons having them are usually very well designed. This one has engraving on each corner and a cross is engraved on the darkened brass background, behind the ivy draped fence, which is in high relief. Ivy is said to symbolize the weakness of humanity, clinging to the strength of God. This symbolism and the cross make the Religious category, a suitable one for this button, also. $8.00.

PLATE 64

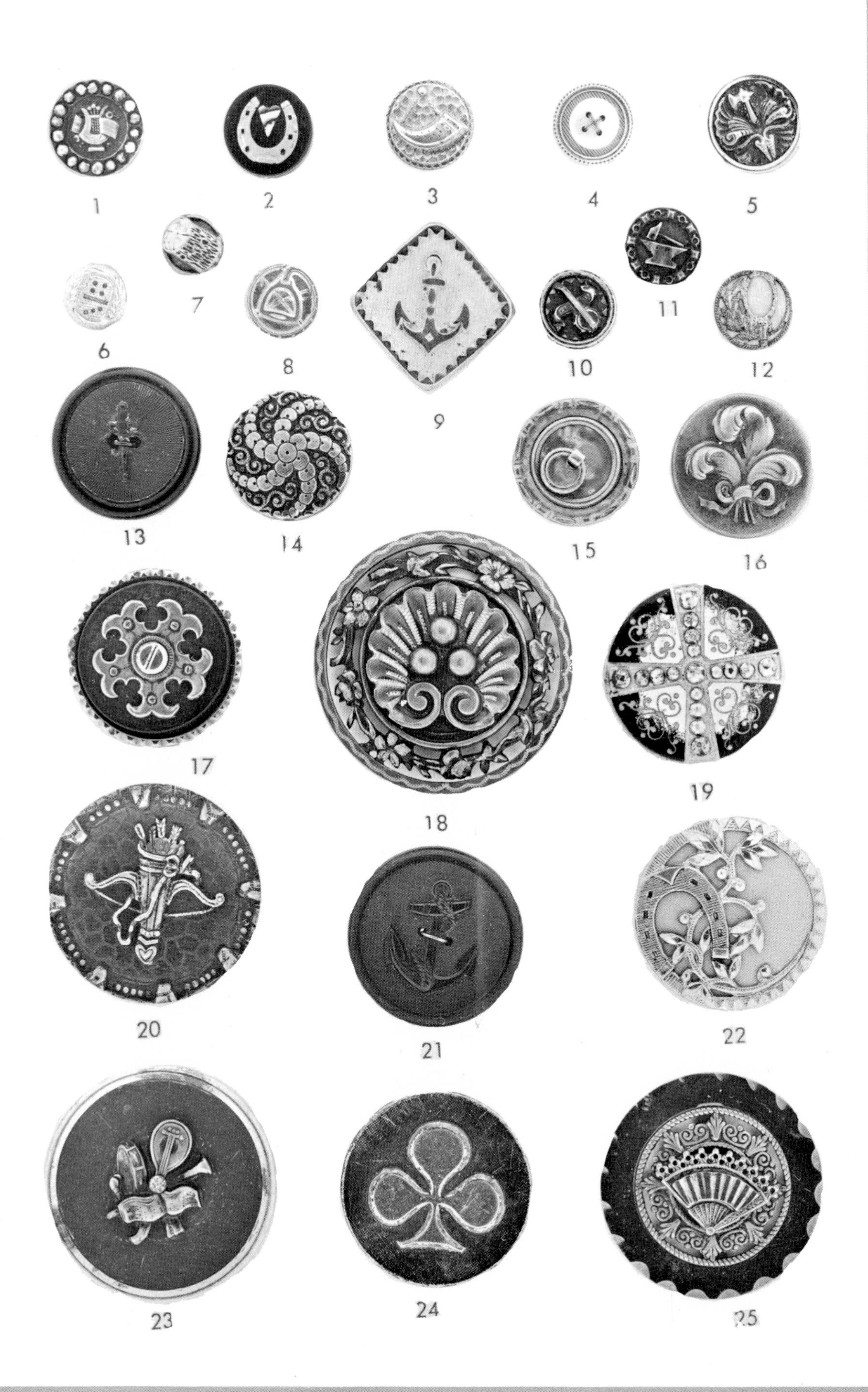

PLATE 64

PICTORIAL OBJECTS

Many inanimate objects can be found pictured on buttons.

An arrangement such as Plate 64 can be made or this classification can be broken down into separate ones such as, Anchors, Baskets, Buckles, Crosses, Hands, etc. Religious symbols and objects which suggest old superstitions are also interesting types for which to search.

1. A LYRE, one-piece brass with cut steels in the border. $1.00.
2. Paper-mache, inlaid with a silver HORSESHOE and a pearl HEART. $1.75.
3. A two-piece, pressed brass POWDER HORN in high relief. $1.00.
4. This little button has a pearl center, with gold wire representing thread, a border of pink celluloid, and a gold-filled rim and shank. A waistcoat button of the gay 90's. $1.00.
5. A tin HATCHET, mounted in a pierced brass, rococo design. The rim is of tin. This design might possibly have been inspired by the French historical incident which involved Jeanne Hachette. $.75.
6. A brass DOMINO. The spots and dividing line are pierced to show a tin liner. $1.00.
7. A cut LOG. Pressed brass with the log in very high relief. $.75.
8. A STIRRUP, the strap of which forms the rim of this two-piece button. $.75.
9. An ANCHOR, unusual in that it is square and of rich gold color. $1.75.
10. A BANJO; one of the small brass musical buttons that is quite scarce. $1.25.
11. ANVIL AND BLACKSMITH'S HAMMER. The border design shows square horseshoe nail heads alternated with pierced holes that let a tin liner shine through. $.75.
12. A cut out design showing the outline of a HAND MIRROR and a leaf spray, over a background of celluloid. The brass design is tinted pink and blue. $.75.
13. A pressed horn, sew-through button with a DAGGER in the center. As is often the case with these interesting horn buttons, the design is centered between the holes. $1.50.
14. This brass PINWHEEL is made up of sequin-like shapes. The entire top is of one-piece brass, turned under at the rim. $1.00.
15. An "Early Victorian" DOOR KNOCKER. The brass knocker is mounted on dyed pearl. Rim and border are of brass. $1.50.
16. PLUMES. When three plumes are shown in this manner, they are often referred to as, "Prince's Feathers" for three feathers in a similar arrangement appear in the crest of the Prince of Wales. Pressed brass with feathers in high relief. $1.50.
17. SCREW HEAD. This button is a "Steel Cup" with a wood background. A brass, five armed, cross-like escutcheon shows five tiny screw heads and a larger screw holds all parts together. $3.50.
18. A brass SEASHELL. The brass border is made of lovely flower forms, pierced and the shell and rim are hand chased. Exceptional. $6.50.
19. A CROSS. A brass button, enameled, forms the background for a brass cross which is decorated with cut steels. $7.50.
20. BOW, QUIVER AND ARROWS of pewter form an escutcheon on this one-piece brass button. $3.50.
21. Dyed, pressed horn ANCHOR; a sew-through button. $1.00.
22. A pierced HORSESHOE, floral spray and rim of brass, silver tinted, over a celluloid background. $2.00.
23. MUSICAL INSTRUMENTS in relief on a tinted brass background; brass rim. $3.50.
24. One piece of tinned zinc forms the front and turned-under rim of this CLUB. $1.75.
25. An ornamental brass disk is centered by a brass FAN. This is mounted on a darkened brass background. The fan's decoration and the scalloped border are of steel. $3.50.

PLATE 65

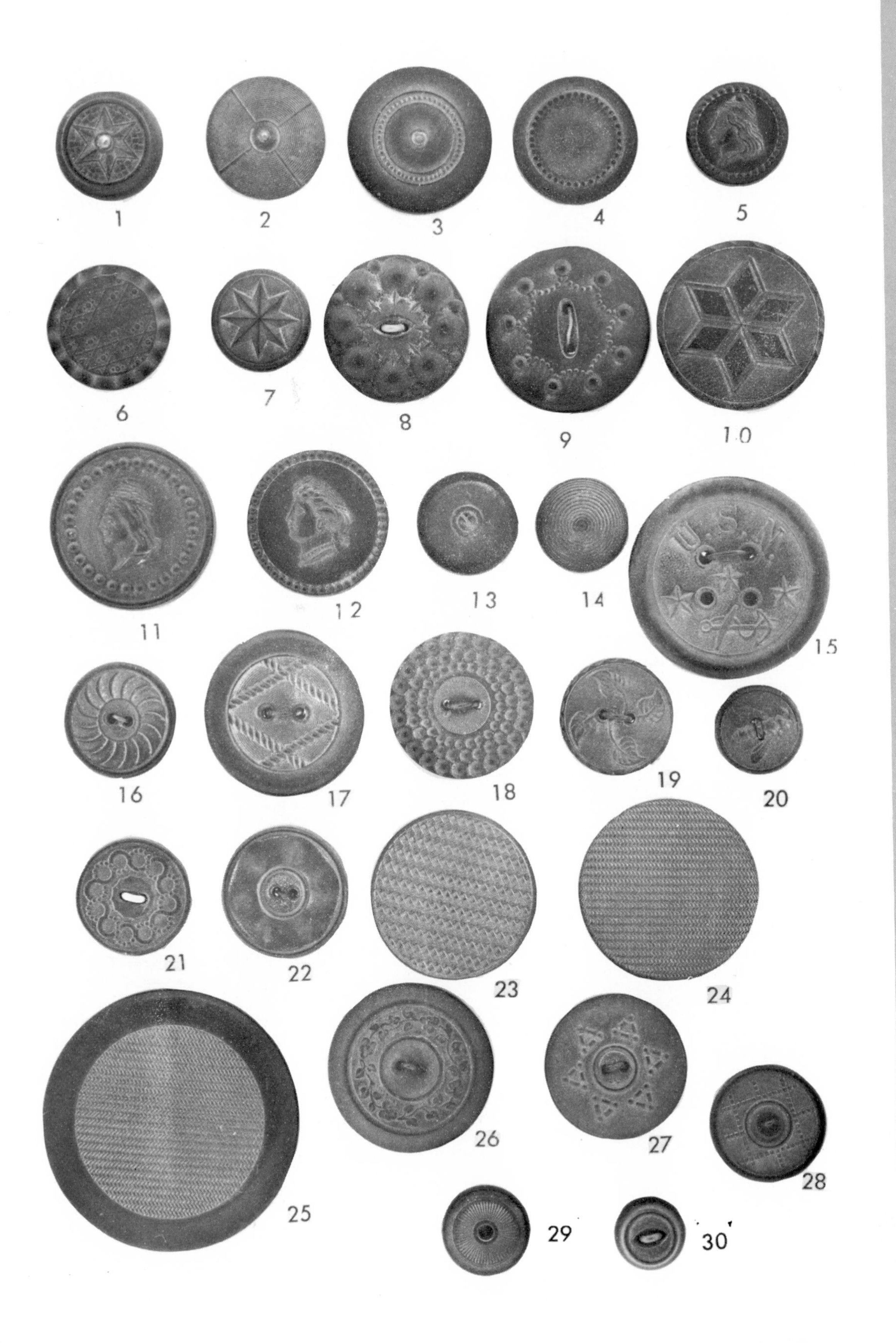

1
2
3
4
5
6
7
8
9
10
11
12
13
14
U. S. N.
15
16
17
18
19
20
21
22
23
24
25
26
27
28
29
30

PLATE 65

GOODYEAR HARD RUBBER BUTTONS

By Mary Seymour

Following the patenting of the process of vulcanizing rubber by Charles Goodyear, a discovery involving the addition of sulphur and sometimes shellac to India rubber, created the product we know as hard rubber. Nelson Goodyear discovered and patented this process on May 6, 1851, and assigned the use of this material to manufacturers for whatever use they might find for it. Two companies, The Novelty Rubber Co. of New York and New Brunswick, N.J. and the India Rubber Comb Co. of New York, made all the rubber buttons bearing the Goodyear name and patent date.

The Novelty Rubber Co. made the greatest assortment of patterns and types, including sew throughs, metal shanks, and all the pin shank types. All of the self shank buttons were made by the India Rubber Comb Co., together with a variety of sew throughs. There are only two known patterns with metal loop shanks made by the I.R.C. Co. One is the Gail Borden Eagle Brand uniform button and the other a plain, shiny finished, solid top button, found in two sizes. Textile designs are the most plentiful among the patterns made by the I.R.C. Co. Backmarks are in both impressed and raised lettering.

Variety is great among patterns made by the Novelty Rubber Co. Besides the conventional and geometric designs, there are many pictorials - animals, classic heads, and symbols. There are two patterns of U.S. Navy uniform buttons - the upright anchor and the horizontal anchor. There are U.S. Infantry officer's buttons (I in recessed shield) and the lined shield type worn by enlisted personnel during the Civil War period. Buttons for both the Republican and Democratic candidates were produced by the N.R. Co. for the campaign of 1868. Some of the most desirable types are those combined with other materials. There are a number of patterns rimmed with metal and some inlaid with metal, glass, or pearl. There is indeed infinite variety and interest to be found in the collecting of Goodyear hard rubber buttons.

Values expressed for unfaded, clear cut, unworn patterns.

1. Pinshank, star, plentiful, Estimated value, $.75.
2. Pinshank, plentiful, Estimated value, $.50.
3. Pinshank, fairly scarce, Estimated value, $.75.
4. Rose head in center of concave well, scarce, $.75 to $2.50.
5. Small Liberty Head, plentiful, Estimated value, $.50.
6. Ruffled edge, scarce, N.Y. in back-mark, Estimated value, $.75 to $1.50.
7. 8 point star, plentiful, Estimated value, $.50.
8. Unusual pattern, fairly scarce, Estimated value, $.75.
9. 9 point star, scarce, May 6, 1851 date, Estimated value, $1.50.
10. 6 point star, plentiful, May 6, 1851 date, Estimated value, to $1.00.
11. Medium size Liberty Head, plentiful, May 6, 1851 date, Estimated value, $1.00.
12. Classic Head, plentiful, Estimated value, $1.00.
13. Odd shape, estimated value, $.50, screw head center.
14. Bee Hive shape, red color, Estimated value, $.75.
15. Navy, horizontal anchor, scarce, Estimated value, $4.00.
16. Swirl pattern, no patent date, Estimated value, $.50.
17. Rope, May 6, 1851, scarce, Estimated value, $1.00.
18. Dotted design, plentiful, Estimated value, $.50.
19. Leaves, scarce, Estimated value, $.50.
20. Wasp, fairly plentiful, $.75.
21. Chain type pattern, scarce, $.50.
22. Fluted with rim, no patent date, plentiful, Estimated value, $.75.
23. Textile pattern, I.R.C. Co., plentiful, Estimated value $.50.
24. Textile pattern, I.R.C. Co., plentiful, Estimated value, $.50.
25. Largest size found in Goodyear's, 1 3/4 inch, scarce, value, $1.50.
26. Violet wreath, scarce, no patent date, Estimated value, $1.50.

    Numbers 16, 22, 26 and 28, having only NOVELTY RUBBER CO. on the back, are generally believed to have been made after the patent period had run out, sometime between 1870 and 1880. There are many patterns so marked which are also found with the patent date on them (No. 16 and No. 22) and about an equal group which we have never found with the date. Mrs. Lebers includes them with her Goodyear's.

27. Star, plentiful, $.75.
28. Whistle, no patent date, scarce, Estimated value, $.75.
29. Whistle, I.R.C. Co., back-mark, scarce, $.50.
30. Odd shape, fairly plentiful, Estimated value, $.10.

All buttons shown on this Plate are from the collection of Mary Seymour.

PLATE 66

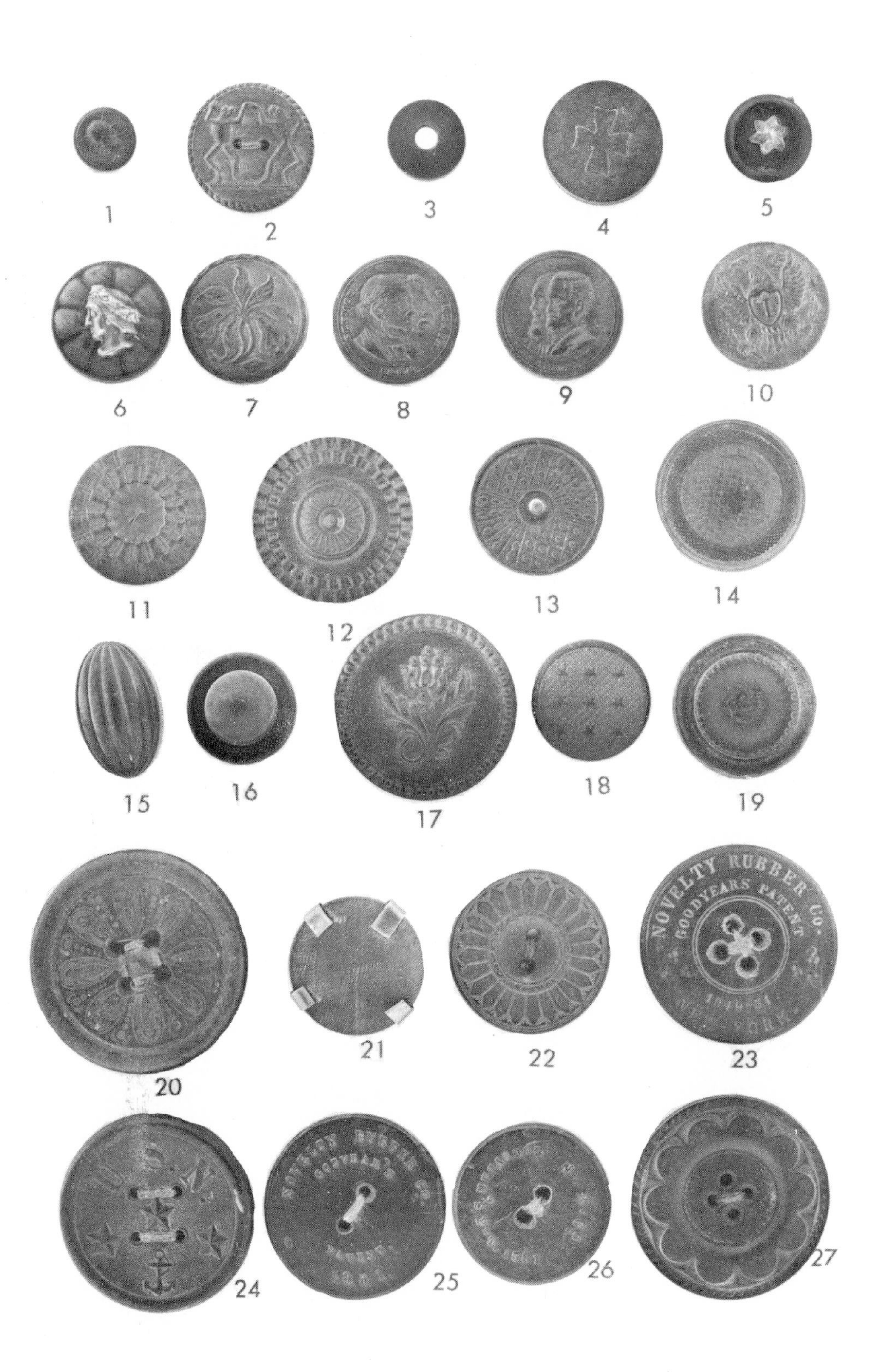
1
2
3
4
5
6
7
8
9
10
11
12
13
14
15
16
17
18
19
20
21
22
NOVELTY RUBBER Co.
GOODYEARS PATENT
23
24
25
26
27

PLATE 66

GOODYEAR

All Goodyear buttons shown are from the collection of Mary Seymour, unless otherwise stated.

1. Bug. 3/8" Back: N.R. Co. P/T. This is one of four patterns (bug, cross, rose head, and ball) that are found also in diminutive size, but with no backmark. Estimated value, $1.00.

2. Dancing Frogs. Back: N.R. Co./GOODYEAR'S P-T. 1851. Also found in small size. Scarce. Estimated value, $10.00 and up.

3. Opalescent glass center. Back: N.R. Co./GOODYEAR'S P-T. Rare. Estimated value, $5.00. From the collection of Mrs. Clarence Reeds.

4. Cross, white metal inlaid. Back: N.R. Co./ GOODYEAR'S P-T. 1851. Scarce. Estimated value, $3.00.

5. Pinshank, 6 point cut steel star. Back: N.R. Co./GOODYEAR'S P-T 1851. Rare. Estimated value, $1.50.

6. Pinshank, brass head. Back: N.R. Co./GOODYEAR'S P-T 1851. Rare. Estimated value, $3.00.

7. Figs. Back: N.R. Co./GOODYEAR'S P-T. 1851. Scarce. Estimated value, $2.50.

8. Political campaign button from Presidential election year, 1868. Democratic candidates - Horatio Seymour for President and Francis P. Blair for Vice-President. Back: N.R. Co./GOODYEAR'S P-T. 1851. Rare. Estimated value, $45.00.

9. Political campaign button from Presidential election year, 1868. Republican candidates — U.S. Grant for President and Schuyler Colfax for Vice-President. 13/16". Back: N.R. Co./GOODYEAR'S P-T. 1851. Rare. Estimated value, $35.00 - $45.00.

10. U.S. Infantry Officer's button. Worn by sharpshooter regiments, Civil War period. Much scarcer than the general service pattern with striped shield. Back: N.R. Co./GOODYEAR'S P-T. 1851. Rare. Estimated value, $45.00.

11. Scarce ruffled pattern in the rarest color, tan. Has one of the older types of backmark. Back: N.R. Co./GOODYEAR'S P-T. 1851. Estimated value, $3.00.

12. Pinshank, double ruffled border. Back: N.R. Co./GOODYEAR'S P-T. 1851. Scarce. Estimated value, $3.00.

13. Pinshank, brown. Back: N.R. Co. N.Y./GOODYEAR'S P-T. 1851. Scarce. Estimated value, $3.00.

14. Brass rimmed, basket weave center, brick red color. Back: N.R. Co. N.Y./GOODYEAR'S P-T. 1851. Rare. Estimated value, $5.00.

15. Melon-shaped. Back: N.R. Co./P-T (in recessed circle). Estimated value, $5.00.

16. Two-piece pattern, ball and saucer. This is found in several small sizes. Back: N.R. Co./GOODYEAR'S P-T. Scarce. There is one other two-piece pattern called "top hat", which is more rare. Estimated value, $.75.

17. Floral pattern. 1 1/8". This attractive pattern is in plentiful supply, but highly desirable for its not so plentiful back-mark. Back: N.R. Co./GOODYEAR'S P-T May 6, 1851. Estimated value, $1.00.

18. Nine stars on textile pattern background, red brown color. Self-shank. Desirable because it is the only symbol pattern found among those made by the India Rubber Comb Co. Back: I.R.C. Co./1851/GOODYEAR (in incised letters). Estimated value, $.75.

19. Rose head in bottom of concave reeded center, brick red color, brass rim. Back: N.R. Co./GOODYEAR'S P-T. 151. Rare. Estimated value, $5.00.

20. Beautiful pattern with oldest backmark. 4-hole sew through. Large sizes and also the small size seem to be rarer than the medium size with the 1849-51 backmark. Very rare. Estimated value, $15.00. See No. 23 for backmark description.

21. Moire pattern with canvas shank. Rare backmark. Back: N.R. Co. N.Y./GOODYEAR'S PATENT '49-'51. Very rare. Estimated value, $15.00.

22. Unusually beautiful pattern, 2-hole sew through 1849-51 backmark. See No. 23. Estimated value, $12.00.

23. Mounted to show the desirable oldest type backmark found on Goodyear rubber buttons. The lettering is incised and arranged in two concentric circles. Outer - NOVELTY RUBBER CO/NEW YORK. Inner - GOODYEAR'S Patent 1849-51. $15.00.

24. U.S. Navy enlisted man's button, upright anchor pattern. Back (in raised letters): NOVELTY RUBBER CO./GOODYEAR'S PATENT/1851. Rare. Estimated value, $5.00.

25. This button is mounted to show one of the intriguing errors in spelling to be found in the backmarks of Goodyear buttons. The error "GODYEAR" occurs on many buttons both in medium and small size. $5.00.

26. Another error. The date is 1581 instead of 1851. $5.00.

27. Unusual pattern in large size 4-hole sew through button, made by the I.R.C. Co. Plain and Textile patterns are more commonly found in this size. Back: I.R.C. Co./GOODYEAR 1851 (incised lettering). Scarce. Estimated value, $2.00.

PLATE 67

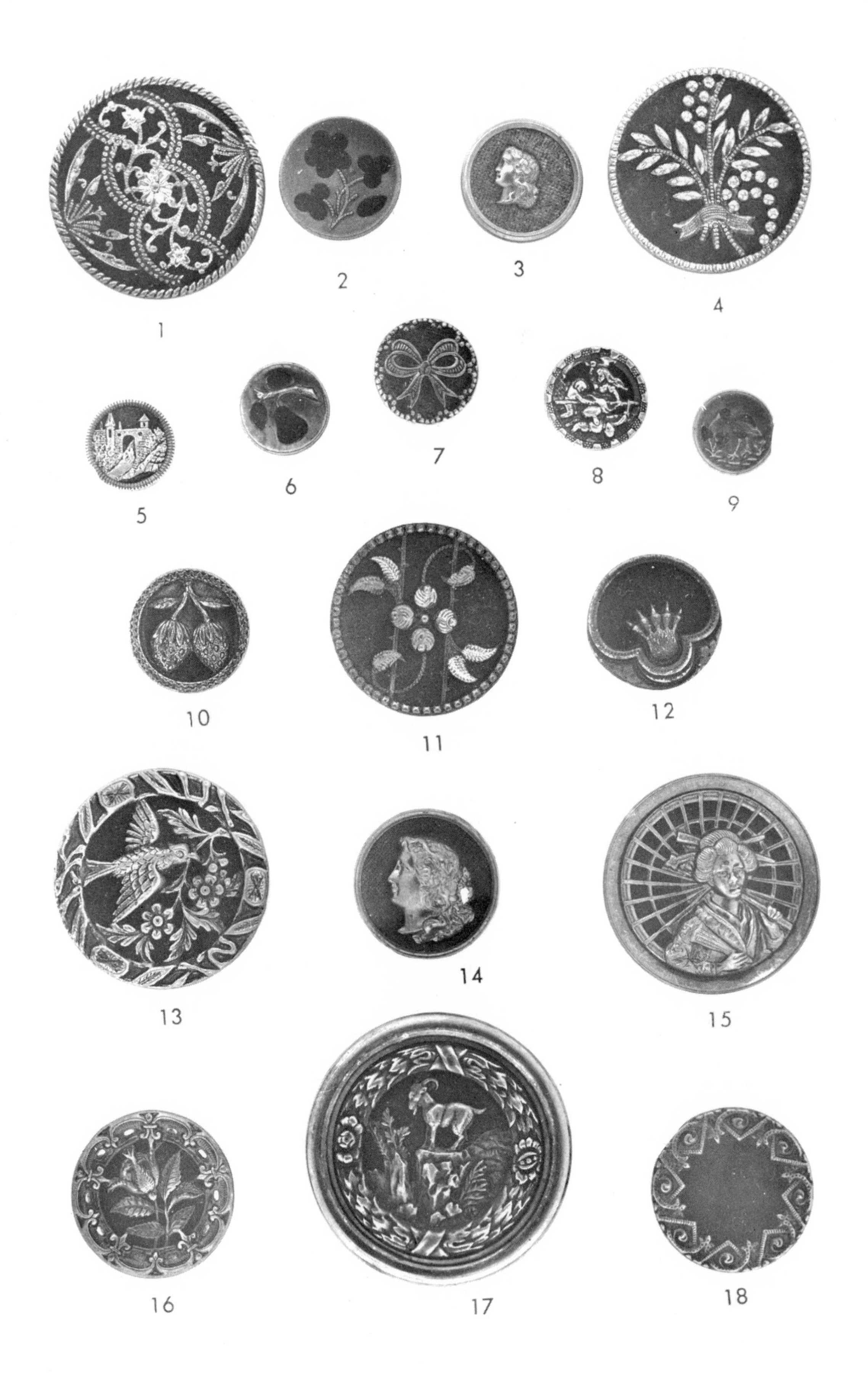

PLATE 67

VELVET BACKGROUNDS

The class of buttons known as, "Velvet Backgrounds" forms a charming group and can be assembled into a very attractive arrangement. Usually a metal design has been placed over a background of velvet, which has been secured by sizing, to a metal back. A metal rim is applied and forms a frame for the center design. In some cases the velvet is covered with a thin sheet of metal which has a cut out design, allowing the velvet to show through and make or enhance the design.

1. A large button with fine cut out design and rope border of brass. Value, $2.50.
2. A metal face, cut out showing flowers and leaves of red velvet. The button has a reddish tint and flowers and stems are raised. Value, $.75.
3. A brass head superimposed on green velvet. Value, $2.00.
4. A spray of faceted leaves and berries, tied with a BOW superimposed on black velvet. The rim and decoration are of silvered brass. $3.50.
5. A pewter CASTLE with brass rim and brown velvet background. Value, $1.50.
6. Similar constructon and color to No. 2. The PEAR and leaves show the red velvet background. Value, $.75.
7. A brass BOW KNOT; ornamental border and dark brown velvet background. $.75.
8. JEANNE HACHETTE in brass with brass border, steel mirror liner and red velvet background. Value, $1.75.
9. A brass face with a design of a BIRD and flowers is cut out so that the background of velvet forms the flower petals and body of the bird. The bird has a long bill and resembles a baby stork. $1.00.
10. STRAWBERRIES; brass with brownish tint; brown velvet background. Value, $1.50.
11. Brown velvet background with a LEAF and floral arrangement of tinted brass. Value, $3.50.
12. A CLAW, set in a brass border with red velvet background. Value, $2.50.
13. DOVE OF PEACE, with a dark brown velvet background. Value, $4.00.
14. A lovely purple tinted brass head of a GIRL with flowers in her hair. She probably represents Spring. Superimposed on purple velvet. Value $3.00.
15. YUM YUM with parasol; brass with brownish tint and brown velvet background showing through the ribs of the umbrellas, Value, $3.50.
16. A lovely MOSS ROSE; brass with a blue tint and dark blue velvet background. The border has a fleur-de-lis design and a steel mirror lining shows through the cut out sections. Value, $2.50.
17. This is called ROBINSON CARUSO'S GOAT and by some, MOUNTAIN GOAT. It is an extra large button with a highly raised design in brass, over a dark brown velvet background. Value, $15.00.
18. An interesting brass border, tinted black, showing a black velvet background which forms the entire center. $1.00.

PLATE 68

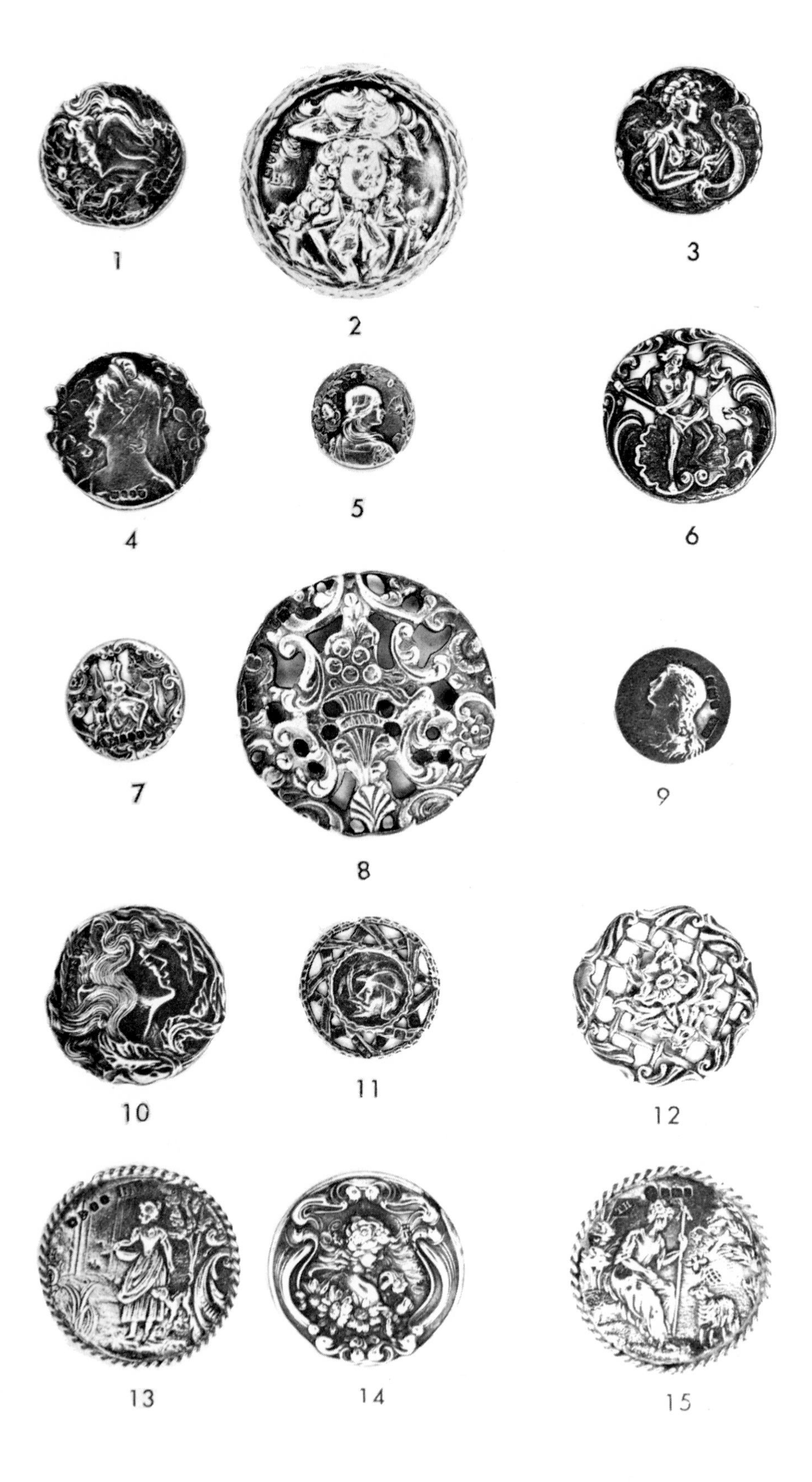

PLATE 68

HALL MARKED SILVER

A hallmark is a mark of genuineness, an official stamp on gold or silver impressed at the assayer's office. It appears on many silver buttons and consists of the maker's mark, the place of origin and the date.

Marks of origin most often found are: Leopard's head denoting London; a castle, Edinburgh; Anchor, Birmingham; a shield and sword, Chester. All buttons illustrated are hallmarked.

1. Profile of a LADY. $12.00.
2. HERTZOG VON BERWICK. Hallmark at left. $35.00.
3. Called MUSIC. Probably represents Euterpe, the Muse of Music. $12.00.
4. Another lovely PROFILE. $15.00.
5. MIGNON. $6.50.
6. NEPTUNE WITH SEAHORSES. Hallmark at right. $18.00.
7. DIANA. $8.00
8. BASKET OF FRUIT. Hallmark at left. $15.00.
9. JOAN OF ARC. Hallmark at right. $8.00.
10. SEASONAL HEAD. $15.00.
11. MAN'S HEAD with lovely pierced border. $8.00.
12. TRELLIS with flowers entwined, leaves forming border. $10.00.
13. A domestic SCENE, hallmark clearly visible at top. Rope border. $25.00.
14. SPRING. $20.00.
15. SHEPHERDESS, rope border. $25.00.

See JUST BUTTONS for April 1959 for a comprehensive article, "The History of English Hall Marks" by Faith Russell Smith.

PLATE 69

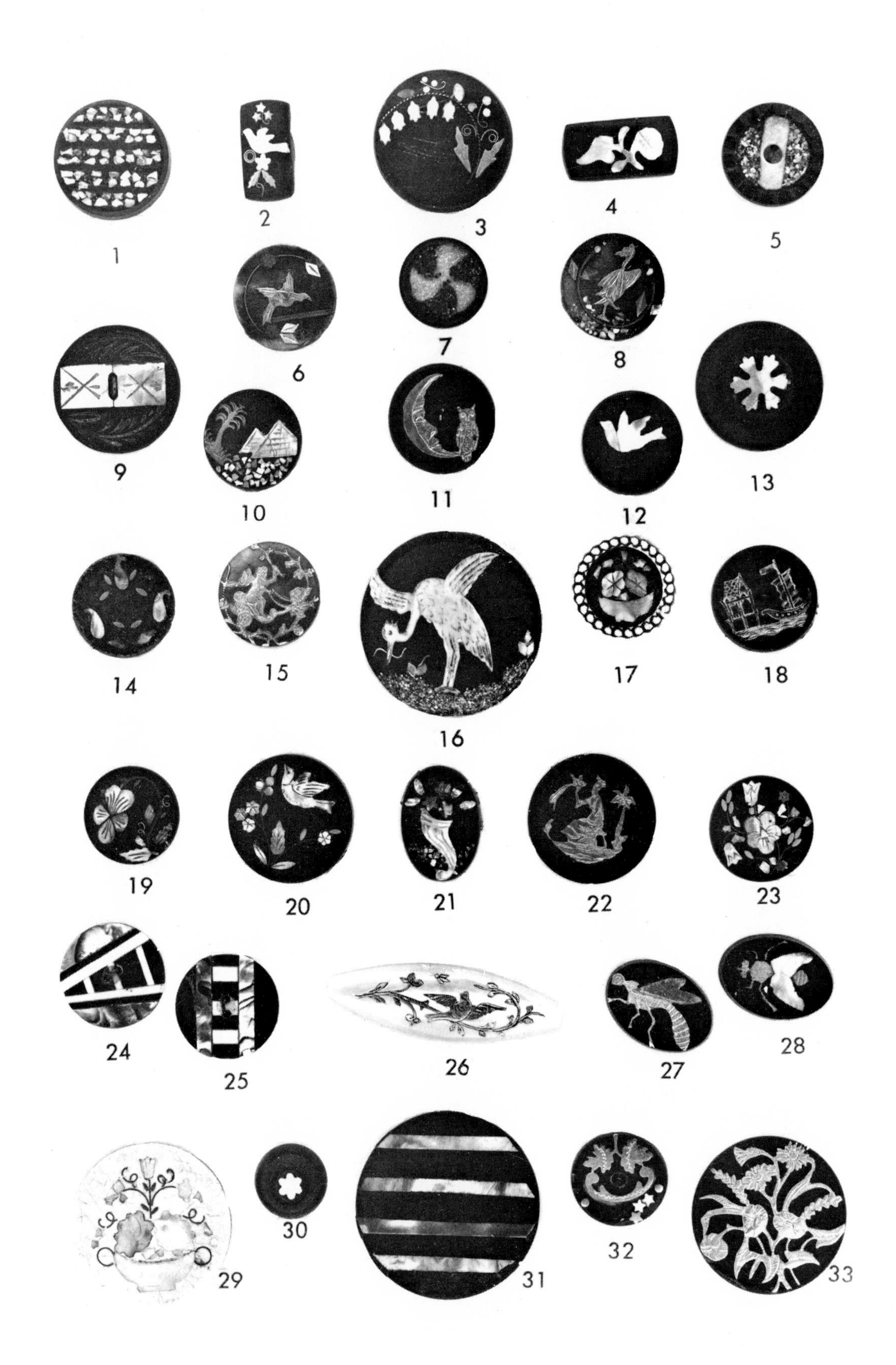
1
2
3
4
5
6
7
8
9
10
11
12
13
14
15
16
17
18
19
20
21
22
23
24
25
26
27
28
29
30
31
32
33

PLATE 69

INLAYS

Buttons of many different materials have the surface ornamented by setting in pieces of other decorative material, such as ivory, pearl, silver, foil and glass. Sometimes the inlaid portion forms a design, but often it is a pictorial object or scene. Birds and insects were popular. This inlaying was done in two ways, either by impressing or inserting. If the base material was one, such as horn or rubber, that could be softened by heat, the "inlay" was pressed into it, while in a plastic state and thus embedded. If the base material was hard like ivory, bone, pearl or wood, the inlaid decoration was inserted into spaces which had been previously prepared in the base, and secured. Another method used was veneering. These buttons have a thin piece of material, different from the base. cemented, or laminated. to the base. Mosaics and marquetry also belong in this classification.

1. Pearl Chips, called "THRIFT", impressed in horn. $1.50.
2. Dyed horn with impressed pictorial design of pearl and silver. $2.00.
3. Dyed horn with floral design; ivory LILY OF THE VALLEY FLOWERLETS on a twisted silver wire stem with white metal and pearl leaves and berries, impressed. Rare. $4.00.
4. Brown dyed horn with impressed iridescent pearl leaf design. $2.00.
5. A whistle button of horn (called on old store cards, "buffalo horn") with foil impressed. $.35.
6. Pressed horn, colored, to represent tortoise shell with silver and pearl inlay of BIRD and flower form. $2.00.
7. Another horn button which was sold under the trade name of "Buffalo Horn". These buttons have been dated from the original cards as having been made from 1871-1884. The back and border of this one is dyed a reddish brown and the decoration is formed by bits of pinkish foil, impressed. These interesting buttons can be found in many different styles and colors with attractive designs which are usually of inlaid foil. $.50.
8. Pressed horn colored to represent tortoise shell with design inlaid in white metal and pearl. Flecks of "thrift" (pearl chips and foil) are impressed at the bottom. $3.00.
9. Composition with a leaf design and two squares of pearl, having pigmented engraving, inlaid; a two-hole sew-thru. $.75.
10. Dyed horn with pearl PYRAMIDS, white metal palm and pearl chips impressed. Pyramids are made to look more realistic by a few lines of engraving. $2.50.
11. Dyed black horn with silvered MOON AND OWL impressed, a whistle button. $2.50.
12. Brown dyed horn with pearl BIRD, inlaid (impressed). $2.00.
13. Black dyed horn with iridescent pearl design. $1.00.
14. Dyed horn with bits of bright colored foil impressed in the face and a floral design, as well as three paisley forms, inlaid in pearl. $1.50.
15. Natural horn with silvered design of, "CUPID IN CART drawn by butterfly" inlaid. $2.50.
16. Convex black dyed horn with engraved ivory STORK, silver snake in his mouth; "thrift" impressed at the base to represent the ground and small pearl leaves with silver stems also inlaid. Rare. $22.50.
17. A brown horn base, with a laminated ivory border, over which a brass chain border has been inserted; basket and flowers inlaid in pearl in the center. $3.00.
18. Composition, two-hole sew-thru with silvered CHINESE JUNK and small fishing shelter, inlaid. $2.00.
19. Dyed horn with a pearl VIOLET, dyed pink and blue, brass wire stem, and tendrils, pearl leaves, impressed. The flower and leaves are engraved to give detail. $2.50.
20. Pressed horn, dyed black with design of iridescent, engraved pearl, inlaid, brass wire stems. $7.50.
21. Oval shaped, black dyed horn with colorful, tinted and engraved pearl CORNUCOPIA and flowers, inlaid; pearl chips at base of Cornucopia. $2.00.
22. A one-piece cut out design of engraved silver, showing seated figure, bird and palm tree; inlaid in black horn. $3.00.
23. PANSY and bell flowers of tinted and engraved pearl; stems and leaves of metal in black horn. $2.50.

24. and 25. are ivory, two-hole sew-thru buttons with veneers of abalone, ivory and tortoise shell laminated to the bases. $1.00 each.

26. This white pearl base was carved and the silver design of branch and BIRD, inserted. Rare. $7.50.
27. Papier mache, with metal WASP, inlaid. $2.50.
28. Papier mache with inlay of silver, engraved FLY with pearl wings. $2.50.
29. Composition base with ivory veneer into which is inserted, engraved pearl VASE AND FLOWERS with gilt leaves, stems, tendrils and handles. $8.00.
30. Black composition ball with pearl inlay $.50.
31. Black composition with strips of mother-of-pearl, inlaid. $1.25.
32. Tortoise shell with all-silver design except for three pearl STARS, inlaid. $2.00.
33. Red horn with engraved, silver floral design, impressed. $5.00.

Many buttons on this Plate are from the collection of Agnes Smith.

PLATE 70

TRELON
WELDON
&
WEIL
1
2
3
4
5
6
7
8
9
10
11
12
13
14
15
16
17
18
19
20
21
22
23
24
25
26
27

PLATE 70

T.W. & W. BACK MARKS

"T.W. & W Paris" is the back mark of Trelon, Weldon & Weil, a leading French firm which was in business from 1814-1864. All buttons made by T.W. & W. were very well designed and excellently finished. Some are two-piece buttons and others are one-piece, although some that appear to be in one-piece are actually made in two parts, fitted with a Plaster of Paris-like substance and so skillfully put together that they appear to be one-piece. Nos. 20 through 27 clearly show that they were made in two or more parts. Many of the better picture buttons have "T.W. & W" back marks. All shown here, excepting 8 and 23, have firm loop shanks and are all more than a century old.

1. PALM and flower. $1.00.

2. THE HERALD. Very well defined. $2.00.

3. This rare button is from the collection of Edith Rodway. The backmark is "T.W. & W.", while the "front mark" is the company name in full. It is a uniform style button and whatever its purpose may have been, the number made must have been very limited, as this is the only one that we have ever seen. $25.00.

4. THE LIGHT CAVALRYMAN from Gene Louis Andre Gericault's painting, 1812. $2.00.

5. THE WOUNDED CUIRASSIER — from a painting by the same artist as No. 4 about 1814. No. 4 and 5 identified by Lillian Smith Albert (N.B.B. March, '50). $12.50.

6. and 7. CHILD WITH NEWFOUNDLAND DOG. Medium size. $1.00.

8. This rare button, pad shanked, T.W. &. W, has a conventional STAR shaped design on the front. $3.00.

9. LION OF ST. MARKS, Venice - the inscription on the tablet is in Latin and translated reads, "Peace to the Evangelist, Mark". $2.00.

10. YOUNG GIRL, DEFENDING HERSELF AGAINST LOVE, from a painting of the French Artist, Adolphe Wm. Bouguereau 1825-1905. Helen Wegener identifies this from a print in American Art Review, Vol. I-1880, Page 488. $4.00.

11. A silver-tinted TULIP. Rare. $2.25.

12. ANCHOR, gold-tinted brass. $1.25.

13. PEARS, silver-tinted brass. $1.50.

14. BULLDOG IN SEASHELL, centered in a raised square $2.25.

15. ROOSTER SERENADER (N), brass with a silver tint. $10.00.

16. CORN. $.75.

17. DRAGON. $3.00.

18. FISH, with silver tint. $1.00.

19. BAMBOO ROOT, stem and leaves forming border and center design, pierced, over darkened brass background. $1.25.

20. DOG HEAD and rim are brass with a pearl background, not often used by T.W. & W. This is an early Victorian coat size, possibly one of a set of hunting coat buttons. $3.00.

21. WILD ROSE, the design is cut out and in one piece with the turned under rim, rose tinted brass with cut steel trim. $.75.

22. CHARLEMAGNE, ruler of the Franks (742-814) about whom many legends are told. Same construction as No. 21. $2.00.

23. This has a conventional pierced and silvered design with copper colored rim but unusual feature in the shank. Two slits were made in the back and the strap left, was stretched to form a shank. This type is often mistaken for a shank used on certain buttons that were not well constructed and made since 1900. The back mark of T.W. & W. is proof that this "split shank" was used before 1865. Scarce. $1.50.

24. A LEAF escutcheon is the only decoration on this 3 part all-brass button. $1.25.

25., 26. and 27. are quite similar. Each has a cut-out design attached to the border, under which is a steel liner. The rim of each is turned under. No. 27 has the sea shell motif and both 26 and 27 have cut steels applied. $1.75 - 2.00.

PLATE 71

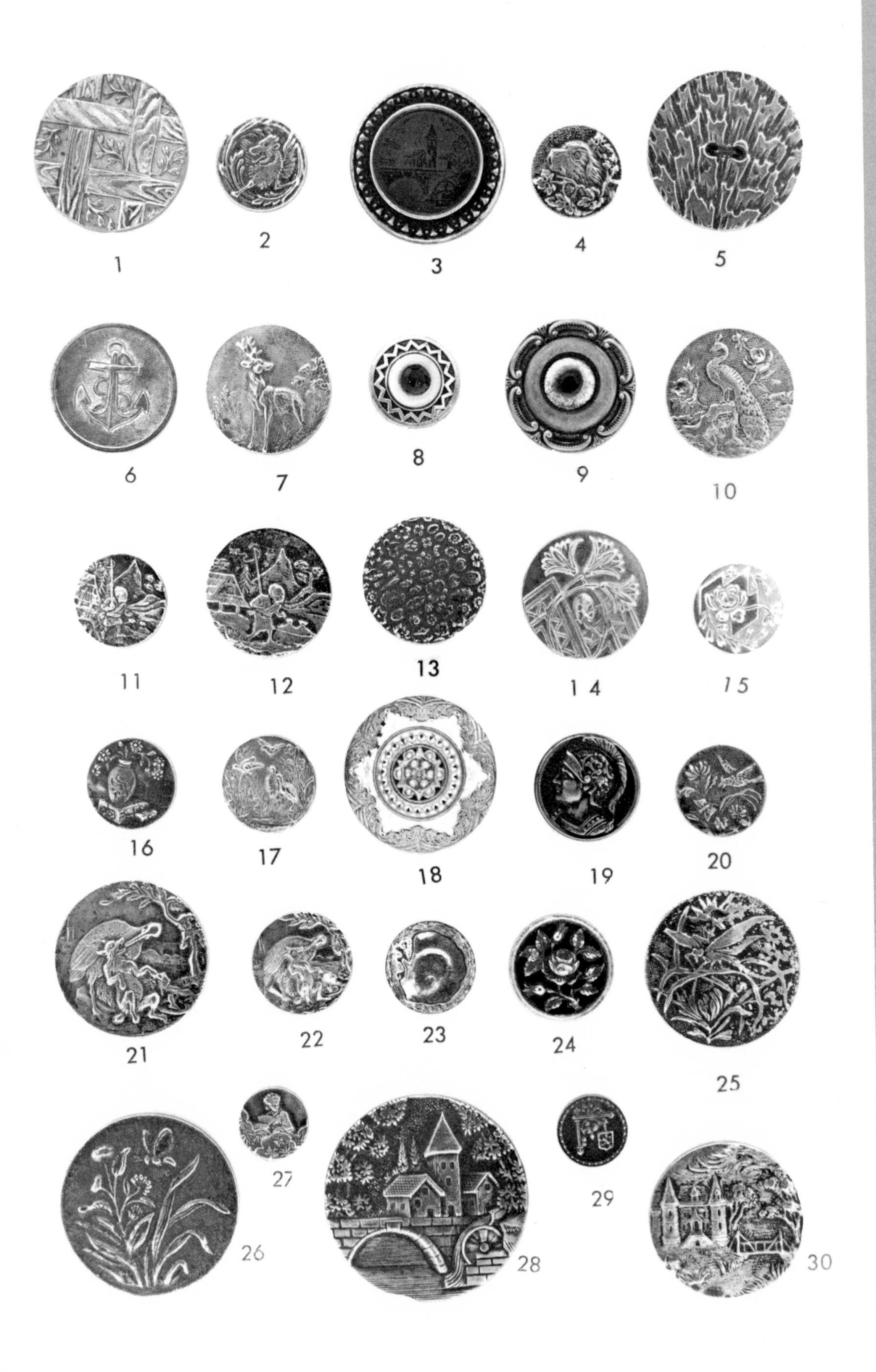

1
2
3
4
5
6
7
8
9
10
11
12
13
14
15
16
17
18
19
20
21
22
23
24
25
26
27
28
29
30

PLATE 71

OTHER PARIS BACK MARKS

Many of our finest buttons were made in France. Here we have given a sampling of some of the fine 19th century pictorials, as well as two jewel types having Paris Back Marks. All have loop or self shanks of metal except No. 5, which is a sew-thru. Many of these buttons were for some time called one-piece, but actually they are two-piece brass buttons, so expertly welded together that little evidence of the joining can be seen.

1. INTERLACED CROSS, silver tinted brass with back mark, "A. P. & Cie Brevete, Paris." Brevete means Patented. A. P. & Cie stands for "Albert Parent & Co." $1.50.

2. A brass DRAGON, marked, "INDUSTRIE, PARISIENNE". $.75.

3. A SCENE of pressed Gutta Percha, mounted in brass, marked, "A.P. & Cie, Paris, Depose". $3.00.

4. A SPANIEL DOG'S HEAD, pushed through foliage; brass; A. P. & Cie, Paris, Soldaire". Solidaire means, "jointly and separately liable" and has to do with the patent. $1.25.

5. A brass sew-thru, the design somewhat resembles the Aurora Borealis; "A.P. & Cie, Paris". $1.50.

6. An Anchor of brass in relief; "A. P. & Cie, Paris, Soldaire Bte, S.G.D.G.". S.G.D.G. stands for, "Sans garantie du gouvernement" which means that the article is patented but not guaranteed by the government. $1.00.

7. STAG, ALERT; brass, back-mark the same as No. 6. $1.75.

8. Silvered brass with a chevron border; center of faceted cranberry, transparent glass, set in opaque, clambroth, glass, "P. H. Paris". P. H. stands for "Parent and Hamet", the firm name which later became "Albert Parent & Co." $1.50.

9. PEACOCK'S EYE of green and blue, set in brass with ornamental scallop border. "A. P. & Cie, Paris. $3.50.

10. PEACOCK, stamped brass; "A.P. & Cie". $2.00.

11. and 12. ORIENTAL WITH KITE, stamped brass with tinted background; "Industrie Parisienne". $.75 & $1.75.

13. An all-over design of flower heads, sea shells and leaves; pressed brass. The back-mark is enclosed in a circular buckled belt and says, "J. B. M. Paris. $.75.

14. LOTUS FLOWER, symbol of a Christian life, silver tinted brass, "A. P. & Cie". $1.00.

15. Another floral in the small size, design and construction very similar to No. 14; the same back-mark as No. 14. $.50.

16. VASE OF FLOWERS on small chest with one open drawer; "A.P. & Cie"; stamped brass. $.75.

17. A pressed brass design of GAME BIRDS; "Qualite Solide". $1.00.

18. A convex brass button with a six point STAR in the center design and the same star formed again by the border. Back-mark, "A Walter, 14 R De La Banque, Paris". $2.00.

19. WARRIOR.This is a one-piece pressed brass button, three strap-like, curved, brass pieces are attached to the rim at the back and a loop shank is applied in the center where they join. The back-mark is found in the three pieces that are attached, "A.P. & Cie, Paris, Depose". $1.00.

20. CRESTED BIRD AND BUTTERFLY, stamped brass, "A. P. & Cie. $.75.

21. and 22. THE WOLF AND THE STORK, pressed brass, the small size, silvered. "A. P. & Cie, Paris". $1.25 and $.75.

23. A sea shell of silvered brass. "A. P. & Cie. $1.00.

24. A PIERCED ROSE design, attached to rim, over a purple tinted background; tin back is marked, "P. H. Paris". $1.75.

25. Pressed brass DRAGONFLY; "A. P. & Cie, Paris, Brevete". $1.00.

26. Pressed brass BUTTERFLY and flower; back-mark has the initials, "S.A." on opposite sides of the self shank; above and below, "Industrie Parisienne". $1.25.

27. Stamped brass ORIENTAL LADY WITH FAN, two small butterflies in the foreground; "A. P. & Cie". $1.00.

28. The same scene as No. 3 in stamped brass with darkened background; "A. P. & Cie, Paris, Solidaire, Bte S.G.D.G." $3.50.

29. "AT THE SIGN OF THE LION", a tavern sign; pierced brass, superimposed on a darkened brass background; "A. P. & Cie". $1.00.

30. CASTLE, a pressed brass scene; "A.P. & Cie, Brevete, Paris." $2.00.

PLATE 72

PLATE 72

CELLULOID

"Celluloid" is a trade name in the U.S., applying to the first known synthetic, plastic material. The method of making celluloid from cellulose nitrate, camphor and alcohol, under heat and pressure, was developed by J.W. Hyatt and I.S. Hyatt of Newark, N.J. in 1870. Earlier investigations had been made in Great Britian by A. Parke and D. Spill.

Many buttons were made from celluloid during the late 19th and early 20th centuries. The most destinctive were made to imitate ivory but a variety can be found; different colors, opaque and clear, molded, combined with different materials, inlaid, etc.

Celluloid can be distinguished by placing a hot needle along the back of the button. If celluloid, it will smell strongly of camphor.

1. A two-piece button with background of celluloid, shading from brown to light cream color; a brass BOW is attached to the scalloped brass rim. $1.00.
2. Pierced grey celluloid, set in ornate brass border with clear glass "jeweled" design in center. $2.00.
3. Background of shaded, grey-tinted celluloid; silvered brass rim and floral spray; gilt, scalloped border. $1.25.
4. A two-piece button, capped with celluloid, painted in a geometric design with gold outline and green, black and red sections against a tan background. $1.00.
5. Brown and white celluloid, set in brass rim with a square of pearl inserted in the center. $1.00.
6. Green and white plaid cloth under clear celluloid forms the center; two stamped brass borders are painted green and white to harmonize; two-piece. $2.00.
7. A celluloid, pin back, portrait button, such as were made and sold at County Fairs during the 1900's; sepia and white. $1.50.
8. Two-piece with colored cloth design, capped by transparent celluloid. $1.50.
9. Pierced celluloid with cobalt blue glass "jewel" and brass flower heads inserted, set in brass with ornate border. $2.00.
10. Pierced celluloid background of red, shaded to black; tin floral design inserted; brass rim; two-piece. $2.00.
11. A four-hole sew-thru, not common, set in brass rim; the ivory colored celluloid is pierced, with simulated cut steels of tin, inserted; the design is pressed and filled with dark pigment to imitate engraving; two-piece. $1.50.
12. Background of ivory-tinted celluloid in a basket weave pattern, pierced with insets of tinted metal, repeating the center design of tinted brass, which is enclosed in a bright brass rim; pierced white metal border. $1.50.
13. Black and white checked cloth under transparent celluloid with tin rim and brass back. $1.50.
14. Two-piece with grained celluloid face, the center enclosed by brass rim; pierced with clear glass "jewels" in brass rims, inserted. $1.50.

15., 16., and 17. Small buttons of various colors of celluloid, with pierced designs of tinted brass. No. 1 has a pierced face with the center design inserted. $.25 each.

18. Ivory colored celluloid, pierced to hold Tiffany set "jewel" of faceted clear glass; pierced brass design and border. $2.00.
19. Small four-hole sew-thru of mottled celluloid with gilt design imitating engraving; set in gilt rim. $.50.
20. Pierced green celluloid with pierced brass inset over a tin liner; brass border. $.25.
21. A brown celluloid back and rim holds a frosted glass, domed inset with molded design of a PEACOCK; the "eyes" in the tail feathers are filled with gilt and the glass is enclosed in a gilt filigree border. $3.00.
22. Brown celluloid with tinted floral design; brass rim. $.25.
23. Blue-tinted, pierced brass rim and tin circlet; blue-tinted celluloid face. $.25.
24. A lovely pierced brass WREATH joins tan center, which has tinted floral design, with capped rim. $1.50.

25. and 26. Small and large size; mottled grey celluloid, pierced in the center, silver lustered inset, tin collet and brass rim. $.35 and $1.25.

27. The small size, matching No. 3. $.35.
28. THREE-LEAFED CLOVERS in a pierced design, attached to brass rim, over shaded blue celluloid background. $2.00.

PLATE 73

PLATE 73

IVOROIDS

Ivoroid is a name given to celluloid that has been colored, grained and embossed to look like ivory. Such buttons are scarce and considered very desirable by collectors. Those shown here are from the collection of Florence Leggett.

1. FLORA AND THE HIND. This illustrates a a fairy tale, called "The Hind in the Forest" by Kate Douglas Wiggins. $12.50.

2. A HOUSE WITH NOBODY IN IT. Brass rope border. $1.00.

3. Probably an adaptation of the Thorwaldson design, CUPID CARESSING THE SWAN, from a bas-relief called "Summer". Twisted rope border of brass. Fine detail. $15.00.

4. LADY SARAH LENNOX AT HOLLAND HOUSE. Adapted from a painting by Sir Joshua Reynolds. This has the same brass twisted rope border as No. 2. & 3. (See J.B. March, '48). $2.00.

5. THE WHITE OWL IN THE BELFRY, (N), tin collet and back. $6.50.

6. STEEPLE CHASE. Inner brass rim and tinted brass collet. 15.00.

7. SCENE. Tin collet. $1.00.

8. THE KARLSKIRCHE, VIENNA with the same metal rim as Nos. 2, 3, & 4. $3.50.

9. FLOWER form; pierced ivoroid set in metal rim. $2.00.

10. CASTLE, metal rim. $3.00.

11. DAISY: pierced, ivoroid set in metal rim. $2.00.

12. HUNTER AND BIRD are of brass. An embossed fence with ivy is in the foreground. The sky is sepia tinted and shows a crescent moon with face and also stars and clouds. The border is brass. $25.00.

13. A WINDMILL. Metal rim. $3.50.

14. LUCY AND HILDEGARDE. $2.50.

15. LUCY ASHTON AND EDGAR. $2.50.

16. EMPRESS ELIZABETH OF AUSTRIA. The same moon and stars as in No. 12. $22.50.

17. IVY LEAF. $1.00.

18. ORIENTAL FIGURES. $2.50.

19. BAREFOOT BOY. Scarce. $20.00.

20. BAREFOOT BOY, small size. $3.00.

21. The same as No. 22 in a small size. $2.00.

22. BALMORAL CASTLE, the highland residence of Queen Victoria, situated on the River Dee, in the midst of fine and varied scenery. It is built of granite and has a massive, imposing appearance. It is now the reigning monarch's Scottish summer residence. Very artistically done. Plain brass rim. $22.50.

PLATE 74

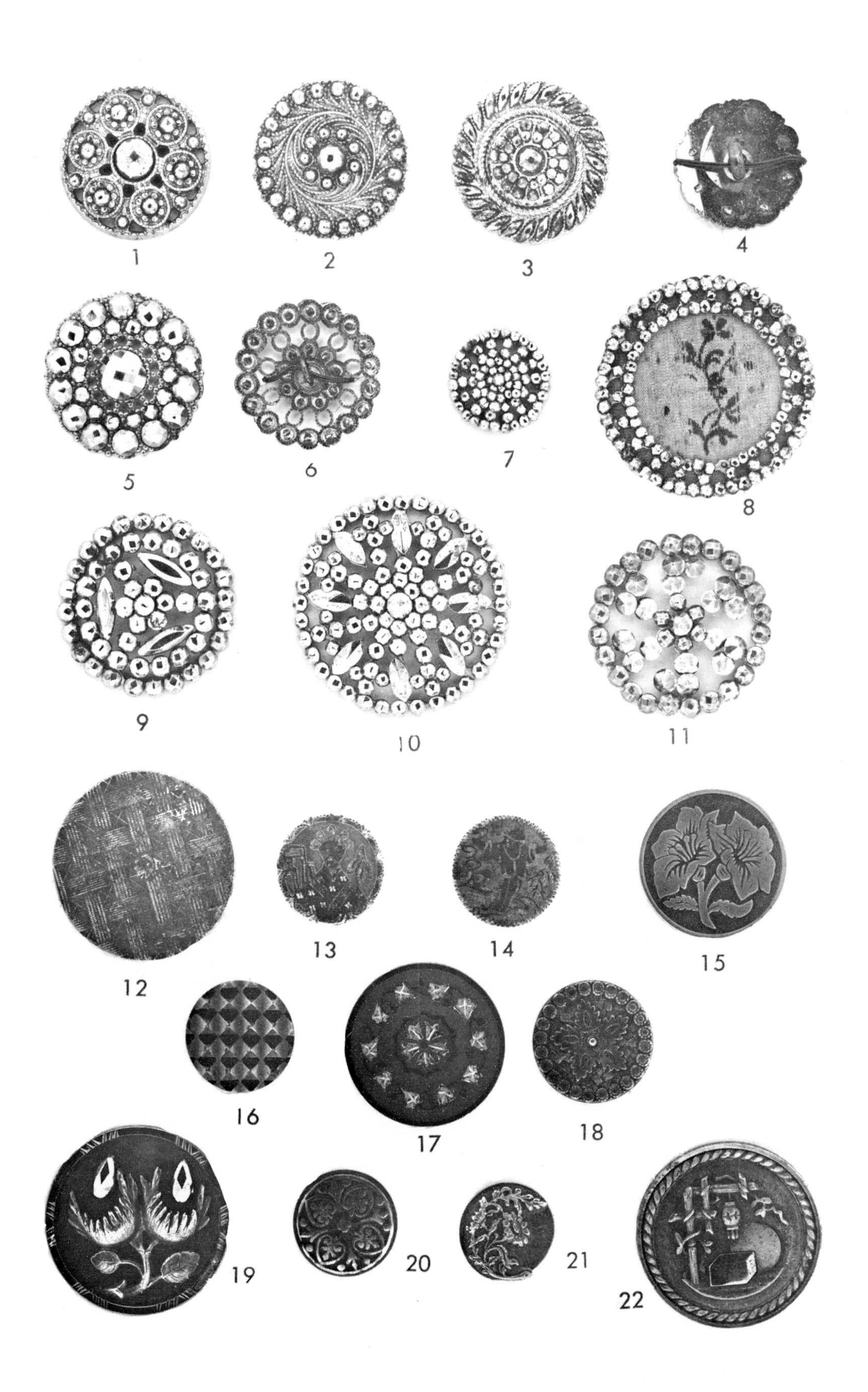
1 2 3 4 5 6 7 8 9 10 11 12 13 14 15 16 17 18 19 20 21 22

PLATE 74

STEEL, VARIOUS TYPES

Steel, an alloy of iron and carbon, has been used to fashion or trim many of our buttons. Matthew Boulton (1728-1809), English manufacturer and engineer is credited with inventing cut steel buttons. Steel was used during the eighteenth century in making jewelry and other artistic objects, such as snuff boxes, seals, and buckles. Buttons of this period were carefully made of separate faceted and handpolished pieces of steel that were riveted into place on prepared bases. These early buttons had great brilliance.

During the nineteenth century, imitations of the early cut steel buttons were made and flat steel buttons, often tinted, were produced. Steel will attract a magnet and this test is used to verify the presence of steel in a button.

The top row of this Plate shows four of the eighteenth century Boulton Steels, the property of Mrs. Robert Smith. Number 4 shows the flat, heavy polished steel back of one button with the riveted stemsof the cut steels showing. 1, 2, and 3 plainly show the mille-grain setting that was stamped on the face. The steels in these buttons were set as carefully as jewels.

1. A medium sized Boulton steel with 61 mille grain mounted cut steels. Estimated value, $25.00.

2. Another Boulton steel of the 18th century with only 31 cut steels but a lovely background. $25.00.

3. This 18th century Boulton steel has 27 elongated cut steels slanted in a border with mille grain settings. The 29 center steels are mounted on a separate disk. $25.00.

4. A slightly smaller steel button of the same period, shown in reverse to familiarize the collector with the perfectly plain back of these early types. $18.00.

5. and 6. Front and back of the 19th century cut steel, studded buttons; the steels riveted on a pierced background. The pressed design of No. 6 can be seen plainly on the back. 5, $1.00, 6, $.50.

7. This small button is an early one with about 70 tiny cut steels. $1.75.

8. A Stevenograf bit of silk in colors of green and red on a cream background with wide, pierced border, set with small, brilliant cut steels. $18.00.

9. Faceted cut steels of the nineteenth century, riveted on pierced backs. No. 9, $1.50; No. 10, $2.50; No. 11, $1.00.

12. A flat, stamped steel button of the Colonial Period. This specimen had been corroded by moisture, destroying it's sheen and reducing the value to $5.00.

13. A small, one-piece, stamped and etched steel button showing a strange looking lady. Rare. $1.50.

14. A stamped steel button, etched to show the figure of a man and bits of foliage. The design is tinted blue. $1.50.

15. One-piece stamped steel with floral design in relief. $1.00.

16. Stamped steel with alternate diamond shapes, tinted blue. $.75.

17. Stamped steel with design gilded and tinted. Ivy wreath. $2.00.

18. One-piece steel. The designs of these buttons were struck from dies that were very similar to those used for pewter buttons of this same period (1790-1810). $1.75.

19. Steel cup with silvered floral design applied. Flowers have cut steel stamens. $1.75.

20. Stamped steel with dark background and polished design of conventional hearts. $.50.

21. A flat steel background with a pierced brass floral design, applied. $.50.

22. A steel cup with pressed brass center. The design is an Oriental garden with hanging lantern and moon rising behind the arbor. A rectangle of cut and polished steel represents a seat. $3.50.

PLATE 75

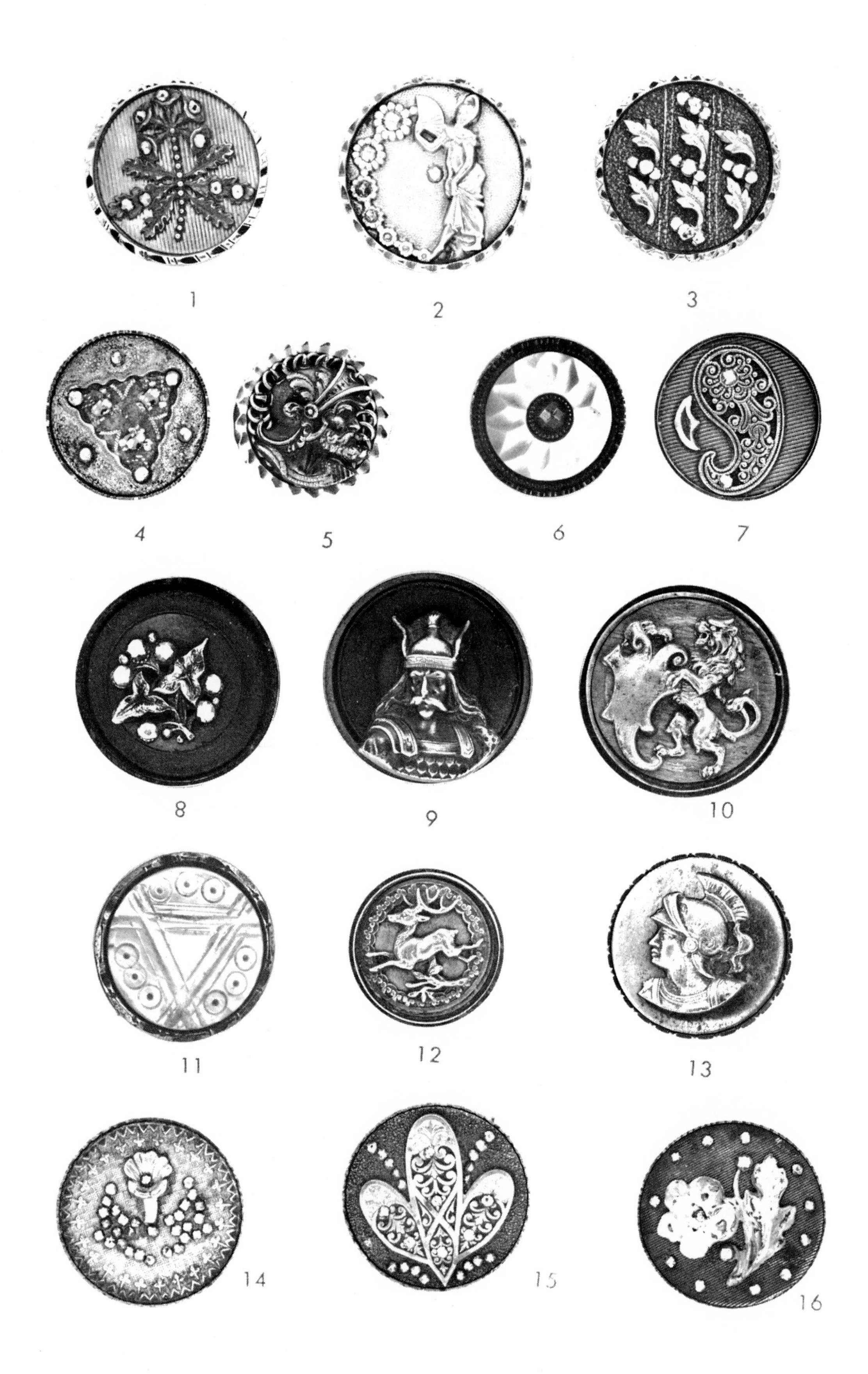

PLATE 75

STEEL CUPS

"Steel Cups" are buttons having a steelback which is fashioned like a shallow cake pan with a standing rim. A shank is attached and the centers are of various materials and designs. One may find centers of pearl, wood, enamel, brass, pewter, cut steels or other materials with a design or picture applied. They can be found in small, medium and large sizes. All buttons shown on this Plate have steel cup backs so only the centers are described.

1. Iridescent ribbed steel forms the backing of this center. Cut steels fasten the brass oak leaves and also form acorns. $1.75.

2. A brass lady "FOP" with the usual fan, and a crescent of cut steel-centered flowers are fastened to a pebbled brass center. $4.50.

3. Brass WINDBLOWN LEAVES, ornamented with cut steels which fasten them to the brass, chased center, are the motif of this steel cup. $2.00.

4. This has a brass center decorated with painted PINK FLOWERS, green leaves, and engraving. Cut steels give added decoration and fasten the center to the steel cup. $1.50.

5. A brass head of KING ARTHUR is mounted on a coiled brass wire center. This is a fine head with chased beard and armor. $3.50.

6. A green iridescent PEARL center is held in place by a large cut steel, mounted in a brass ring. A larger brass ring outlines the pearl and meets the steel rim. $1.25.

7. A brass, pierced, PAISLEY DESIGN ornamented with cut steels and a crescent shaped cut steel decorate this brass center. $2.25.

8. Here we have a thick wood center decorated by brass IVY LEAVES and cut steel berries. This button could also be classed with "wood backgrounds" or with the "Plant Kingdom". $2.25.

9. A bronzed brass head of LOHENGRIN is applied to a center of wood. This is one of finest steel cups to be found and may also be classed with "Heads" "wood backgrounds" or "operas". $6.50.

10. RAMPANT LION of brass applied to center of wood. This also can be classed with "wood backgrounds" as well as "Heraldic Designs". $1.75.

11. A plain center of iridescent, engraved ocean pearl. $1.25.

12. A RUNNING DEER of brass, attached to a pierced brass border, decorates this plain center. $2.50.

13. A brass head in high relief of HECTOR, leader of the TROJANS, applied to a concave brass center. $3.00.

14. A brass EASTER LILY with a cut steel center and leaves, is applied to a brass center disk which has a border formed by 24 crosses. $2.00.

15. This pebbled and bronze tinted brass center is decorated with cut steels and a leaf motif that has been painted in colors. $2.00.

16. A darkened and lined brass center is decorated with a brass FLOWER which is painted in blue and white. Cut steels form a border. $2.00.

PLATE 76

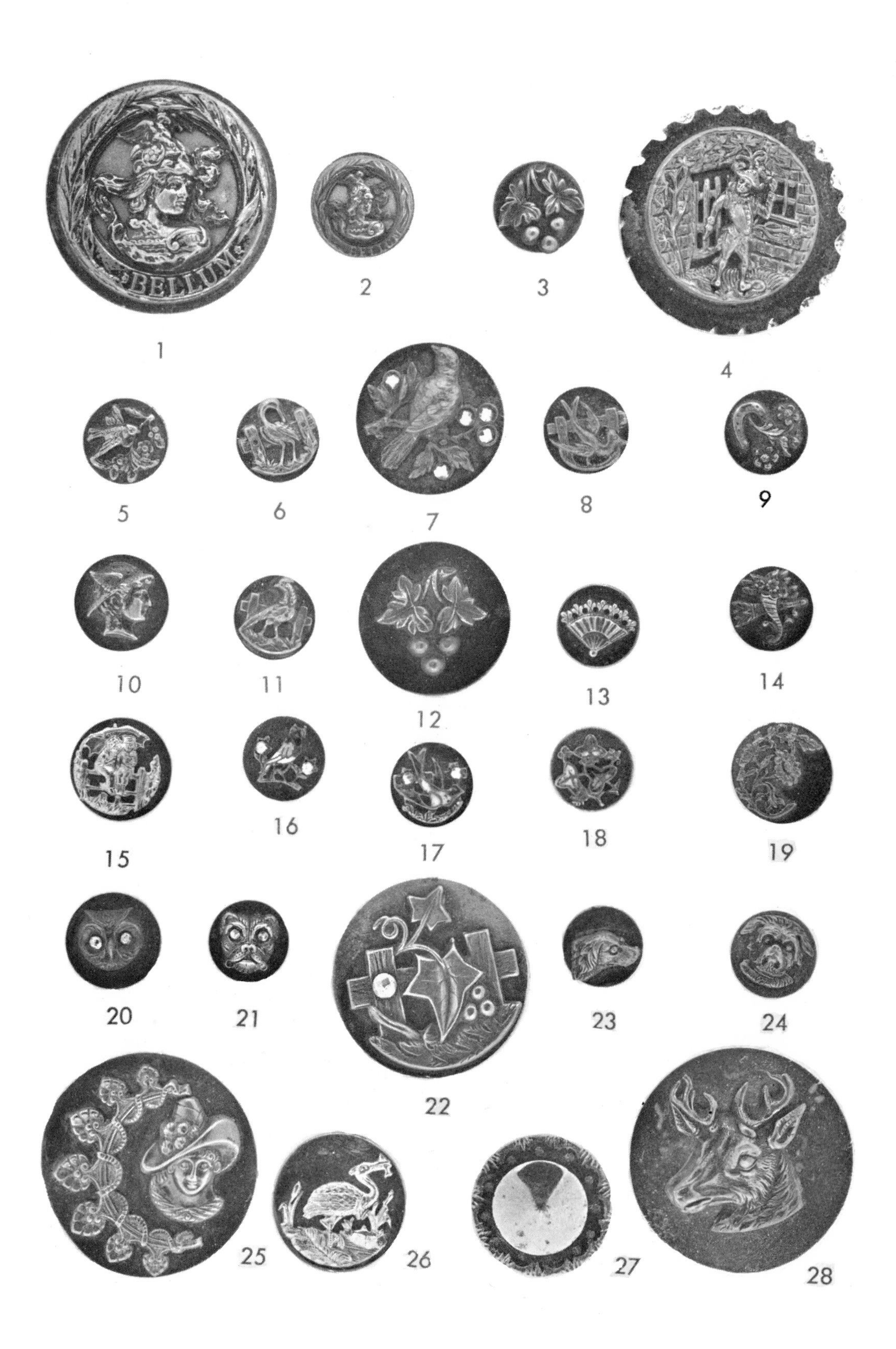

PLATE 76

FLAT STEEL BACKGROUNDS

These buttons belong to the nineteenth century. All have flat steel backgrounds and brass designs, superimposed, unless otherwise stated. These designs, in most cases, are escutcheons attached to the brass loop shanks, through a hole in the button.

1. A pressed, pierced design in high relief, called, "Bellum" (War). A similar button with head facing in the opposite direction, is a companion button to this and is called, "Pax" (Peace). $6.50.

2. The same as No. 1, in the small size. $1.00.

3. GRAPES AND GRAPE LEAVES. $.50.

4. Stamped and pierced design, showing PUNCHINELLO in high relief. $8.50.

5. BIRD on a flowering branch. $.75.

6. CRANE, in front of gate. $.75.

7. BIRD ON BRANCH, a medium sized button, flowers trimmed with cut steels. $1.25.

8. A design similar to No. 6 but a different BIRD. $.50.

9. HORSESHOE and flowers. $.50.

10. The background of each button in this row is tinted a brilliant blue. This gave a pleasing contrast to the brass design and probably helped to prevent rusting, which happens so easily when steel is exposed to moisture. This one has a head of MERCURY. $1.00.

11. A COCK PHEASANT, with gate behind him. $.75.

12. The same GRAPE design that was used on No. 3, but this time we have a medium size. $1.75.

13. A FAN. The blue background shines through the pierced design in the top of the fan. $1.00.

14. A CORNUCOPIA WITH FLOWERS and A QUIVER WITH ARROWS. $.75.

15. SUMMER, a Kate Greenway design. The design here is of pressed and pierced white metal. $3.50.

16. An enameled OWL, the flowers have cut steel centers. $1.50.

17. The same design as No. 8 but here the BIRD is enameled and the fence has cut steels, representing nails. Background is tinted purple. $1.50.

18. THREE LEAFED CLOVERS. The leaves are enameled and background tinted blue. $1.25.

19. FLORAL DESIGN, which is fastened to the background by attached pins which go through holes in the steel and are clinched at the back. $.50.

20. An OWL HEAD in high relief with cut steel eyes. $1.00.

21. BULLDOG'S HEAD, in high relief with cut steel eyes. $1.00.

22. The familiar FENCE but this time with IVY and BERRIES. $2.50.

23. A SETTER DOG'S HEAD. $.75.

24. SCOTTIE DOG HEAD. $.50.

25. A curved design which partly encloses a HEAD OF LADY, wearing a large, high hat. $3.00.

26. Pierced, white metal design of CRANE WITH FISH IN MOUTH. Cattails can also be seen in the design. $2.00.

27. The background of this button has a chased border and a cone-shaped, steel piece is superimposed for the center decoration. $1.00.

28. Brass DEER HEAD in very high relief. $6.50.

PLATE 77

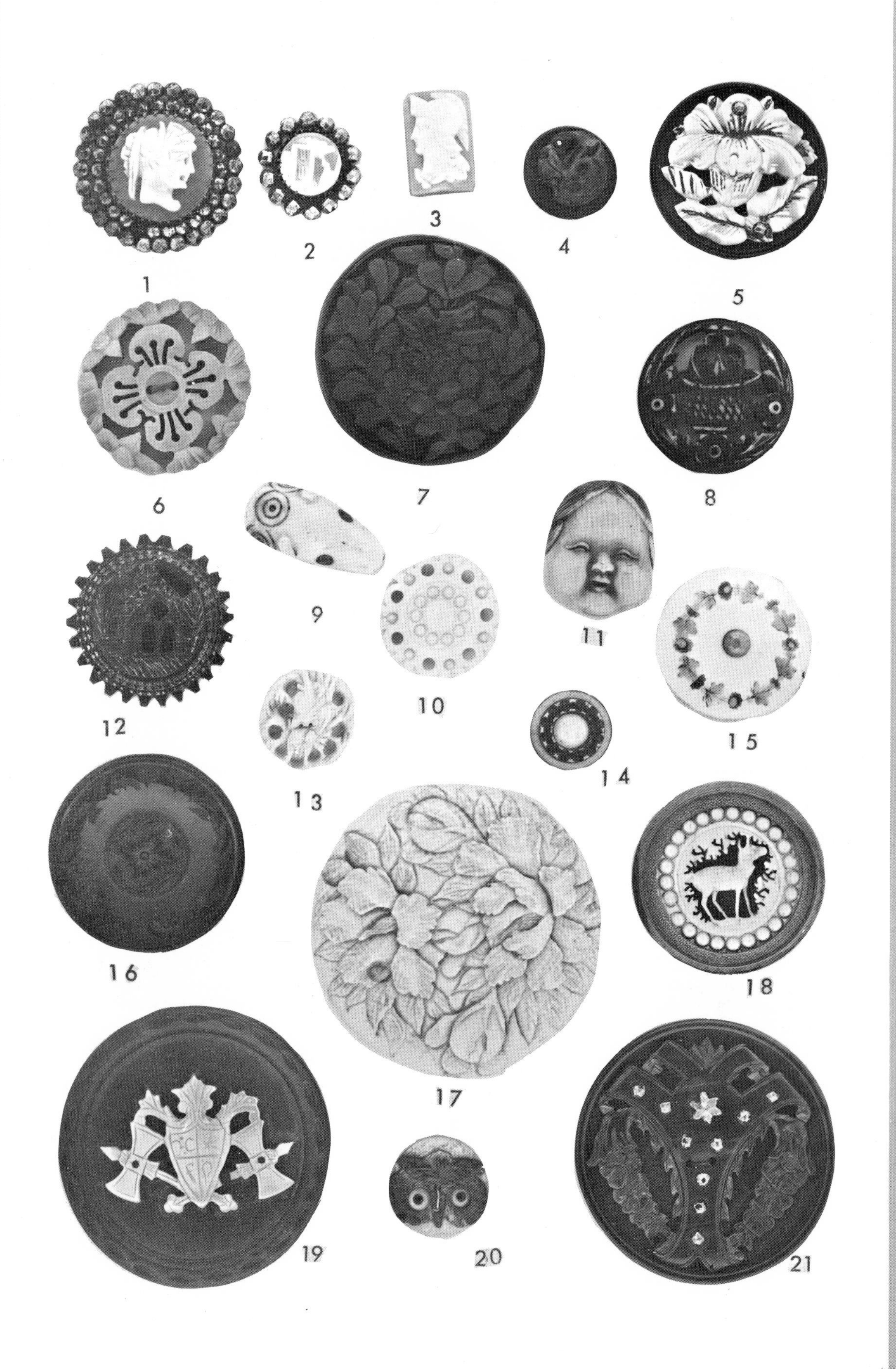

PLATE 77

ASSORTED MATERIALS

1. A shell disk with a CLASSICAL HEAD, cameo cut, in a prong setting. Border made of two rows of riveted cut steels. $20.00.

2. A small cameo-cut shell with WOMAN AND BUILDING. Prong setting, border of riveted cut steels. $6.50.

3. Shell with cameo-cut HEAD, wearing Greek helmet, probably intended to represent Minerva. The back of the shell is concave and a brass shank is inserted. $6.00.

4. A carved wood BULLDOG'S HEAD, applied to a darker, cup-shaped wood back. The dog has a very realistic glass eye, amber with dark pupil. Brass loop shank. $5.00.

5. A wooden button with a beautiful, iridescent carved pearl FLOWER in the cupped center. The two cut steels have pins that go through the wood to the back of the button and help hold the design in place. It is also a two-hole sew-thru. Portions of the flower are filled with pigment to give accent. From the collection of Agnes Smith. $15.00.

6. A CONVENTIONAL FLOWER DESIGN of bone, carved and pierced. A two-hole sew-thru, tinted green. From the collection of Agnes Smith. $4.00.

7. Cinnabar, showing FLOWERS, FOLIAGE AND A BIRD. Natural Cinnabar is a bright red ore from which mercury is obtained. Deposits of this ore are found in Spain, China, some of our western states and in several other countries. The Chinese mix this ore, or the residue, after mercury has been extracted, with raw lac and obtain a distinctive lacquer which is used for the type of articles, known as Cinnabar. A foundation of wood or metal is used and successive layers of lacquer are applied. When the surface has been built up to the desired height, it is hand-carved with characteristic Chinese designs. Some Cinnabar buttons are round, some are square but all are easily identified. The older ones are carved more deeply. Value of this specimen, $10.00.

8. Carved and pierced ivory, dyed black. The center design is an urn or BASKET. $5.00.

9. AN ANIMAL'S HEAD, made of carved and engraved ivory, portions of the carving are filled with pigment to make it look more realistic. From the collection of Edith Rodway. $5.00.

10. BONE, pierced and carved. Made about 1810. Brass shank. $3.00.

11. A carved ivory NETSUKE. This is a mask of a moon-faced, homely woman called "Okame". Netsukes are made of wood, jade, coral, ivory or any material that can be carved. They have two holes, either in the back or the base and were originally worn by the Japanese with a draw-string run through the holes, to anchor a man's tobacco pouch, purse or other useful articles to his kimona sash. They always represent something of significance to the Japanese and some tell a story. The earliest were carved in a round shape that fitted nicely into the palm of the hand. They are no longer worn by the Japanese but since they have been prized by collectors, they are still made and exported to us. They belong in the class of Specialties. Value of this, $12.00.

12. Black, deeply carved BOGWOOD. This is the wood of oak, usually, that has been preserved in peat bogs. During the Victorian Era it was used for jewelry, as well as buttons. It resembles ebony and carves easily. This specimen has two holes on each side of the standing rim and was probably part of a bracelet. $4.00.

13. Twentieth century carved and pierced BONE. $2.00.

14. Carved and dyed BONE. $.75.

15. Eighteenth century Ceramic disk with painted WREATH and pin shank, fired and glazed. Back unglazed. $25.00.

16. NATURAL HORN with a pressed and pierced design. The center and border are dyed. The undyed portion between center and border is very thin and practically transparent. $5.00.

17. This button is of carved ivory and is a MANDARIN BUTTON; its origin, China. It has a shank which unscrews. These buttons were worn on the top of a mandarin hat. When a Chinese gentlemen wished to change his hat, he could remove the ornamental button and put it on a different hat. $35.00.

18. Carved and pierced ivory DEER, mounted in brass. Tin back, marked "Extra Fein". $25.00.

19. PEARL SHIELD AND CROSSED BATTLE AXES, mounted in the center of a dyed horn button, with border that has a pressed design. From the collection of Agnes Smith. $12.00.

20. A carved pearl OWL'S HEAD with yellow glass eyes, black glass pupils. $10.00.

21. A lovely carved and pierced PEARL DESIGN, applied to a wood background which has a standing rim. Cut steels ornament the design and two are riveted through the wood and help hold the design. It is a two-hole sew-thru. From the collection of Edith Rodway. $15.00.

PLATE 78

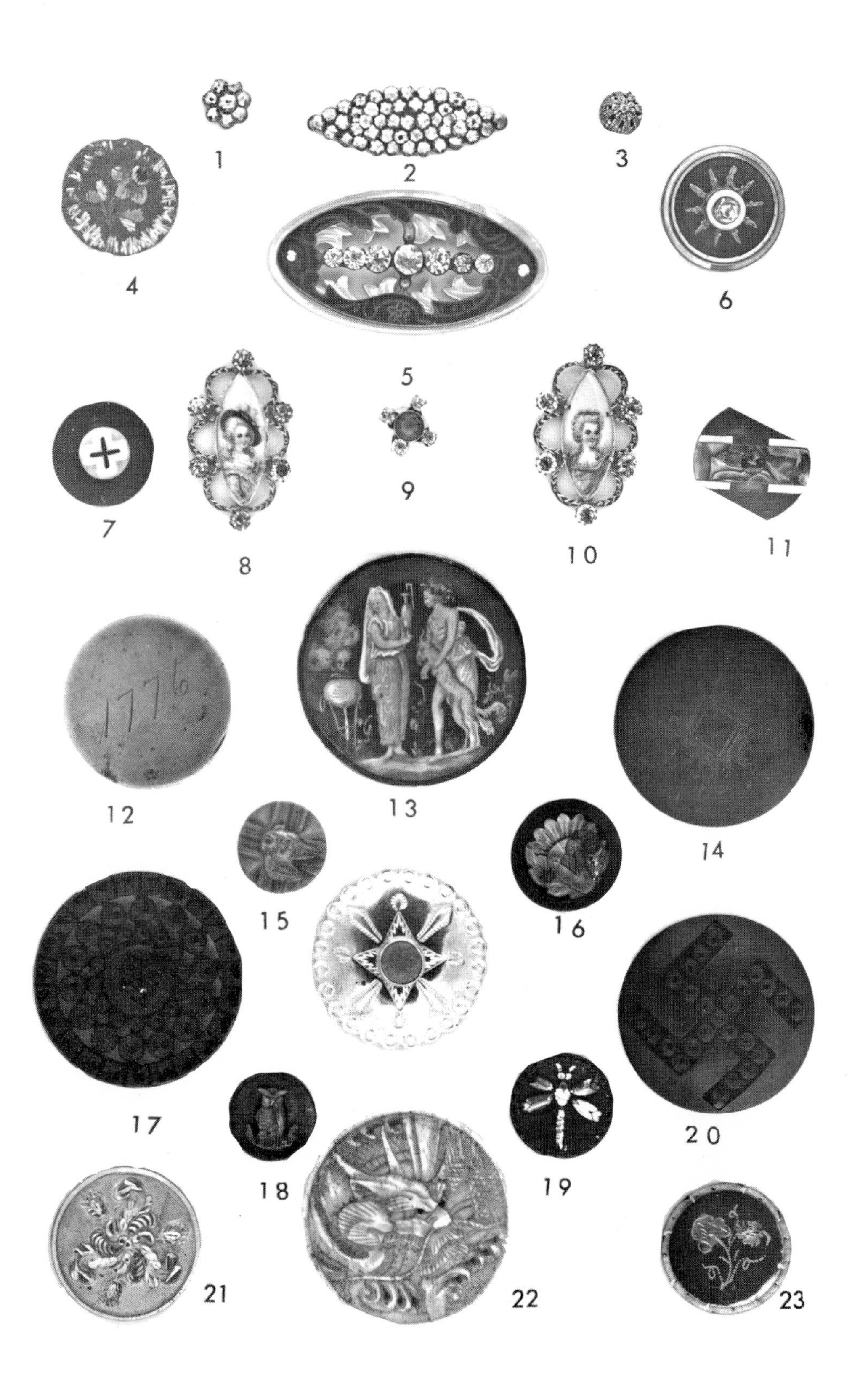

PLATE 78

ASSORTED MATERIALS

1. A diminutive button made of a cluster of cut steels riveted to a scalloped brass background. $.50. A button is classed as diminutive if it is under 3/8 of an inch. Diminutives can be found in all materials and are very attractive when mounted.

2. Riveted cut steels in a SPINDLE SHAPE. $2.00.

3. A diminutive button with a high dome, pierced. A green steel mirror shines through the openings in the face. $.25.

4. An eighteenth century TEXTILE BUTTON, background of pink silk with polychrome embroidery. $7.50.

5. Another SPINDLE SHAPE with an open metal design riveted with two cut steels to a curved and pierced white pearl shape that is slightly larger. The metal border is enameled and paste stones are set in prongs on a bar that extends through the center; shank is attached to the center of this bar. $10.00.

6. A hard black rubber center; and the faceted, clear glass "jewel" has a collar setting. This, the ten point star, and applied rim are gold filled. This is typical of buttons made by Hammond Turner & Sons of England just prior to 1900. $2.50.

7. A TEXTILE BUTTON of brown silk with a cross molded in white milk glass. The center of the cross is incised and filled with brown pigment. $1.00.

8. and 10. Miniature polychrome paintings on ivory, set in gilt frames with paste stones in prong settings, ornamenting the borders. The paintings are under slightly convex glass and are backed by white kid, a precaution which was taken with ivory paintings to protect them from atmospheric changes. $35.00 each.

9. A JEWEL TYPE with faceted blue glass center in collar setting. Four paste stones in prong settings, border it. $1.00.

11. A sew-thru, bone backed with laminated veneers of tortoise shell, iridescent pearl and abalone. $1.50.

12. A TOMBAC BUTTON (described on Plate 83), engraved with the date 1776. $27.50.

13. An eighteenth century polychrome painting on ivory, under convex glass, mounted in silver. The painting shows TWO FIGURES; one with a goat, the other holding an ewer; both are gazing at a brazier on a tripod which emits flames and clouds of smoke. $75.00.

14. A COPPER COLONIAL (explained on Plate 83). The center has a simple, hand-chased design. The background is etched in squares and has a border of circles. Prominent is the date 1736. $37.50.

15. A bone background with a carved cross and a DOG'S HEAD escutcheon of brass. $2.00.

16. Wood with a concave center, in which is mounted a carved pearl OWL'S HEAD. The eyes are cut steels with pins that rivet the head to the back. $2.00.

17. An unusual large, four-hole, sew-thru PASSEMENTERIE, made of black glass pieces, cemented to an open-work, solid metal back. $5.00.

18. A dark iridescent pearl, concave with a pewter escutcheon which is an OWL ON A BRANCH. $.75.

19. Concave 19th century pewter, tinted dark blue, with bright, tinted DRAGONFLY applied. $.75.

20. CROSS REBATED, a riveted, black glass design, applied to a metal screenback. The shape of the design is pierced in the metal face of the button which has a dull black finish; convex.$2.50.

21. A lovely gilt button, backmarked, "Wadhams Coe & Co. Extra Rich". A two-piece button, die-struck and hand chased. $2.50.

22. Twentieth century CARVED BONE, A DRAGON, with beady, glass eyes. $4.00.

23. Another "EARLY GILT". This is one-piece with a hand-chased floral design and border. Backmarked, "Wadhams Coe & Co. Extra Rich". $2.00.

PLATE 79

1
2
3
4
5
6
7
8
9
10
11
12
13
14
15
16
17
18
19
20
21
22
23
24
25
26
27
28
29
30

PLATE 79

VICTORIANS

These buttons get their name from the fact that they were made and worn during the Victorian era. They sometimes are referred to as Victorian Jewels, as they are constructed primarily of glass centers set in metal. Drum buttons are also Victorians and can be included with any of the so-called Victorians, but a Victorian button is not a drum unless it has straight sides. All buttons shown on this Plate, have brass rims, unless otherwise stated and all except 9, 22, and 27 have loop shanks. The three mentioned have pad shanks.

1. A clear glass Dewdrop center, set in a scalloped gilt border which has a pressed design of grapes and leaves. $1.25.

2. A rim of white metal, tinted black, holds an inset of amber glass, molded in a flower design. $.75.

3. A convex, amber glass inset, molded on the back to resemble dewdrops; enclosed by a gilt circlet; black lacquered, Ogee rim. $1.00.

4. A domed, frosted glass center into which has been cut an eight point star; backed by amber foil; the rim is gilded and serrated at the top. $1.00.

5. A Glory center; eight point star backed by gold foil. $1.50.

6. A green transparent, cone shaped glass center with border extension covered with bits of galena. $1.50.

7. Milk glass molded center, acorn design, in high relief. $1.00.

8. A molded amber glass acorn, set in a silvered copper disk. $1.00.

9. Molded milk glass with dog's head in high relief, in an Ogee brass rim. $1.50.

10. Black glass house fly, molded and set in a white metal rim, lacquered black. $2.00.

11. Black glass in a lacquered black rim, foil decoration. $1.25.

12. Molded black glass head of woman, set in a pebbled brass border. $2.00.

13. Molded, clear glass head of woman, backed by silver foil; the surface surrounding the head is painted black for contrast. $.75.

14. A brass head set in disk of early composition, which is seldom found in good condition. $2.00.

15. Molded milk glass head, wearing helmet, mounted in a pierced brass face, two-piece. $1.00.

16. A black glass disk with milk glass "sheet overlay", which has a black transfer of a classical head, wearing a laurel wreath. $7.50.

17. A molded milk glass head on a black disk, inserted in a border extension which is covered with galena; brass rim originally painted black. $2.50.

18. Milk glass disk with center hole, through which the escutcheon type pressed brass head is attached to the pin shank. $1.50.

19. A black glass disk with molded head, wearing helmet, inserted in lacquered black metal face. $1.75.

20. Molded black glass disk with seasonal head, in high relief, dull finish. $1.25.

21. Molded, opaque gray glass disk with head in high relief, the flat section of the disk is painted black for contrast, black rim. $2.00.

22., 23. and 24. have molded opaque glass sea shell shapes inserted in different type rims. No. 22, $1.50. Nos. 23 and 24, $1.25 each.

25. Crackle glass center in a gilded brass rim. $1.00. Colored crackle glass centers can be found also more scarce and more costly.

26. A small disk of abalone, rimmed by brass set in black celluloid. $1.00.

27. A silver tinted metal disk with molded glass inset, leaf design. $2.00.

28. A fine early specimen of jewelers quality; a silver rim with crimped top, holding an iridescent pearl disk which has an inset of black onyx with a diamond paste center. $5.00.

29. Milk glass disk, containing particles of copper, known as adventurine, set in gilded brass. $1.50.

30. High domed, faceted, opalescent glass center, backed by foil; rim has original dark tint. $1.50.

PLATE 80

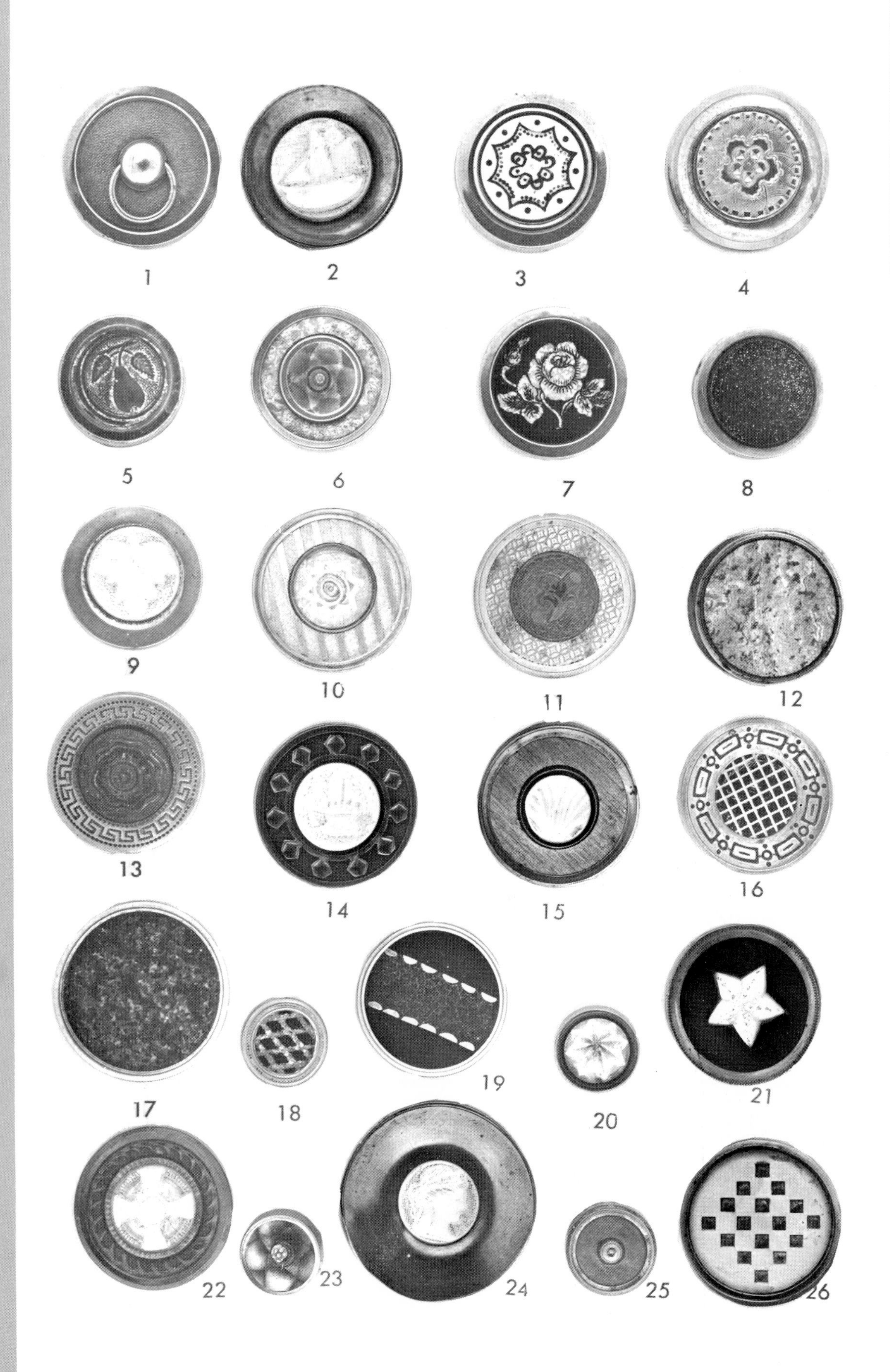

PLATE 80

DRUMS

Drums are a variety of Victorian buttons used from about 1840-1870, having straight sides. The depth or size is not considered, when admitting them to this classification, although those having higher sides, have a closer resemblance to musical drums from which they get their name. They are usually made of brass with tin backs and if taken apart, they are found to be filled with many layers of tightly compressed paper. The variety of their centers is what probably gives them the most appeal. Buttons on this Plate vary from one-eighth to one-fourth inch.

1. This one is all brass, except for the tin back. The center is recessed and has a door knocker, with movable ring, for a decoration. This could also be classed with Pictorial Objects. $2.50.

2. Brass rim which slopes deeply in the center and has a molded milk glass inset with a sailing ship design. $2.50.

3. Brass with a milk glass inset, which has a molded intaglio design, filled with pigment. $2.00.

4. The brass rim here slants toward the center where a gilded, brass inset, with pressed design, is slightly elevated. $2.00.

5. The brass rim fits over a molded black composition disk, with pear design; sides of drum are tinted black. $2.50.

6. This brass rim fits over a circle of crystallized tin; in this is a concave brass center with a star design, silvered; this star has a green glass center with brass head attached to a pin shank. $1.25.

7. This is a rare specimen, having a reverse painting on glass, the background and outlines of rose are black and the rose itself is of iridescent pearl chips. $8.00.

8. Brass sides and rim with inset of goldstone, Goldstone being glass is often scratched, and one should look for a specimen which is not. $1.25.

9. A molded milk glass center with pebbled background and leaf design. $1.50.

10. The brass rim encloses a circle of white metal, silver striped, which has a domed, clear glass inset, molded on the back in the shape of an eight point star and backed by gold foil. This is called a Glory center; very lovely and rare. $2.50.

11. Brass rim enclosing a silvered copper circle which has a raised center inset of molded amber glass. $2.00.

12. Instead of a tin back, this drum has a thread back and the inset is of green, mottled paper, varnished; an early type. $2.00.

13. The center is a molded black glass disk and the brass border has the Greek key design. $1.50.

14. A molded milk glass center with a basket of fruit for the design, inserted in a pressed brass border which is enclosed by the brass rim. $2.00.

15. A molded milk glass seashell forms this center; circled by copper ring. $1.50.

16. Brass with sloping sides decorated by an ornamental border which encloses a metal disk, probably aluminum; this disk has been painted black, then engraved to show the bright, silver colored metal and form a checkered pattern. $2.00.

17. This center is a reverse painting, flecks of pearl, backed by gold, metallic foil add color and sparkle. $1.50.

18. A small drum painted in reverse with a black, diamond pattern which is backed by iridescent pearl chips. $.75.

19. Another reverse painting; the white scallops were first painted on the glass, then the two outer sections painted with black and the center filled in with brown which contains pieces of glitter. This has a pad shank. $2.50.

20. A small drum with Glory center; a blue foil backing reflects through the eight point star. $1.00.

21. A molded, five point milk glass star is set in black celluloid; slanting brass rim, serrated at the top. $1.75.

22. The sides and rim of this Drum still have a nice gunmetal tint, sides sloping to center have an ornamental, pressed border and the molded milk glass cross is set in a narrow, serrated, gilt circlet. $2.00.

23. A waistcoat size, identical in construction to the center of No. 6, the glass here is red with slightly larger brass head than No. 6. $.75.

24. This is the only large size Drum shown here. It has low sides, a concave rim with an inset which is a milk glass ladies' head, molded. Drums in this size are scarce. $2.00.

25. This small Drum has an inset, covered with blue cloth with a brass knob in the center. $.75.

26. The glass inset of this Drum is lined with white paper, having a pierced design of tiny squares, which is backed by gold foil. Lovely. $2.50.

Nos. 1, 2, 3, 4, 6, and 7 are from the collection of Thomas W. Owens, Jr.

PLATE 81

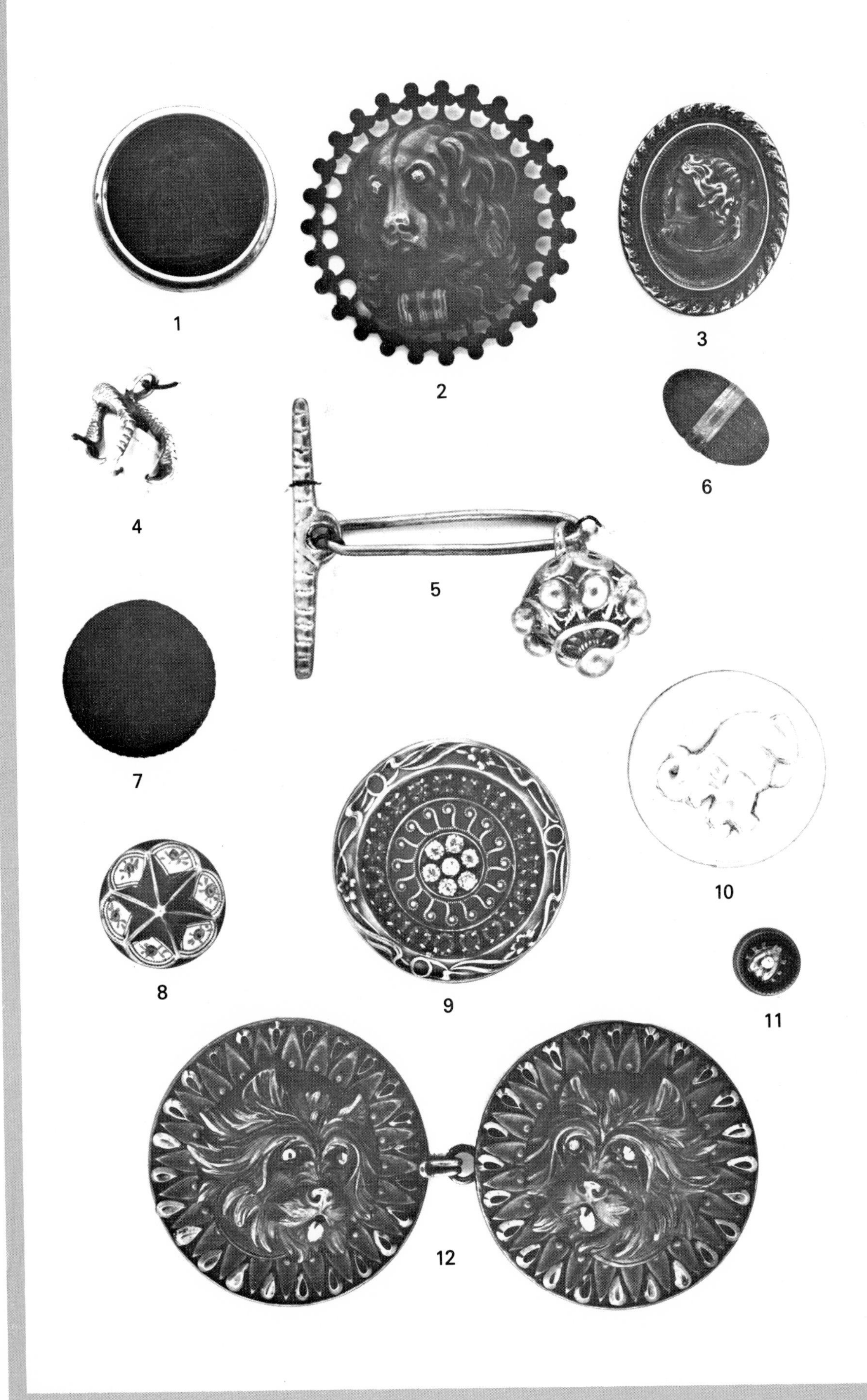

PLATE 81

ASSORTED FASTENERS

1. This button shows two figures in high relief, molded. It has a self shank and a tin rim is applied. $2.00.

2. A ST. BERNARD DOG with whiskey keg around his neck, in very high relief. Cut steel eyes and pierced metal background. These dogs were trained to rescue travelers, chiefly at the monastery at the Great Saint Bernard Pass in the Swiss Alps. $10.00.

3. A brass head of JOAN OF ARC, as identified in N.B.B., May '56. Superimposed on an oval composition background, brass back and "collar" setting with a brass border applied. $8.50.

4. A hallmarked silver CLAW, holding an ivory animals tooth, said to have been worn on leather Alpine clothing. $12.50.

5. This fastener is called a TOGGLE. It is made of heavy silver and shows much wear. This type of button was used for several centuries in various European countries. $7.50.

6. Called a VEIL BUTTON and said to have been worn by ladies dangling from their veils to keep them in place. Cloth covered, brass bound with a brass shank attached to the brass band. This specimen is brown. $1.00.

7. A FABRIC button which has a velvet background, star-shaped ornamentation in the center, crocheted border and thread back. $1.50.

8. This has a center of silvered brass, in the shape of a six-point star which comes to a high point. The outer points of the star are connected to the scalloped border which has the same finish. The other sections are painted with silver and tiny pink roses with green leaves. These sections are outlined with two rows of gold and silver lines extending from each scallop to the top of the star. $2.50.

9. A JEWEL button of white metal, silvered and pierced. The center has clear paste stones set with prongs in a cluster and a border is formed by faceted amber glass stones. Convex. $5.00.

10. A twentieth century carved ivory button with self shank, showing a CIRCUS ELEPHANT. $5.00.

11. A brass BEETLE mounted with one cut steel in concave drum-shaped, brass button. $1.00.

12. Here we see two large buttons that by having a brass hook and eye soldered to the edges, were made into a buckle. Many other buttons were converted to buckles in this manner and collecting them makes an interesting "Specialty". These buttons show a pair of CAIRN TERRIERS. The heads are in extremely high relief, made of tinted brass and fastened to the brass background by two pins which go through the metal and are clinched to the back. The eyes are round cut steels and the tongues and ornaments in the border are diamond shaped cut steels. Value of the pair, $35.00.

PLATE 82

CROWN
OVERALL
Carhartt's
O'BRYAN BROS
B&L
OSH KOSH
B'GOSH
KEYSTONE
MOGUL
SWEET
ORR
THE
BRAND
THE
FREELAND
FREELAND
S.O.&CO.
N.Y.
S.O.&CO.
H.W.CARTER
& SONS
GOLD
MEDAL
BRAND
ANTHRACITE
A-WEAR-WELL
HEAD
LIGHT
1
2
3
4
5
6
7
8
9
10
11
12
13
14
15
16
17
18
19
20
21
22
23
24
25
26
27
28
29
30

PLATE 82

WORK CLOTHES OR OVERALL BUTTONS

Overall buttons were used by manufacturers of men's work clothes with the greatest production, during the first 25 years of this century. There are many hundreds of designs. One firm alone has 1300 patterns on its sample boards. We have shown here a few of the different types. Much information can be found in the N.B.S.'s Classification Series, Volume III, "VICTORIAN OVERALL BUTTONS" by Jane Ford Adams and Lillian Smith Albert. Values given here are from several collectors and dealers.

1. CROWN OVERALL, used from 1900-1908. $.75.

2. and 3. CARHARTTS, on heart shaped button, 1910-1912. $1.00 and $.75.

4. PINE TREE WITH STAR. No caption, 1918-1919, $1.00. The Pine Tree Brand garments, made by the Sawyer-Baker Co. of Portland, Maine.

5. GANDER'S HEAD, O'Bryan Bros., 1900-1908. $1.00.

6. THE RAILROAD, 1900-1908. $.50. There are many pictorial overall buttons showing different Railroad Engines and having various captions.

7. B. & L. CROWN OVERALL MFG. CO., Cinti., O. $.25. The pictorial overall buttons are more sought after, which makes the purely verbal ones, less expensive.

8. A very small STEAM LOCOMOTIVE in oval, no caption. Sometimes this same button says, "Union Special". $1.00.

9. OSH KOSH B'GOSH. This is very plentiful. $.25.

10. KEYSTONE TRADE MARK, in use about 1908-1910. $.25.

11. STEAM ENGINE. Although this is a later engine than many, it is not a common one. $1.00.

12. SWOFFORD'S MOGUL. 1900-1908. $1.00.

13. An EARLY ENGINE with no capiton. $.75.

14. SWEET ORR. 1921. $1.00. The Tug of War indicates the strength of the garment.

15. THE BRAND, with car and heart between the twc words; meaning, "The Carhart Brand". 1900-1908. $1.00.

16. THE FREELAND, with map of the U.S. Freeland is a small city in Pa., where the Freeland Mfg. Co. is located. $1.25.

17. FREELAND. $.50.

18. S.O. & CO. N.Y., with early engine. S.O. & CO. N.Y. signifies Sweet Orr & Co. of New York City. 1900-1908. $.75.

19. Similar to No. 18. $.75.

20. IDEAL, with head of Unicorn. Scarce. 1900-1908. $1.50.

21. Another LOCOMOTIVE, no caption. $.75.

22. H.W.C. & SONS, which signifies H.W. Carter and Sons. 1900-1908. $1.00.

23. CARTER'S LEBANON, N.H., same firm as above, showing early engine. 1908-1910. $1.00.

24. H.W. CARTER AND SONS, found more often than Nos. 22 and 23. $1.00.

25. GOLD MEDAL BRAND. $.25.

26. K.S. CO., letters entwined. Plentiful. $.50.

27. ANTHRACITE WEAR WELL. $.50.

28. HEAD LIGHT. $.50.

29. BROOKFIELD, J.A. WHITE & CO. with star below. 1912-1913. $.50.

30. SOUVENIR. The placard is held by a shaggy dog. This is not positively identified as an overall button but it is so similar to the Buffalo's Head which holds a placard that we feel it belongs with OVERALLS. $2.00.

PLATE 83

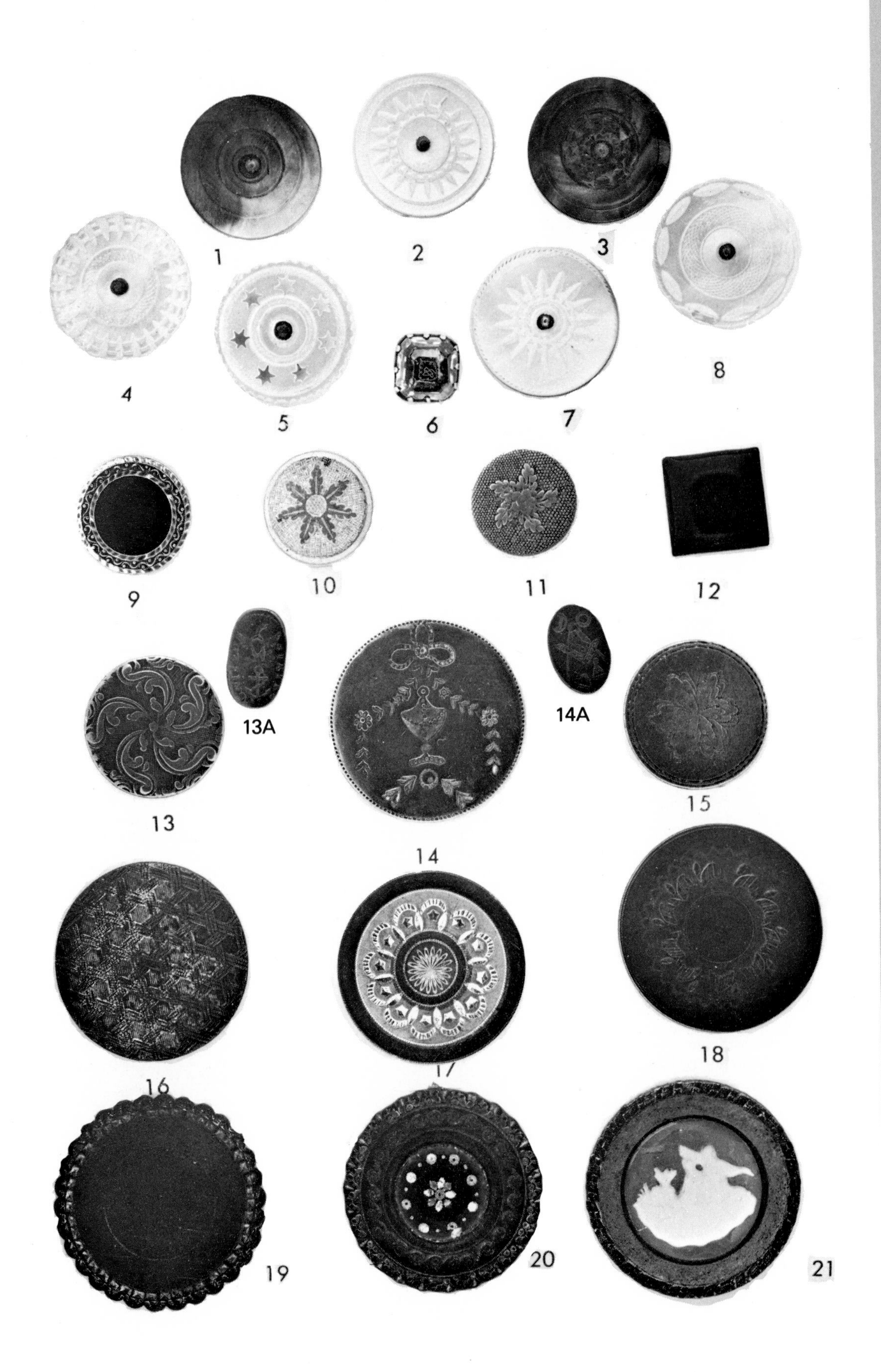

PLATE 83

FROM THE COLONIAL PERIOD

Most of the buttons shown on this Plate were made during the Colonial Period, and are designated as "Colonials". This name was given to them by button collectors when the hobby was in its infancy and it clings to them for lack of a better term. Although large hand-wrought buttons of this type were made and worn by the early American Colonists. manv that fall into the categorv of "Colonials" were made in Europe. The first that came to the attention of collectors had been handed down in families since early colonial times. They were large, usually 1 3/8 inches, made of copper or brass in one piece, with hand drawn metal shanks that were brazed to the button. The solder used in brazing was much like brass itself, whereas ordinary soft solder is a grayish color. Colonial buttons were decorated with hand-engraved, chased or engine turned designs and borders. These designs are usually geometrical and after studying various specimens and examining the shanks, they can be easily identified.

Some Colonials have decorative centers of pearl, molded glass, enamel, reverse painting or jasperware and with these the metal-work forms a border. However, one can recognize the characteristics that are common to all "Colonials". These more elaborate examples probably will be found to have originated in Europe.

Some buttons of the plainer type have been found at the sites of Revolutionary battles which is understandable, as regulation uniform buttons had not yet been designed and few Revolutionary soldiers had uniforms. The pearl buttons, first shown on this Plate are said to be the type worn by American Revolutionary officers on their dress uniforms.

The period of colonization ends with the eighteenth century but the large Colonial buttons were worn from the seventeenth century until well into the nineteenth century. From this period we also find one-piece silver, pewter, and tombac buttons, either plain or decorated with chased and engine-turned designs.

1.,2.,3.,4.,7., and 8. are COLONIAL PEARLS. All so-called Colonial pearls have pin-shanks. A brass nail (or pin) head is visible on the front. This is attached to a pin which goes through a hole in the button and is turned into a heavy brass shank at the back. They are thick pearl disks which have straight sides and the face is carved or engraved with a geometrical design. They are usually the size shown here but small ones exist and were probably sleeve buttons. Many were made from white pearl shell (oyster) but some such as 1 and 3 were made from black pearl oyster shell. The latter are more rare. No. 7 has a white face and dark back. Value of the dark pearls, $3.00 each. The white, $2.50.

5. This is a pierced pearl with a real garnet set in the center, attached to the heavy brass shank. Eighteenth century. $5.00.

6. This little square button has a flat-crown with faceted sides, clear glass in a silver prong setting. The glass is backed by red foil with a square center of black which has a design in gold outline. 18th century. $5.00.

9. The center of this button is tortoise shell and the border is silver, an example of Sheffield Plate (silver over copper.) The entire back is copper and also the shank. $10.00.

10. and 11. are Hard White Pewters. The N.B.B., Jan '56 shows 30 different buttons of this type with manufacturer's backmarks, dating them from 1800 - 1827. The N.B.B. for May '58 contains the research of H. Campbell Scarlett. Recently much more research has been done by Jo and Bob Ferguson with their findings published in Just Buttons. In the center of the back these buttons are raised into a Mound, in which a Ring Shaped Shank, usually of brass wire, is embedded. None are known to have been made later than 1830. All have become quite scarce and should be priced accordingly.

12. This square button is made of iron, lacquered. Rare. $5.00.

13. Brass with a copper finish and a brazed, brass shank. $6.50.

13a. and 14a. are link buttons that were worn by an officer during the American Revolutionary War. One has the Masonic emblem, the other the Federal eagle, an anchor, and the words, "United States." Many English generals were also members of the Masonic fraternity and it is said that when Generals of both sides established the fact that each were Masons, prisoners were exchanged freely. The pair are from the collection Agnes Smtih and valued at $12.50.

14. This lovely Colonial is called, "THE GEORGE WASHINGTON URN". It is thought that this may be a George Washington memorial item but there is no proof of its real identity. Value, $50.00.

15. A Tombac button of medium size with engraved design and border of fine lines. Tombac metal is a variety of brass, originating in the eighteenth century. Most buttons of this type are from ½" - 2" in size and although some are without decoration, many are hand stamped with punch tools and others decorated with gilt and brass. Shanks vary but are usually flat iron wires, applied in different ways. $3.00.

16. A copper "Colonial" with a basket-weave design. This is "capped" (the face is turned-over a brass back and crimped.) $12.50.

17. A "Colonial" with chased design. Sheffield plated with borders left in copper, unplated, for contrast. $35.00.

18. Copper "Colonial" with simple hand-chased designs. $17.50.

19. A copper "Colonial" with scalloped and hand chased edge which is rare. $25.00.

20. This copper, engraved "Colonial" has a center ceramic inset which is enameled cobalt blue, and has a design made up of green and gold paillions. $35.00.

21. A copper "Colonial" with chased border. The center holds a blue and white jasperware cameo (probably Wedgwood) under convex glass. $50.00.

PLATE 84

PLATE 84

HERALDRY

By Marion Moxley

Since time immemorial, and in all parts of the world, men have used symbols to express ideas and sentiments in visual form. Early in the 12th century, at the time of the Crusades, it became a necessity for practical purposes. Heralds conducted Tournaments and also carried messages from Princes to their Knights fighting in the field, and as the Knights were completely covered with armour, it was necessary to show some device to distinguish friend from foe. Because of this, the Heràlds learned these devices and kept records of each device. So the practice was called "Heraldry". Heraldry is the science of armorial bearings, and in olden times it was as much the study of the scholar as the science of chemistry is today.

The Shield was the most important part of the Armour, and at first it was very simple, perhaps just a color, or one line dividing it; but as the practice grew, it was necessary to add more lines, birds, flowers, beasts, monsters, etc. This device on the Shield became the Coat-of-Arms for the Bearer. The Crest was either some portion of the Coat, or something depicting an outstanding event in the life of the Bearer. The Motto was probably a War Cry.

From left to right:

1. Bishop's Mitre, Ecclesiastical Heraldry. $1.50.
2. Cardinal's Hat, 15 red tassels, Ecclesiastical Heraldry. $2.00.
3. Bishop's Mitre, Crossed Banners, Armoured fist holding sword, Ecclesiastical Heraldry. $1.50.
4. Fitchee Cross denotes Crusader (point was stuck in ground). $1.50.
5. Lozenge - Shield of Widow or unmarried lady. $2.00.
6. Shields of husband and wife Accolle (side by side); Crest; Supporters and Motto. $2.00.
7. Shields of husband and wife Impaled, as she is not an heiress; 2 Crests; Motto. $1.50.
8. Shield of husband with wife's "in escutcheon", as she is an heiress; Crest; Supporters; Motto. $2.00.
9. Shield; Helmet of Peer; Mantling; Motto. $2.00.
10. Shield; Crown of Viscount Crest; Supporters; Motto. $2.50.
11. Shield with Pavillion (or Tent) Mantling, denoting Royalty. $2.50.
12. Shield with Pavillion Mantling; Duke's Crown Crest; Supporters; Motto. $2.50.
13. Crest on Chapeau, or Cap of Dignity. $2.00.
14. Crest on Duke's Crown. $2.50.
15. Crest on Wreath (Angel is rare on crest). $2.50.
16. Shield Embattled; Crest on Wreath; Collar and Star of Most Distinguished Order of St. Michael and St. George. $3.50.
17. Label (on side of stag) denoting first son. $1.50.
18. Shield with Crescent, denoting second son. $1.50.
19. Mullet (or star) denoting third son. $1.50.
20. Martlet (bird without feet) denoting fourth son. $1.50.
21. Mural Crown. $2.00.
22. Earl's Coronet; 8 lofty rays, five visible. $2.00.
23. Baron's Coronet; 6 large balls, four visible. $2.00.
24. Viscount's Coronet; 16 balls, 9 visible. $2.50.

All buttons pictured on this Plate and the following Plate are from the collection of Marion Moxley. All values given for these buttons are approximate.

PLATE 85

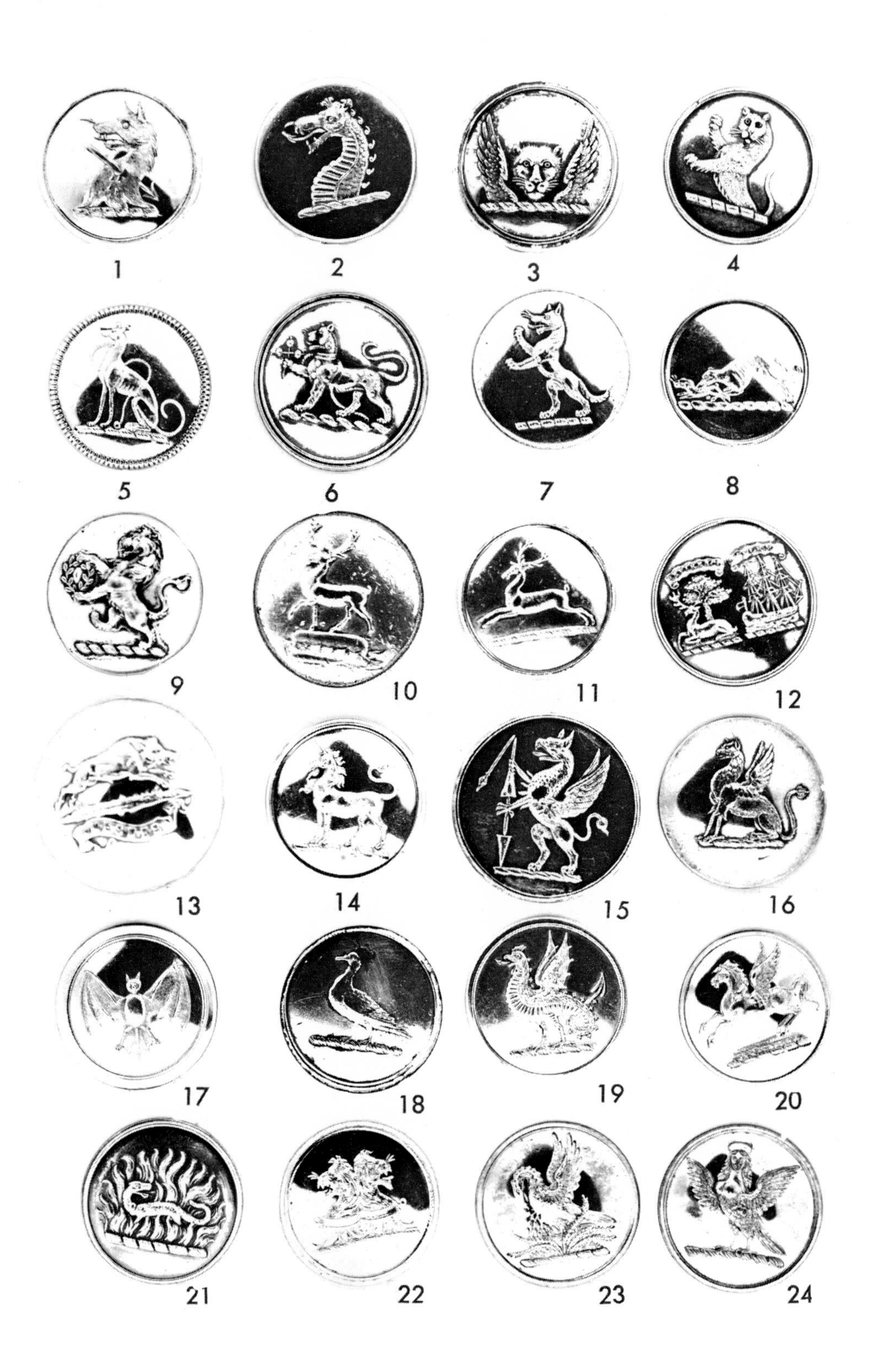

PLATE 85

HERALDRY

1. Crest on Wreath, Erased (torn off jagged); Augmentation (arrow through neck). $2.00.

2. Crest on Wreath, Couped (cut off even). $2.00.

3. Crest on Wreath, Cabossed (full-faced, no neck). $2.00.

4. Crest on Wreath, Demi-lion Half Guardant (facing spectator). $2.50.

5. Crest Sejant (sitting). $2.00.

6. Crest Passant (walking, 3 feet on ground, right front foot raised, profile). $2.00.

7. Crest Passant Erect (walking erect). $2.00.

8. Crest Salient (leaping on prey). $2.00.

9. Crest Rampant (left hind foot on ground). $2.50.

10. Crest, Stag Trippant (walking). $2.00.

11. Crest, Deer "At Speed" (running). $2.00.

12. Crest on left, Deer Couchant (resting on belly, legs under). $2.50.

13. Crest Courant Re-Courant (running contariwise, facing Sinister). $3.00.

14. Crest Statant (4 feet on ground). $2.50.

15. Crest, Griffin Segreant. $2.00.

16. Crest, Griffin Sejant (sitting). $2.00.

17. Volant (flying). $2.50.

18. Trussed, or closed (wings). $2.00.

19. Cockatrice. $2.50.

20. Pegasus. $2.50.

21. Salamander in flames. $2.50.

22. Addorsed (back to back). $2.00.

23. Pelican in Piety (feeding young birds). $2.50.

24. Harpy (fabulous monster, represented as bird with virgin's face, neck and breasts, and vulture's body and legs). $2.50.

PLATE 86

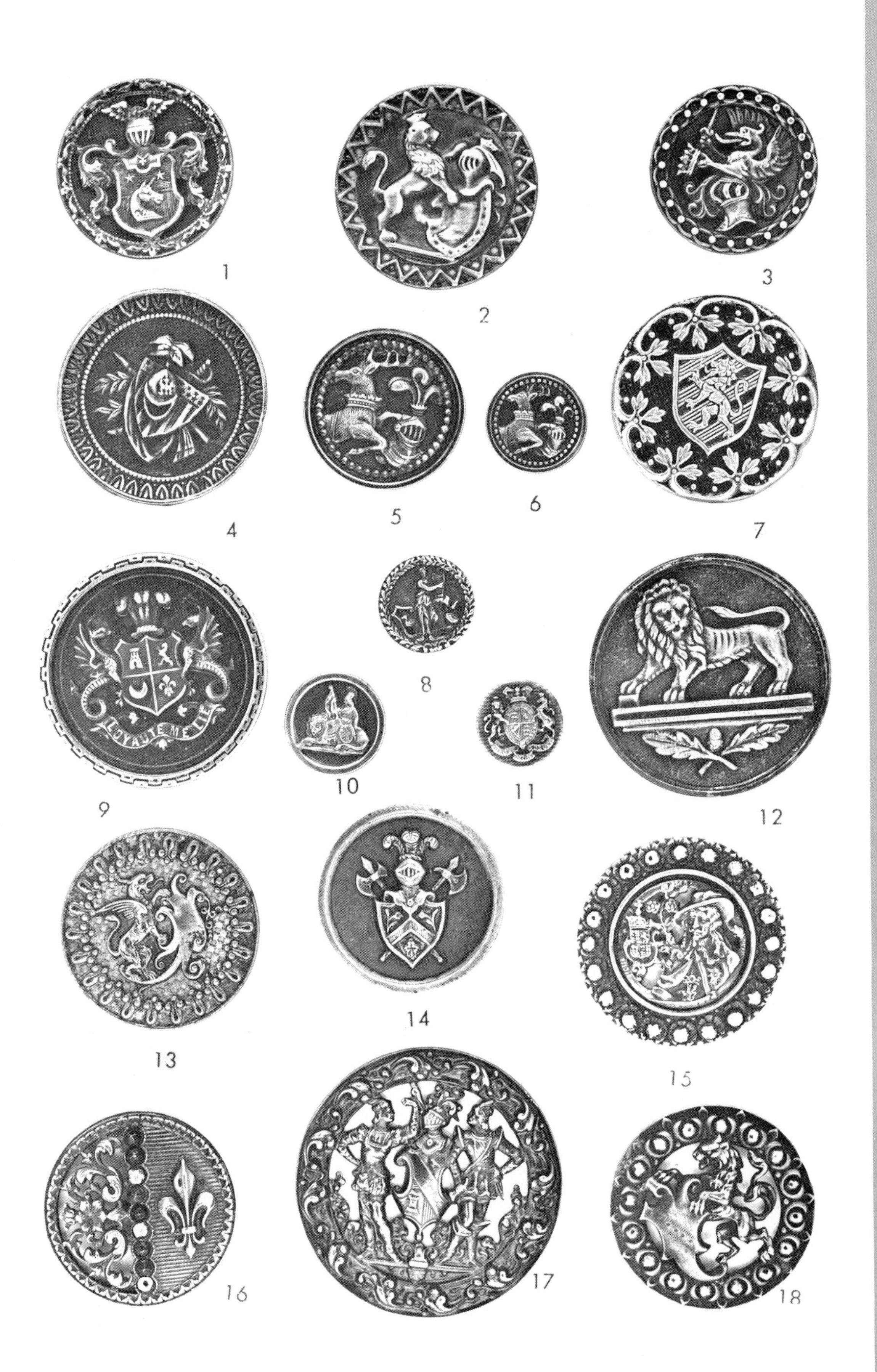

PLATE 86

HERALDRY

These buttons are called Heraldic Buttons because an heraldic device is used as a means of decoration.

1. This shows a complete COAT OF ARMS, topped by the British sovereign helmet. It is of tinted brass with a leaf and fleur-de-lis border. $3.00.

2. Here we see the RAMPANT LION, crowned, with shield and Peer's helmet; two-piece pressed brass with a pierced saw-tooth border, showing a steel liner. $2.00.

3. A GRIFFIN with crown and sword, topping a plumed helmet; two-piece brass, chain border. $1.50.

4. Shield, helmet, plumed with open visor, sword, scarf, pike and laurel branches; two-piece pressed brass. $2.00.

5. STAG with crown around his neck, front foot resting on a helmet, which has three plumes like those of the crest of the English Prince of Wales; two-piece pressed brass, darkened. $1.50.

6. Same as No. 5 in the small size. $.75.

7. SHIELD WITH LION RAMPANT (left hind foot on ground); brass darkened background with leaf border. $2.00.

8. ERATO, Greek muse of lyric poetry (should be classified with Music). Brass with tin back. $1.00.

9. SHIELD with marks of cadency supported by two Cockatrices, motto underneath and three plumes above. $3.50.

10. MINERVA with shield, showing Greek cross. $1.00.

11. LIVERY BUTTON with heraldic device. $.75.

12. The LION GUARDANT (facing spectator), crossed oak leaves and acorn under base; brass in high relief on tin background. $3.00.

13. RAMPANT GRIFFIN with Shield; brass on a brass background in basket weave effect; fleur-de-lis border. $2.50.

14. SHIELD WITH CHEVRON, plumed helmet above, halberd and battleax behind shield. $2.00.

15. PORTRAIT OF KING CHARLES I OF ENGLAND, showing the Royal Arms, the Rose, Thistle and Shamrock, and the Star of the Order of the Garter. Circling all this is the Motto of the order. "Honi Sait Qui Maly Pense." One-piece brass with a pierced border, ornamented by cut steels. $8.00.

16. A lovely button of silvered metal, with a center separation of tinted cut steels. One side has a pierced leaf design and the other a FLEUR-DE-LIS in high relief. The fleur-de-lis is a Mark of Cadency that is a symbol denoting the sixth son. $1.75.

17. Two FALCON HUNTERS, in complete hunting attire, one has a falcon balanced on his wrist. Between the two is a shield with Bend and marks of Cadency visible, surmounted by a plumed helmet. One-piece brass, with this lovely pierced design and leaf border. $12.00.

18. LION RAMPANT with shield; one-piece brass cut out with an ornamental border, decorated with cut steel. $3.50.

BUTTON MATERIAL IDENTIFICATION

Simple tests to identify various button materials as demonstrated at a program of the N.B.S. in 1947 by one of the authors. Heat a needle until red-hot and quickly touch an inconspicuous spot; the spot touched will smoke and the resulting odor will identify the material as follows:

Celluloid — odor of camphor.

Bakelite — Carbolic acid or lysol.

True Jet — Coal gas or soft coal smoke.

Horn, Hoof — Burning feathers.

Hard Rubber — Burning rubber.

Vegetable Ivory — Burned English Walnut Shells.

Composition of various kinds — Burning sealing wax or lacquer.

Zinc — Does not respond to the magnet.

SIZE SPECIFICATIONS

Buttons are classed, according to size in the following way:

Large — 1¼ inches and over.

Medium — ¾ to 1¼ inches.

Small — 3/8 to 3/4 inches.

Diminutive — up to 3/8 inches.

POLITICAL CAMPAIGN BUTTONS

By Thomas W. Owens, Jr.

For the collector with a lively interest in American history, our political campaign buttons will have an extraordinary appeal. The Washington Inaugurals, in a class by themselves, are presented separately on Plate No. 89. Beginning with a button issued for the first campaign of Andrew Jackson in 1828, buttons may be found to reflect the political activity of the two major parties, with some exceptions, for the next ninety years, being gradually replaced by the more versatile lapel studs and celluloid pins.

From 1828 to 1848, political campaign buttons were made in the style of men's coat buttons and were apparently used as such. Plain gilt buttons were in fashion during the 1820's. While the maker's name or quality mark was placed on the back of the button, the face was innocent of the slightest decoration. So it was for the Jackson campaign button. On the reverse side of the plain gilt button is found the legend ANDREW JACKSON — MARCH 4, 1829. In conjunction with the decorative types, plain gilt buttons continued in use throughout the Golden Age (1830-1850). Evidence of this is found on the back of another plain gilt button which bears the legend HENRY CLAY — SUPERIOR. This has been attributed to Clay's first unsuccessful bid for the presidency in 1832 but it would not have been unfashionable for the 1844 campaign.

With the log cabin and cider barrel as its popular emblems, the Harrison campaign of 1840 easily sets the record for number and variety of buttons. More than a score of variations of the log cabin pattern have been catalogued. Some are in good supply; others are scarce; all are interesting.

The ultimate in men's gilt coat buttons, the watch-case gilt, had its candidates on the political scene for the Henry Clay campaign of 1844. The most spectacular of these is not illustrated because of the technical difficulties in its photography. The die was made by executing the pattern of Clay's profile in very fine parallel lines, engraved on the oblique, which makes it necessary to tilt the button to the proper angle to see the design. The refraction of light gives Clay's profile an unusual opalescent sheen.

As the end of the Golden Age approached, the sacrifice of quality found in all gilt buttons is apparent in those of the Taylor campaign of 1848. Thin metal, tinned iron backs and mediocre dies do an injustice to the Hero of Monterey and Buena Vista. By mid-century, civilian styles had changed from metal to cloth-covered buttons. In some measure, this may account for the lack of buttons for the 1852 and 1856 campaigns, as well as those of 1860 and 1864 which, doubtless, suffered also from wartime austerity. Except for the two Goodyear buttons for the 1868 campaign, buttons seem not to have been used until 1880. The late political campaign buttons (1880 to 1916) are, for the most part, succinct in their message but woefully lacking in artistry and imagination.

Current values of political campaign buttons may seem somewhat excessive to the experienced collector and somewhat discouraging to the novice. Collectors of political Americana with no interest in other types of buttons have, in recent years, greatly increased the demand for these buttons and, thereby their value. The price range embraces both small and large sizes and makes allowances for the condition of the buttons.

PLATE 87

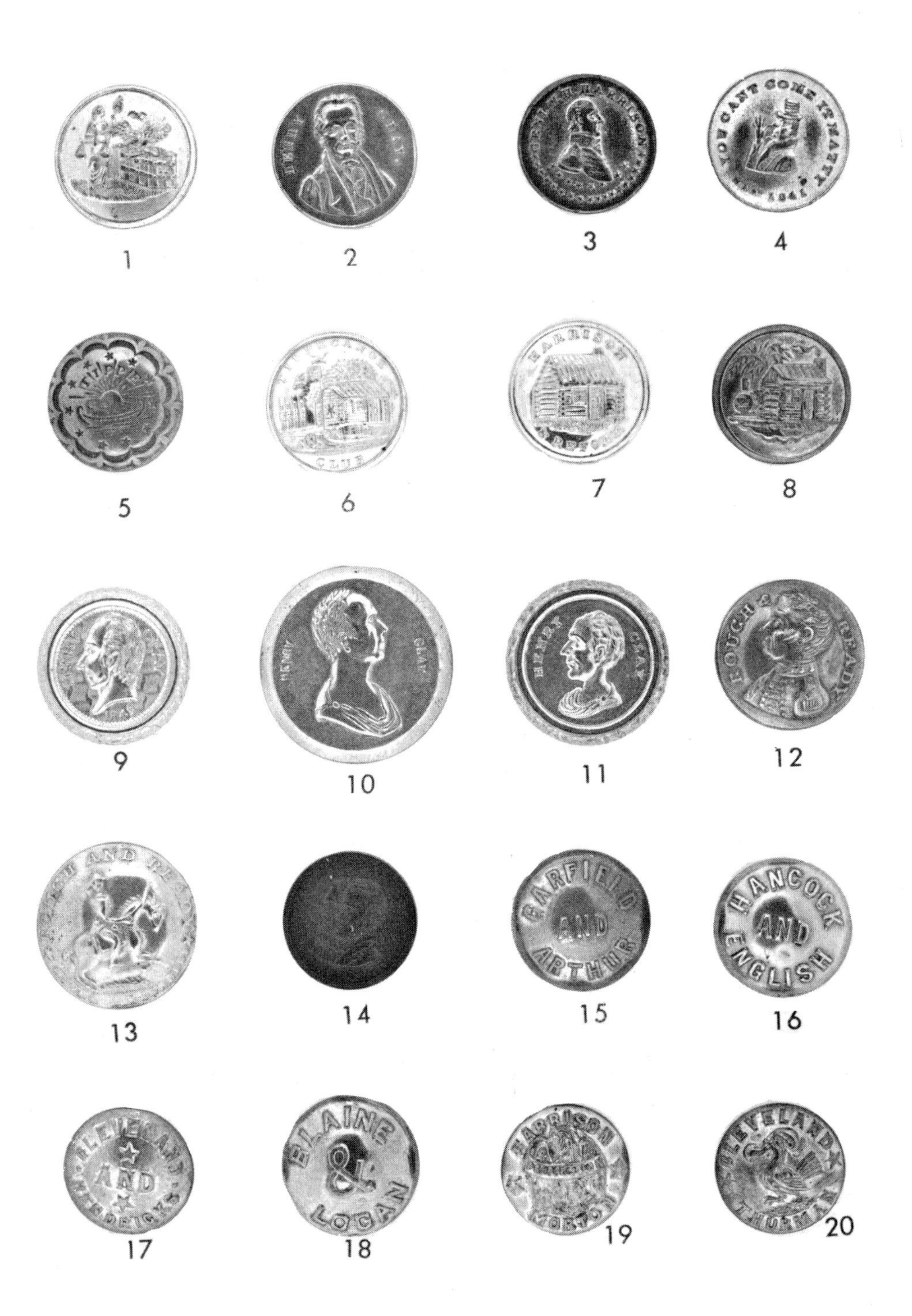

1
2
3
4
5
6
7
8
9
10
11
12
13
14
15
16
17
18
19
20
HENRY CLAY
YOU CANT COME IT MATTY
1841
HARRISON
CLUB
ROUGH & READY
GARFIELD
AND
ARTHUR
HANCOCK
AND
ENGLISH
BLAINE
&
LOGAN
CLEVELAND
AND
HARRISON
CLEVELAND
THURMAN

PLATE 87

POLITICAL CAMPAIGN BUTTONS

All buttons illustrated are from the collection of Thomas W. Owens, Jr.

1. 1840 Campaign (VanBuren). Eagle perched on strong box, holding key, with figure of Freedom standing at his side. Symbolic of the "Hard Money" issue of the Democratic party. Two-piece gilt button by Ives, Kendrick and Co. Estimated value from $30.00 to $45.00.

2. 1832 Campaign (Clay). Bust of Henry Clay in full face. Faced type button, brass over iron body. Estimated value from $25.00 to $40.00.

3. 1840 Campaign (Harrison). Bust of General Harrison in profile. Two-piece gilt button by Scovills and Co. Estimated value from $35.00 to $50.00.

4. 1840 Campaign (Harrison). Anti-VanBuren button with legend YOU CAN'T COME IT MATTY - MAR. 1841 encircling profile of man thumbing his nose. Two-piece gilt button by Scovills and Co. Estimated value from $75.00 to $100.00.

5. 1840 Campaign (Harrison) TIPPECANOE in rebus form. One-piece gilt button marked "Rich Gold Colour". Estimated value from $45.00 to $60.00.

6. 1840 Campaign (Harrison). Log cabin pattern with legend TIPPECANOE CLUB above. Two-piece gilt button by E.E. Pritchard. Estimated value from $30.00 to $45.00.

7. 1840 Campaign (Harrison). Log cabin pattern with legend HARRISON & REFORM. Two-piece gilt button by R. and W. Robinson. Estimated value from $12.00 to $15.00.

8. 1840 Campaign (Harrison). Log cabin pattern. Two - piece gilt button by Waterbury Mfg. Co. Estimated value from $20.00 to $25.00. Many examples of this basic pattern by several makers have been recorded. Great variation in detail adds to their interest. Values range from $25.00 - $30.00.

9. 1844 Campaign (Clay). Head of Henry Clay in profile on wavy line background, with legend HENRY CLAY - 1845 bordering. Two-piece gilt button in watch-case style by Scovills and Co. Estimated value to $45.00.

10. 1844 Campaign (Clay). Bust of Henry Clay in profile on stippled background, with legend HENRY CLAY. Two-piece gilt or plated button marked "Standard Colour". Estimated value from $55.00.

11. 1844 Campaign (Clay). Head of Henry Clay in profile on plain background, with legend HENRY CLAY. Two - piece gilt button in watch-case style by R. and W. Robinson. Estimated value from $35.00 to $45.00.

12. 1848 Campaign (Taylor). Bust of General Zachary Taylor in uniform in profile with legend ROUGH & READY above. Gilt top with tinned iron back. Estimated value from $25.00 to $35.00.

13. 1848 Campaign (Taylor). General Taylor standing beside his horse with legend ROUGH & READY above. Gilt top with tinned iron back marked "Ne Plus Ultra". Estimated value from $45.00.

14. 1868 Campaign (Grant). A jugated design of Grant and Colfax in profile. A Goodyear button by the Novelty Rubber Company. Estimated value from $25.00 to $45.00. A similar button for the opposing candidates is shown on another Plate.

15. 1880 Campaign. Garfield and Arthur. Gilt top with tinned iron back. Estimated value from $4.00 - $6.00.

16. 1880 Campaign. Hancock and English. Gilt top with tinned iron back. Estimated value from $4.00 - $6.00.

17. 1884 Campaign. Cleveland and Hendricks. Gilt top with tinned iron back. Estimated value from $4.00 - $6.00.

18. 1884 Campaign. Blaine and Logan. Gilt top with tinned iron back. Estimated value from $6.00 - $8.00.

19. 1888 Campaign. Harrison and Morton. Gilt top with tinned iron back. Estimated value from $5.00 - $7.00.

20. 1888 Campaign. Cleveland and Thurman. Gilt top with tinned iron back. Estimated value from $4.00 - $7.00.

PLATE 88

PLATE 88

JACKSONIANS

JACKSONIANS is a collectors' name given to a distinctive type of American gilt vest button which employed a considerable popularity from 1825 to 1840. It is a specialized type of Golden Age button which by reason of its construction, may be easily separated from this large group of coat and sleeve or vest buttons. Originally, it was defined as a one-piece gilt button having a plain field with a pictorial design and a plain rim consisting of a separate piece rolled over the edge of the body of the button. Over the years, collectors have insisted upon including similar buttons with conventional designs and those with fancy rims in the Jacksonian family. Reference is sometimes made to Pictorial Jacksonians and to Conventional Jacksonians. Both are properly called Jacksonians today. The pictorial patterns are generally considered the more desirable, despite the fact that several of the conventional patterns are found far less frequently than a few of the more common pictorial patterns.

While these buttons have no direct association with Andrew Jackson, the name is an apt one. Evidence gleaned primarily from the makers' marks on many of the buttons indicates their manufacture to have taken place from 1828 to 1840, corresponding closely with President Jackson's tenure of office from 1829 to 1837. This was the period of the nation's rapid expansion. Only on these small rimmed vest buttons do we find the interests and activities of the people in agriculture, commercial and social pursuits so faithfully recorded. Other buttons of the Golden Age were plain or decorated with ornate floral or conventional designs.

The twenty-five buttons illustrated here were selected from nearly one hundred pictorial patterns on record, including variations of several subjects. Except for a few patterns which are fairly common, including the standing eagle, the eagle displayed, a basket of flowers, a rose, a sheaf of wheat with tools, and one of the several sailing ships, Jacksonians have become scarce. Many patterns are exceedingly rare and, at the present time, a few may be termed unique. During the past decade their popularity has increased greatly, as have the prices asked and unhesitatingly paid by avid collectors. The estimated values appearing below are based upon the rarity and condition of the buttons and the recognition of these factors by dealers and collectors.

All buttons shown are from the collection of Thomas W. Owens, Jr.

1. Bow and Quiver. $15.00 to $20.00.
2. Militia Cadet. $12.00 to $15.00.
3. Flying Eagle. $25.00 to $30.00.
4. Fox Mask. $10.00 to $15.00.
5. Nest with Eggs. $8.00 to $10.00.
6. Cat. $25.00 to $30.00.
7. Rooster. $10.00 to $15.00.
8. Game Bird. $15.00 to $20.00.
9. Turkey. $12.00 to $15.00.
10. Dog's Head with Basket. $12.00 to $15.00.
11. Deer and Trees. $10.00 to $15.00.
12. Steamboat. $20.00 to $25.00.
13. Anchor on Starred Shield. $30.00 to $40.00.
14. Sailing Ship. $4.00 to $5.00.
15. Horse and Jockey. $8.00 to $12.00.
16. Lion. $15.00 to $20.00.
17. Clown's Face. $15.00 to $20.00.
18. Locomotive. $10.00 to $15.00.
19. Fire Pumper. $10.00 to $15.00.
20. Eagle and Snake. $8.00 to $10.00.
21. Liberty Cap with Cornucopias. $10.00 to $15.00.
22. Motto. Liberty - Union. $8.00 to $12.00.
23. Bust of Washington. $10.00 to $12.00.
24. Motto Union Is Strength. $10.00 to $15.00.
25. Liberty Cap with Cannon and Flags. $15.00 to $20.00.

PLATE 89

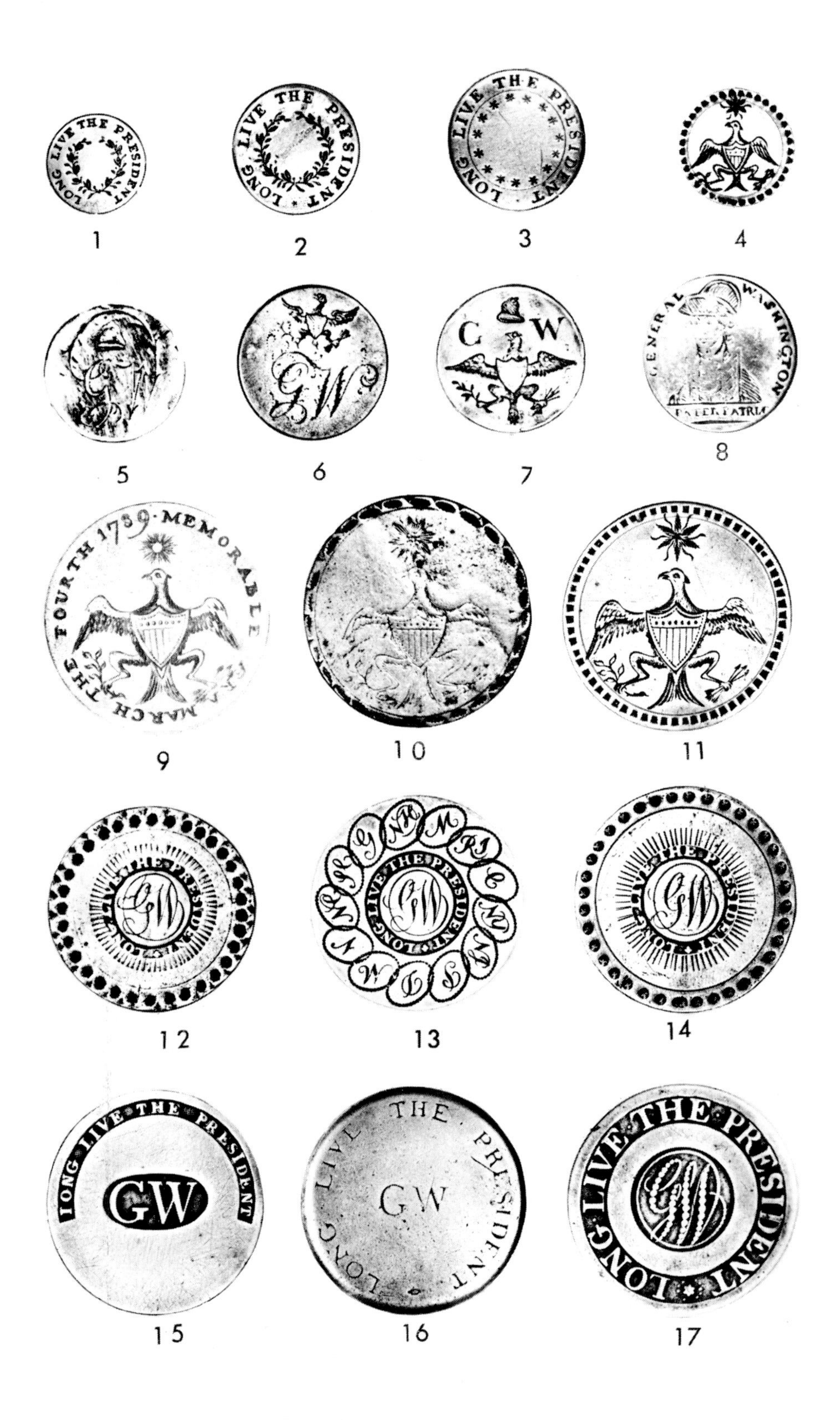

1 2 3 4 5 6 7 8 9 10 11 12 13 14 15 16 17

PLATE 89

WASHINGTON INAUGURAL BUTTONS

The George Washington inaugural buttons are prized highly by collectors as their historical interest gives them special appeal. The pictures shown here were loaned to us by Alphaeus H. Albert, and were photographed by him. The buttons are from Mr. Albert's collection and from the collection of J. Harold Cobb.

The value of these buttons is relative. The condition of the metal, the size and the engraving is of course pertinent. The availability is also a factor, but the pocketbook of the collector and his desire for ownership may cause the greatest variation in price. Some have brought prices that ran into three figures.

The Commemorative button, not shown here, was made for the Centennial of the inauguration in 1889. It is a bronze button, resembling the "G.W." with Linked States border, but is much thicker than the early button. It was made from a die, cut especially for the Centennial and is not a reproduction but collectable as a Commemorative.

1. The Laurel Wreath.
2. The Laurel Wreath with Star.
3. The Fifteenth Star. (Also 15 mm.)
4. The Small Eagle with Star.
5. The "GW" with Liberty Cap.
6. The "GW" with Eagle.
7. The "GW" with Eagle and Liberty Cap.
8. The Pater Patriae.
9. The Eagle with Date.
10. The Eagle with Star of Eight Points. (Also with borders of 21 and 24 punch marks.)
11. The Eagle with Star. (Also with borders of 49, 54 and 72 punch marks.)
12. The "GW" with Indentee Border. (Also with borders of 31 and 32 punch marks.)
13. The "GW" with Linked States Border.
14. The "GW" with Cross in Circle Border.
15. The "GW" in Oval Center. (Also with medium and wide spacing between the G.W.)
16. The Plain Roman "GW".
17. The Dotted Script "GW".

All buttons are one-piece, yellow metal and shown actual size.

PLATE 90

1
2
3
4
5
6
7
8
9
10
11
13
14
15
16
17
18
19
20
21
22
23
24
25
26
27
28
29
30
31

PLATE 90

UNIFORM BUTTONS OF THE UNITED STATES

1. General Service, Revolutionary War; pewter. $100 - $200.
2. 1st Battalion Pennsylvania, Continental Army; pewter. $200 - $250.
3. 5th Connecticut Regiment, Revolutionary War; pewter. $150 - $200.
4. 6th Massachusetts Regiment, Revolutionary War; pewter. $150 - $200.
5. Artillery, Revolutionary War; wood back with catgut shank. $100 - $200.
6. Infantry 6th Regiment, 1798-1802; pewter. $25 - $35.
7. General Service, 1808-1821; pewter. $10 - $15.
8. Infantry 16th Regiment, Officer; 1812-1815; plated one-piece. $50 - $65.
9. Artillery, 1808-1811; one-piece. $15 - $20.
10. Artillery 2nd Regiment, 1813-14; one-piece. $15 - $20.
11. Light Artillery 1st Regiment, 1808-1814; one-piece. $25 - $35.
12. Light Dragoons, 1808-1816; Pewter. $45 - $60.
13. Regiment of Riflemen, 1808-1811; one-piece. $45 - $60.
14. Riflemen 2nd Regiment, 1814-1815; one - piece. $35 - $45.
15. Voltigeurs, 1847-48; two-piece. $35 - $40.
16. Officer, Civil War; staff. $3 - $5.
17. General Service, 1854-1870; two-piece. $1.
18. Artillery, Officers, 1821-1902; two-piece. (Also C for Cavalry, D for Dragoons, I for Infantry, R for Riflemen.) $2 - $3.
19. Topographical Engineers, 1831-1863; two - piece. $15 - $20.
20. Ordinance Corps., 1833-1902; two-piece. $3. - $5.
21. Navy, head of eagle to left prior to 1941; two-piece. $1.00.
22. Marine Corps; two-piece. $1.00.
23. Corps of Engineers; two-piece. $1 - $5.
24. Army General Service, since 1902; two-piece. $1.00.
25. Air Force, since 1947; plated two-piece. $1.00.

CONFEDERATE BUTTONS

26. Officer, 1861-1865; two-piece. $100 - $125.
27. Army General Service, 1861-1865; two-piece. $12 - $15.
28. Infantry, 1861-1865; two-piece. (Also A for Artillery, C for Cavalry, R for Riflemen.) $20 - $25.
29. Engineers, 1861 - 1865; two-piece. $35 - $45.
30. Navy, 1861-1865; two-piece. $50 - $65.

These buttons are from the collection of Alphaeus H. Albert and were photographed and described by him. These relative values are based mainly on the condition and rarity of the buttons.

PLATE 91

1
2
3
4
5
6
7
8
9
10
11
12
MAIN BUILDING
1876
13
14
15
16
17
18
19
20
21
22
23
24
25

PLATE 91

STUDS, ASSORTED

A stud is an ornamental fastener, usually inserted through two button holes in a shirt front. Some were used in men's cuffs and during the Victorian Era when china painting was considered a genteel art for ladies, many china studs were decorated with hand painted roses and other flowers, given touches of gold and used to fasten and adorn the shirtwaists worn at that time.

1. Silvered brass, a CHERUB riding an initial C; the center is convex and letter and figure are in relief. $1.75.
2. Silvered brass with a BROWNIE in relief. $1.00.
3. Silvered brass PAN WITH PIPES; Pan's goat legs can be noted here. $2.00.
4. Gold filled PADLOCK with black background and gold filled border. $1.25.
5. LONG LEGGED BIRD of silvered brass. $1.75.
6. MASONIC SQUARE AND COMPASS, gold filled. $2.50.
7. ARTIST'S PALETTE and brushes, palette engraved, tinted gold. $2.00.
8. BICYCLE, an advertisement of The Ames Mfg., Co., Chicopee, Mass. $2.00.
9. Porcelain painted DOG HEAD; gold rim and special feature which releases back. $2.00.
10. HOUND DOG; copper with silver and gold finish. $2.50.
11. Black glass cameo-like head of MINERVA with gold filled rim and patented device for fastening. $2.00.
12. Black glass intaglio head of WARRIOR with gold rim. $2.50.
13. "MAIN BUILDING 1876"; the Centennial Exposition opened in Philadelphia, May 10th, 1876; this stud is gold filled. $12.50.
14. A floral arrangement of metal foil, under glass, gold rim. $2.00.
15. Gilded HORSE'S HEAD, under glass, gold filled rim. $2.50.
16. Carved pearl, representing a MAN'S CUFF. $2.00.
17. Champleve enamel CHARIOTEER; light blue background with black horse, chariot and man done in shades of red, blue, green, flesh and yellow. $3.50.
18. Red composition COMIC HEAD with green glass eyes. $2.50.
19. Champleve enameled BASKET and foreground, flowers hand painted on white enameled background, then fired. Unusual. $5.50.
20. Gold CROSS with black enameled decoration. Lovely. $3.50.
21. Tortoise Shell with a gold inlaid MONOGRAM and gold inlayed "Greek Key" border. $3.50.
22. Tortoise shell with pierced and engraved silver, showing the Main Building at the 1876 CENTENNIAL EXHIBITION. Philadelphia engraved at the bottom. $15.00.
23. Silver CASTLE inlaid in tortoise shell. $5.00.
24. Tortoise shell with inlay of pierced silver leaves, pearl grapes and gold wire tendrils. $8.00.
25. Tortoise shell with engraved design of gold and iridescent pearl, inlaid. $4.00.

PLATE 92

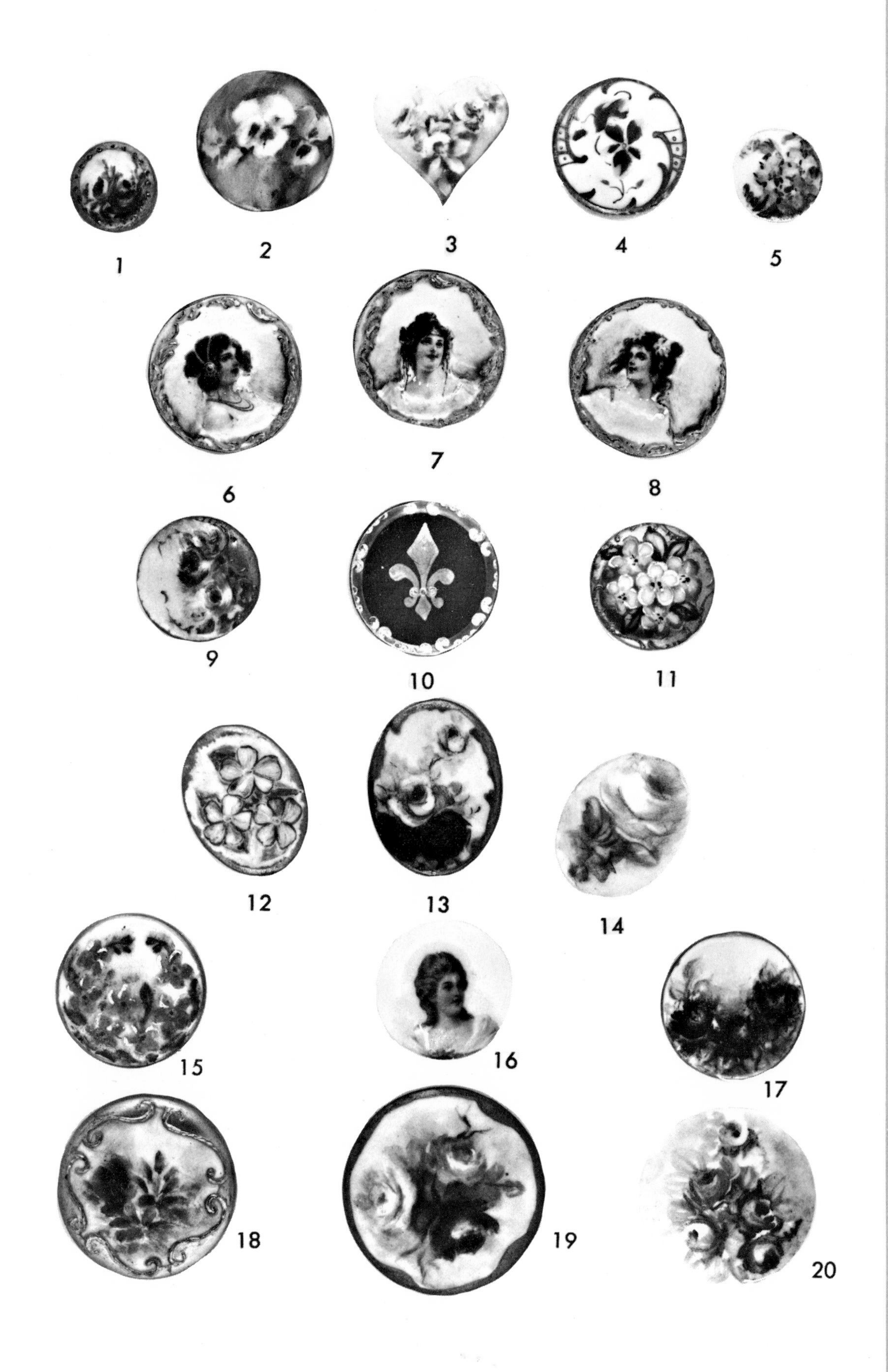

PLATE 92

CHINA STUDS

China painting was considered a "nice" pastime, and in fact, a cultural accomplishment for young ladies during the years which marked the turn of the century (1880-1905). It was something refined and interesting to do during the years between childhood and matrimony. If a young lady did not marry, the supply of hand-painted china grew and grew while her art served as a means of sublimation.

This type of decoration is called "overglaze painting". The painting is done on a glazed surface of porcelain and when fired, the painting strikes into the glaze and is quite permanent.

Victorian ladies who pursued this fad usually "sent away" the painted pieces to be fired, although portable kilns were available. Kits with paints, brushes, all necessary supplies and instructions could be purchased but many young ladies took china painting lessons at a "studio". Lessons were also given by mail.

One could procure various "helps", such as "studies", "stencils", and "transfers". The stencils formed an outline and the transfers could be applied, fired and then "touched up".

When young women began to take jobs outside the home, the art of china painting declined and at the same time, china factories began mass production of china ware. However, many lovely pieces of this Victorian art remain and among them, china studs and brooches are outstanding. Only studs, which served as fasteners, are shown here but hand painted brooches were very similar, having a gold or gilt backing with about six prongs which held the ceramic disk.

1. A very small stud with pink roses, green leaves and a gilt encrusted border. $1.00.

2. A tinted background with yellow pansies and narrow gilt rim. $2.50.

3. This heart shape is especially attractive. Pink roses, green leaves, gold rim. $3.50.

4. Here we see a blue and purple violet and the inevitable gold border is replaced by silver. At first glance this one looks like an enamel. $2.50.

5. A yellow background with blue violets. $.75.

6., 7. and 8. These three are Portrait paintings. Backgrounds are light green, portraits polychrome; borders gold, scroll design encrusted. $5.00 each.

9. More pink roses with an added scallop of gold which might represent a container. $2.00.

10. A cobalt blue background with gold Fleur - de - lis and border. $3.00.

11. The center of this one is completely filled with blue Forget-me-nots and green leaves, gold encrusted border. $2.00.

12. An oval shape with pink flowers, green leaves, gold border. $2.50.

13. Both light pink and deep red roses, a few light blue flowers, green leaves, and nicely shaded background, gold border. $3.50.

14. A green background with a very light pink rose and green leaves. $2.50.

15. Blue forget-me-nots, green leaves and touches of yellow, pink and white, the background left white, except for the slight color given from the paint when the piece was fired. Gold rim. $2.50.

16. Another lovely portrait, polychrome with background untinted. $5.00.

17. Three deep red roses, green leaves, gold rim. $2.50.

18. Blue violets, green leaves, wide gold border with encrusted scroll. $4.50.

19. Large and lovely, pink, yellow and red roses, tinted background, gold rim. $5.00.

20. Pink roses and very light green leaves with only a touch of blue used here. $3.00.

PLATE 93

1
2
3
4
5
6
7
8
9
10
11
12
13
14
15
16
17
18
19
20
21
22
23
24
25
26
27
28
29
30
31
32
33
34
35
36
37
38
39
40

PLATE 93

BUCKLES, HANDS & FANS

PICTORIAL OBJECTS

These three PICTORIALS are favorites with most collectors. Many more than we have shown can be found and the variety is amazing, especially in BUCKLES. Prices in all three categories are comparable to those shown here.

Fans have been in use since very early times. Some authorities say that in China they were known since about 3000 B.C., the earliest being of dyed pheasant or peacock feathers, mounted on a handle. It was during the 18th century that the fan was most elaborately designed and ornamented.

There are two main groups of fans; the screen fan which has a handle and a rigid mount, and the folding fan. Many examples of each type have been used as a motif by button designers and we find the styles reproduced in minute detail.

Hands shown on buttons are very dainty and graceful. Often they hold flowers but many times, a fan. An arrangement of HANDS combined with FANS is very attractive.

1. Molded black glass, the BUCKLE shaped like a horseshoe. $1.00.
2. Black glass with iridescent luster, molded. $1.00.
3. Molded black glass with gold luster. $.50.
4. Black glass silver lustered. $.50.
5. Molded black glass. $.75.
6. A brass BUCKLE with two straps inserted; tinted background. $.75.
7. Small pierced design of BUCKLE only, circled by cut steels. $.75.
8. Oblong brass BUCKLE with one prong and strap curving, over and under. Two-piece brass, buckle and strap in relief with red tinted background. $.50.
9. The same design as No. 7, with a different treatment pierced with cut steel trim. $.75.

10. and 11. The same button in two sizes; one-piece brass showing an engraved BUCKLE and strap on one side, a lovely pierced design on the other. $.50 and $.75.

12. RIGHT HAND HOLDING FLOWER, ruffle at wrist, brass superimposed on a darkened background, tin rim and saw-tooth border. Two-piece. $4.50.
13. A design similar to No.12, HAND of white metal, rim of brass with floral decoration. $1.00.
14. HAND, with cuff and bracelet at the center of a black, pressed horn sew-thru. $.75.

15. and 16. RIGHT HAND HOLDING FLOWERS, two-piece pressed brass with design in high relief on concave tinted background. $3.50 for large. $1.00 for small.

17. RIGHT HAND HOLDING TORCH, possibly representing the hand and torch of the Statue of Liberty. The right arm of the statue arrived nine years in advance of the rest of this gift from France and was exhibited at the Philadelphia Centennial in 1876. This design may have been inspired by this exhibit. Brass superimposed on darkened background. $1.00.
18. RIGHT HAND, GLOVED, HOLDING FLOWER SPRAY. The design is an escutcheon, attached to the brass shank, silvered background, flowers have cut steel centers. Backmarked, "Muster". $2.50.
19. A small steel button with brass RIGHT HAND HOLDING BALL, which is a cut steel; cut steels also form the cuff. This is an escutcheon design and the "ball" is set in a circle of brass and attached to the thumb and finger of the hand, making the entire design movable and attached only to the shank. $.75.
20. Dull black glass, LEFT HAND HOLDING FLOWERS. Back-marked, "Copy'd". $1.00.
21. LEFT HAND WEARING WEDDING RING AND HOLDING CHERRIES, which are cut steels. This is a pierced design, attached to the rim; brass with concave brass background T.W. & W. back-mark. $1.00.
22. An escutcheon formed by a brass RIGHT HAND, HOLDING FLOWERS and a shiny circle of tin. Background of pearl. $1.00.
23. A pink dyed pearl with brass HAND AND FLOWER escutcheon. $1.00.
24. Two-piece pressed brass with floral design and RIGHT HAND. $.75.
25. "EXCALIBUR", the sword of King Arthur. Pierced brass over tinted background, tin rim. $1.00.
26. FOLDING FAN of white metal, inlaid in composition. $.75.
27. Tiny FAN of pressed tin, two-piece. $.50.
28. One-piece brass background, trimmed with cut steel, steel trimmed and pierced FAN, applied. $1.50.
29. Japanned brass, concave with white metal FAN and one cut steel. $.75.
30. Composition with small folding FAN. $.25.
31. Brown-tinted brass background with a pierced design of flowers and fan attached to the border, lustered glass inserted to represent PALM LEAF FAN. $.75.
32. Black glass FAN, gold lustered. $.50.
33. HAND AND FAN, the fan pierced showing a tin liner brass. $.75.
34. Molded black glass design of Madame Chrysantheme, holding FAN. $1.00.
35. The same design as No. 28 but made of white metal. $.75.
36. Pierced brass FAN superimposed on flat steel background. $.75.
37. Lovely white metal FAN on wood background with scalloped tin border and brass rim. $6.50.

38. and 39. Slightly different FANS, etched on lacquered brass, convex. $.75 each.

40. The same FAN as No. 28 but here applied to pierced brass circle and set in a steel border. $6.50.

PLATE 94

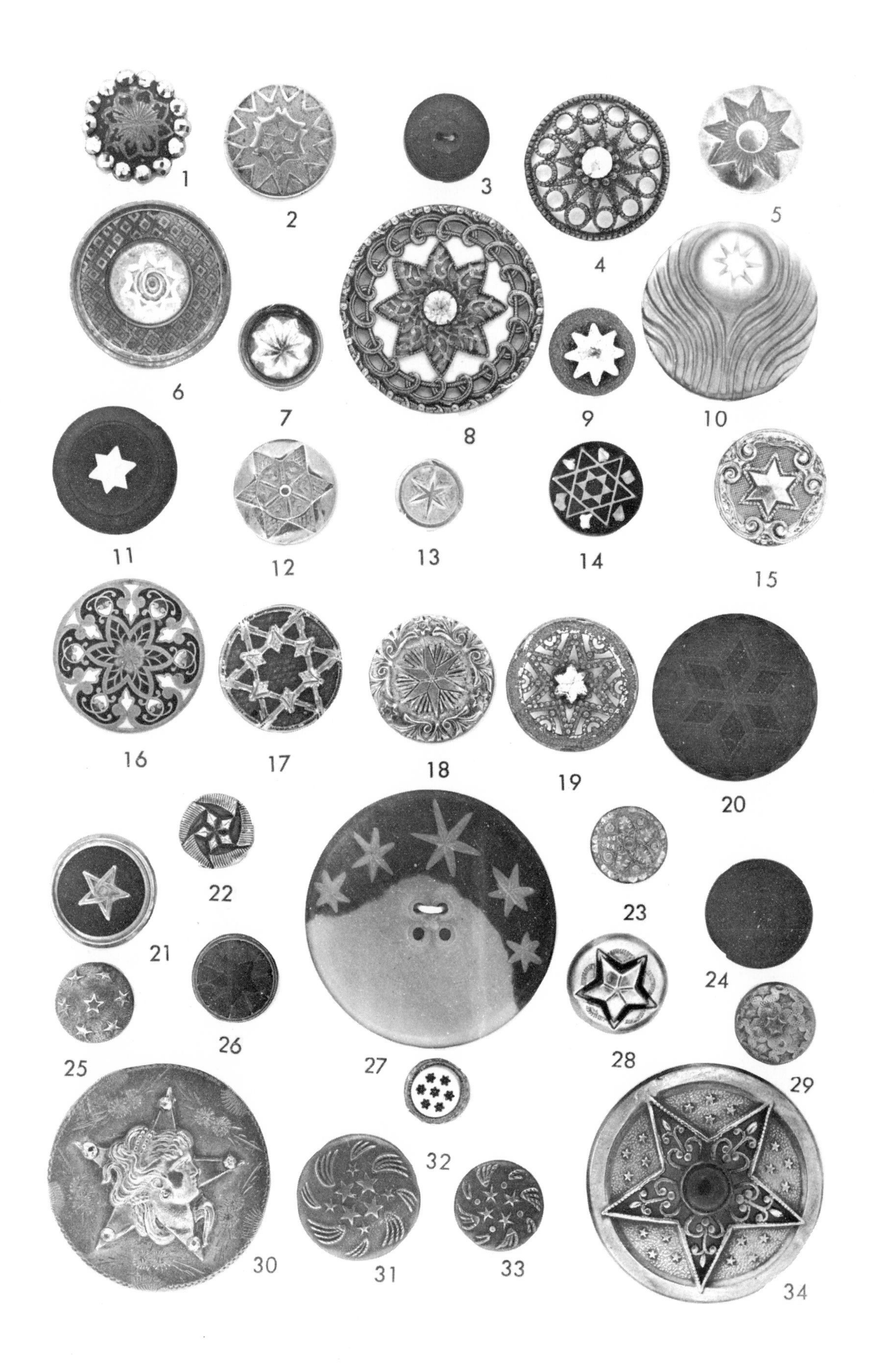
1
2
3
4
5
6
7
8
9
10
11
12
13
14
15
16
17
18
19
20
21
22
23
24
25
26
27
28
29
30
31
32
33
34

PLATE 94

STARS

Star designs, popular with button collectors, are classed as PICTORIAL OBJECTS. Special interest seems to center around the symbolism which has been attached to stars through the centuries. The star motif has been used in many different ways to decorate buttons, all are most attractive and sufficient variety can be found to create a display in any manner that has individual appeal.

1. Red lacquered brass with eight-point, engraved star; riveted cut steel border; one-piece. $.75.
2. A one-piece, "Early Gilt" with a twelve-point star; back-marked, "Extra Rich, Orange Color". $1.25.
3. Goodyear Rubber sew-thru with twelve point star. $1.00.
4. One-piece pressed brass with cut steel center and twelve point star. $.75.
5. One-piece brass "Early Gilt" with eight point star; back-marked, "Rich Gold Color". $1.25.
6. A low drum button with straight brass sides. The center is glass with an eight-point star, having swirled center, molded on the reverse. The glass is backed by gold foil set in a thin circle of tinned copper. $1.25.
7. A small Drum with "Glory" center, eight points. $1.00.
8. An eight-point, brass, filigree star with clear glass "jeweled" center, superimposed on an ivory-centered, celluloid background; ornate border. $2.00.
9. A concave brass, one-piece button with escutcheon type, eight-point star of steel. $.50.
10. A carved pearl, pierced to form an eight-point star. $2.50.
11. Pressed and dyed black horn with an eight-point, carved star escutcheon. $1.00.
12. A six-point star decorating a one-piece brass "Golden Age" button, back-marked; "Rich Orange". $1.25.
13. This six-point star is in relief on a "Jacksonian" button; one-piece brass with applied rim. "Jacksonians" are described elsewhere in this book. $4.00.
14. A pressed horn button with pearl chips and silver stars inlaid. The outer, six-point star is called, "The Star of David". $1.75.
15. A two-piece brass button with original bright blue tint; the six-point star is superimposed on a pebbled disk that is held in place by a bright tin circle, partly covered by the scroll border. $.75.
16. A Champleve enamel, done in green, white, red, and two shades of blue; star center. $8.00.
17. A two-piece button with background of coarsely woven fabric; the design is a pierced brass "Star of David" attached to the rim. $1.25.
18. Six-point Blazing Star, two-piece pressed brass, gilded. $1.00.
19. A one-piece pierced brass button with six-point star design and a cut steel star ornamenting the center, engraved border. $1.00.
20. Rubber with molded six-point star. Back-marked, "Goodyear's N.R. Co., Pat. May 6, 1851". $1.50.
21. This is a hard, black rubber button with five-point, gold-filled star and rim applied; a specimen from the Hammond Turner & Son's pattern books. Rare. $2.50.
22. Pressed tin five-point star with bright tinted background. $.35.
23. Two-piece pierced brass showing a five-point star. $.50.
24. Goodyear Rubber with nine five-point stars. $1.00.
25. Convex two-piece brass with seven five-point stars in relief. $.50.
26. Concave brass, pierced in a five-point star design over a velvet background. $.50.
27. Natural Horn sew-thru with five carved, five-point stars. $2.00.
28. Tinned brass, convex with pierced, five-point star design showing a shining gold colored background. $.50.
29. This button is very similar to No. 25 but the stars are depressed instead of in relief. $.50.
30. ASTRAEA, the head centered in a five-point star with cut steel trim. Astraea was the Greek goddess of justice, living on earth during the Golden Age but taken up to heaven because of the earth's increasing wickedness. Here she was placed among the stars as the constellation Virgo. She is often represented with the scales of justice and a crown of stars. The chased design on the background of this uncommon button forms the shape of a star. $7.50.

31. and 33. Two-piece pressed brass buttons with COMET designs, probably made to commemorate Halley's comet when it appeared in 1910. $.75 and $.50.

32. An early Victorian Waistcoat Jewel type. Opaque, milk-white glass with seven five-point stars forming the design; set in gilt border. $.75.

34. "Gay 90's Jewel". Buttons called by this name were ladies' coat buttons (1880-1890). This one is of brass with pierced design of a five-point star, centered by a cobalt blue "jewel". Four stars also form a design between the points of the large star. $3.00.

For Star Symbolism see "Just Buttons", May 1958 as told by Edith Fairman.

PLATE 95

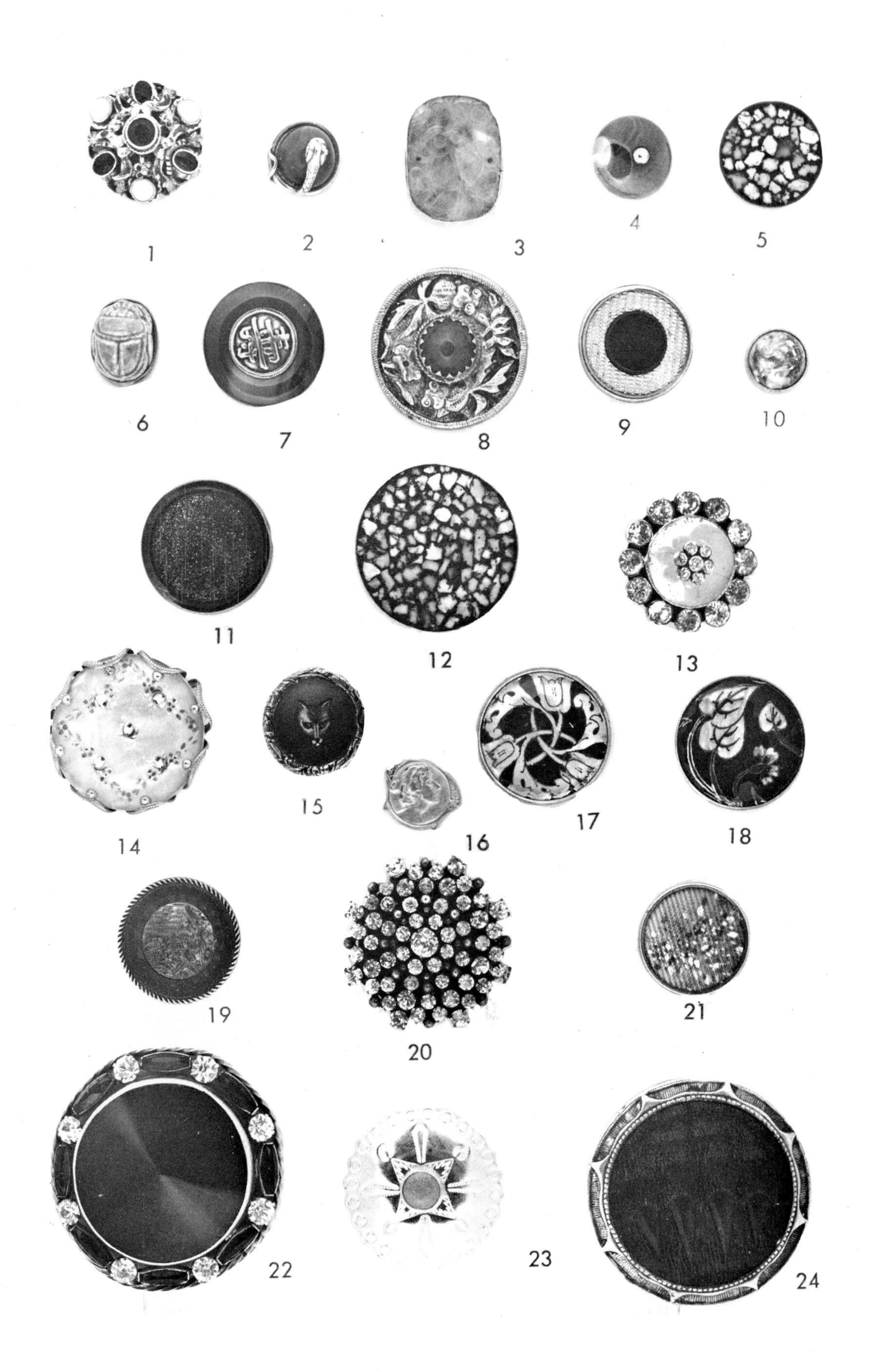

PLATE 95

JEWEL TYPES

1. Hand wrought silver with enameling, set with garnets and turquoise. early Austrian. $15.00.

2. Coral ball with solid gold serpent twisted around coral, gold shank. $15.00.

3. Green jade mounted in gold, with carving of a goldfish, typical of oriental design. $12.00.

4. Agate waistcoat button with silver pin shank. $2.00.

5. Bits of turquoise cemented together, mounted in silver, then polished till smooth. From Iran. Small size. $2.00.

6. Ceramic Scarab. Copper tinted rim and back. $5.00.

7. Chinese Carnelian. Oriental characters on silver center, pin shank. $4.00.

8. Chinese Carnelian, mounted in silver, the button is designed to resemble a goldfish pool with a lotus blossom holding the Carnelian. $10.00.

9. A carnelian set in brass, coat button size, made for the Far Eastern trade about 1890. $3.50.

10. Pink opaque glass with goldstone and white swirls, mounted in brass. $1.50.

11. "Gold stone" mounted in a tinted brass Drum. Early Victorian. $3.00.

12. The same as No. 5 except larger. $8.50.

13. An opalescent center set in silver with paste border and center decoration. 18th century. $15.00.

14. A square wreath of roses and center rosebud are painted on the reverse of the glass, backed by iridescent pearl and set in a gilded, scalloped brass border. $15.00.

15. FOX HEAD painted in color on the reverse of the glass, gold filled rim, fine detail. $8.50.

16. A solid gold button of an odd shape, showing the profile of a lady. The border is set with tiny diamonds. $15.00.

17. and 18. Reverse paintings on faceted glass. The designs are painted in pastel colors, outlined in gold and backed by iridescent pearl. $10.00 each.

19. Iridescent Tiffany-type, lustered glass, molded showing a mill scene. Tinted brass mounting. $3.00.

20. Early paste with an elaborate silver mounting which makes an unusual shape. $7.50.

21. Blue milk glass with darker blue and white flecks, set in gilt rim. $2.50.

22. Dark amythest glass center with a border of paste and oblong amythest, faceted glass; gilded brass rim. $10.50.

23. Indian silver with turquoise center. $4.00.

24. Black glass bear paw mounted in pressed brass rim. $6.50.

PLATE 96

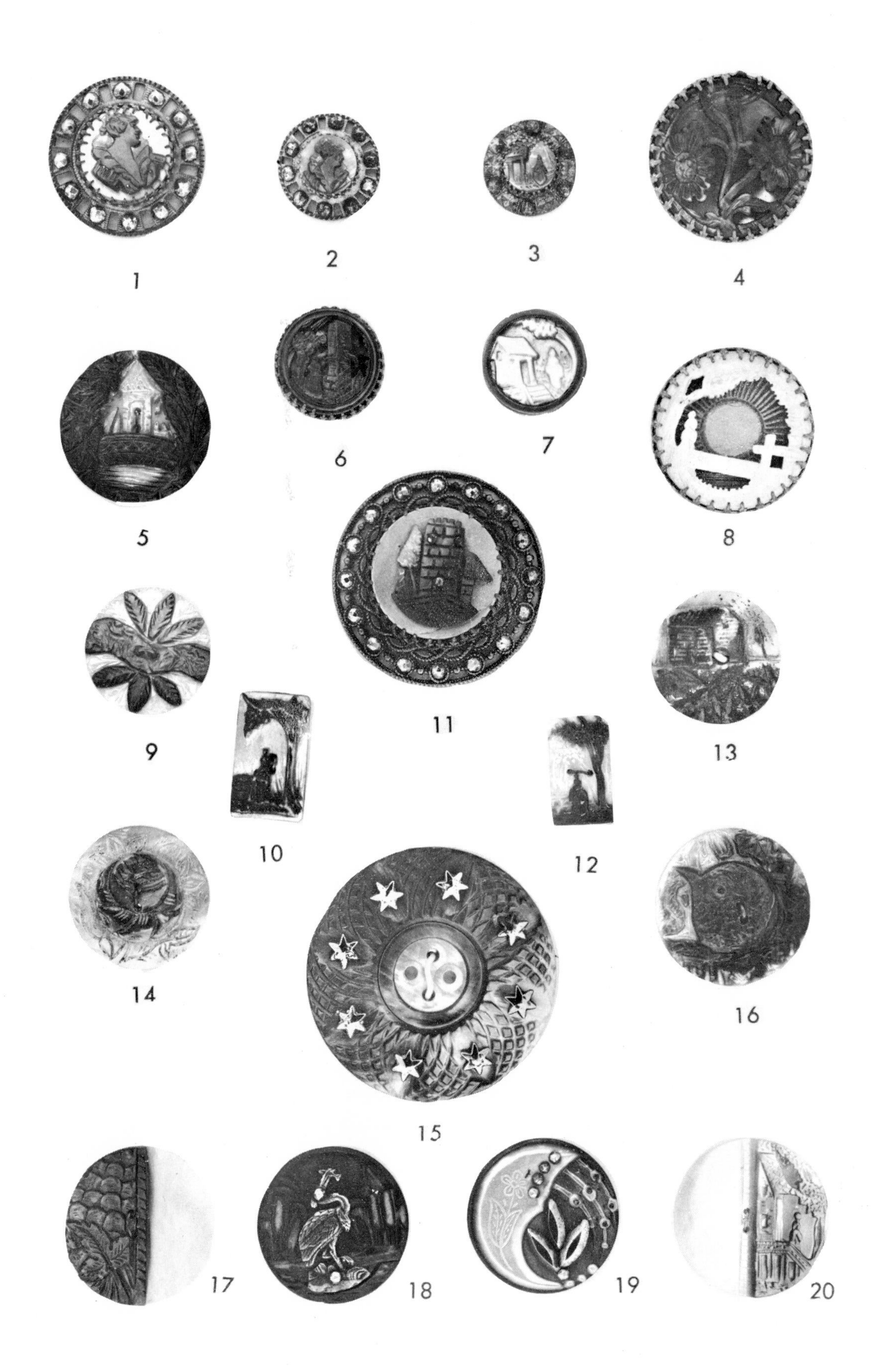

PLATE 96

PEARL BUTTONS

Pearl and shell buttons are available in great variety and form an interesting classification for research and specialization. The N.B.B. for September and October, 1965 gives valuable information. We have tried in three Plates shown here to illustrate as many different types as possible. Carved pearls are highly prized by collectors but many others have special beauty and interest.

1. CAMEO CUT HEAD in a Tiffany setting with pierced, white metal border, set with cut steels. Cameo cut pearl and shell buttons are made from material having layers of different color, so that when the design is cut out, there is a color contrast between background and design. Value of No. 1, $15.00.
2. The same as No. 1, in a small size. $6.50.
3. A cameo cut LADY IN FRONT OF TEMPLE, Tiffany set, with white metal border having cut steel trim. $6.50.
4. This has an overlaying of dark pearl, with a green iridescence, which has been carved and pierced in a FLORAL DESIGN and is placed in a Tiffany setting over light iridescent pearl; metal back. $12.00.
5. Cameo cut and carved TREES, BRIDGE AND WATER, showing carved and pierced white building in the background, green iridescence in the top layer; a two-hole sew-thru. $15.00.
6. LADY AT PUMP. This as well as No. 4 is a fine illustration of overlaying, as the pierced and carved design extends completely over the underlying pearl, which is of contrasting iridescent green and shows through the piercing of the overlay; in a Tiffany setting of white metal. $8.00.
7. LADY AND SMALL BUILDING, carved pearl with brass back and rim. $5.00.
8. Overlaying and carving combine here to make this a most interesting specimen. RISING SUN with face, brightly iridescent and rays deeply carved, behind a frame of trees, carved and pierced from contrasting pearl, with lady and fence in the foreground. The overlaid portion is held in place by a Tiffany setting. From the collection of Gladys Coleman. $18.00.
9. Cameo cut and carved, BRANCH AND LEAVES. $2.50.
10. LADY STANDING UNDER TREE, cameo carved of volute shell; rectangular shape; two-hole sew-thru. $8.00.
11. CASTLE TURRET, TREE AND LADY, cameo-cut and carved, fastened with three rivets to a white pearl disk, which is in a claw setting, with attached, pierced border of brass, decorated with cut steels. $15.00.
12. LADY UNDER TREE, similar to No. 10, but without the pink iridescence of the first button. A two-hole sew-thru. $6.50.
13. Carved, two-hole sew-thru, showing BUILDING with path; the dark portion has a green iridescence. $6.50.
14. Two-hole sew-thru, iridescent pearl with CARVED ROSE, engraving touched with gold. $7.50.
15. Large, conventional, iridescent pearl, four-hole sew-thru, carved and decorated with cut steel stars. $3.00.
16. Two-hole sew-thru, carved HEAD OF BIRD, with glass eye. $12.50.
17. Two-hole sew-thru, carved with LEAF design on one side only. $6.00.
18. Engraved design cattails and grasses on volute shell, which has a lovely rosy color; a silver, gilded CRANE WITH FISH IN MOUTH, applied with two cut steel rivets. $15.00.
19. An overlay of white pearl with etched floral design on a carved background, decorated also with cut steels. $5.00.
20. Carved and pierced design of LADY ON BALCONY, on one side only. Two-tone, two-hole sew-thru. $10.00.

PLATE 97

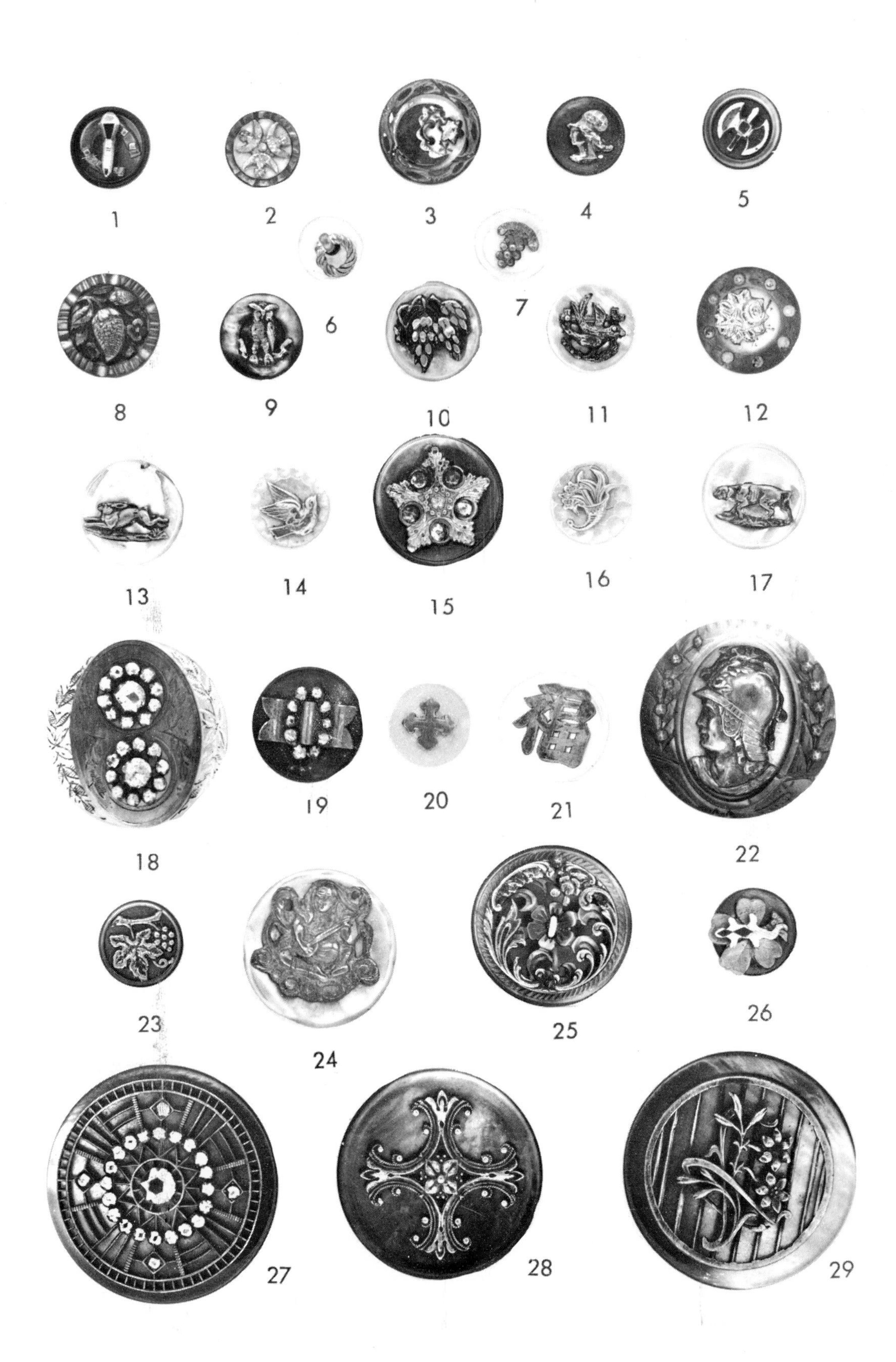

PLATE 97

PEARL WITH METAL TRIM

These buttons show pearl/shell with metal used as a face adornment and no metal rim. Most designs shown are the escutcheon type, fastened through a hole in the button to the shank. Some also have a metal plate on the back for reinforcement. Decorative designs on pearl/shell buttons are listed as, Pictorial, Non-pictorial and Plain. Pictorial designs include, Animal Life, Objects and Miscellaneous. Miscellaneous includes Buildings, People, Transportation, Symbols etc.

1. A steel HORSESHOE AND NAIL (pictorial object), superimposed on dyed pearl. $1.50.

2. A pewter design of CRESCENTS AND CROSSES on white pearl with the rim dyed blue. $.50.

3. A carved pearl with dark rim and light center, steel MOON AND STAR applied; a two-hole sew-thru. $1.00.

4. A steel head of MINERVA on smoky pearl. $1.00.

5. Steel BATTLE AX on smoky pearl, with raised rim. $.75.

6. Gilt KNOCKER on white pearl with raised rim. $.75.

7. Gilt bunch of GRAPES on white pearl with raised rim, slightly engraved. $.75.

8. Brass STRAWBERRIES, flowers and leaves, superimposed on dyed pearl, with carved rim. $1.00.

9. Pewter OWL on pearl, dyed blue. $1.00.

10. Mother-of-pearl with pewter HOPS, tinted, applied. $1.00.

11. Tinted, pewter BIRD (animal life), on light iridescent pearl. $.75.

12. A carved pearl with a FLORAL, brass escutcheon. $.75.

13. A concave pearl disk with brass RUNNING RABBIT superimposed. These buttons are found with dogs, game birds and other animals pertaining to the sport of hunting (see No. 17). They were worn on vests and coats of people belonging to hunt clubs or other sporting associations. $3.50.

14. A silvered BIRD on white metal, pebbled rim. $.75.

15. A white metal, five-point STAR, set with five cut steels, on dark pearl. $1.00.

16. Silvered CORNUCOPIA, holding flowers, on light pearl with pebbled border. $.75.

17. A brass DOG escutcheon, same description as No. 13. $1.50.

18. An oval of dark pearl with two depressed circles in which are cut steel adornments, riveted to the white pearl background by the center steel. Both parts are engraved with a LEAF design. $5.00.

19. A BUCKLE design of brass and cut steels, riveted to the pearl background which is dyed purple. $.75.

20. A brass CROSS on white pearl. $1.00.

21. CHINESE CHARACTERS of brass on white pearl with a raised rim. These characters are said to mean, "good luck and happiness". $.75.

22. A stamped, brass head of MINERVA in high relief, mounted in recessed pearl with carved pearl border in a leaf design, set with cut steel rivets. A beautiful and rare button. $15.00.

23. Brass GRAPE LEAF and grapes on smoky pearl, with raised rim. $.75.

24. ORIENTAL FIGURE with mandolin, gilded brass, pierced on concave pearl. $3.50.

25. A beautiful carved and pierced, dark pearl with brass wreath of ROSES and acanthus leaves, applied. Two cut steel rivets hold the wreath in place. The center is a flower which has two holes to sew through. $3.00.

26. LIZARD of cut steel on a silvered four-leaf clover which is superimposed on dyed, blue pearl. $1.00.

27. A dark pearl, embellished with a pierced, brass design, combined with cut steels. The geometric center design forms an eight-point STAR, outside a circle. $4.00.

28. Dark pearl with silvered CROSS applied. $4.00.

29. Another dark pearl with a pierced brass FLORAL design, applied. $4.00.

PLATE 98

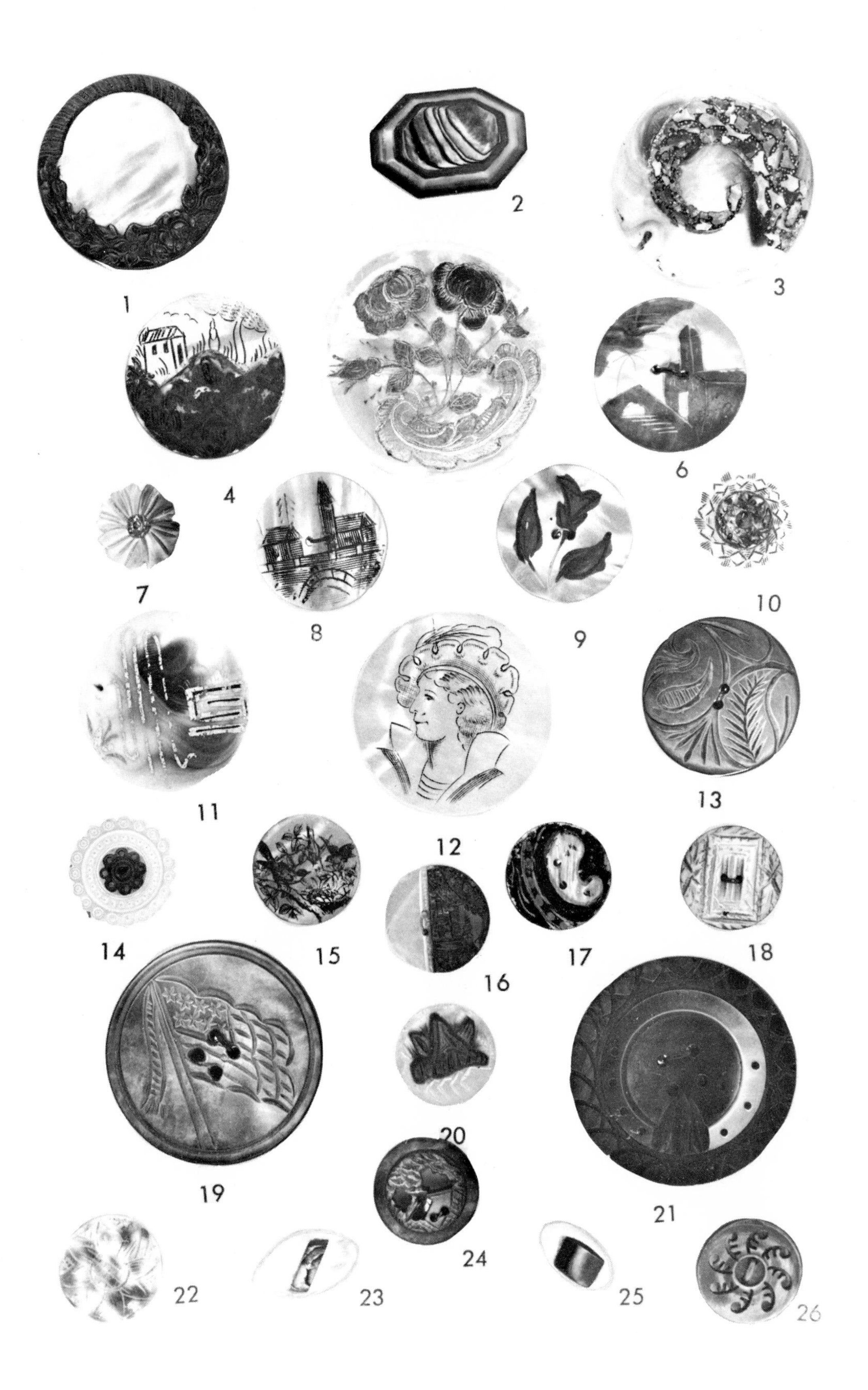

PLATE 98

PEARL & SHELL

Various methods of decoration are shown on this Plate, as well as different methods of uniting two or more materials.

1. An iridescent pearl set in an ornamental, silvered, brass rim; metal back. $2.00.

2. An eight-sided, rectangular shape, showing laminated pearl, the top layer of which is abalone. Laminating, means cementing layer upon layer of pearl/shell, usually in different colors. Sometimes instead of laminating each separate button, an entire sheet of material is laminated and buttons are cut or turned from this. Value of this, $2.00.

3. CONCH SHELL with flecks of nautilus shell applied. Rare. $7.50.

4. Carved pearl sew-thru. The SCENE in the background, on the light pearl has been engraved and the incisions filled with pigment. $12.00.

5. Slightly concave white pearl with lovely floral and scroll design, gilded. "Gilding" includes all pearl buttons decorated with, "metallic paint", gold or silver leaf or colored metal foils. $15.00.

6. This two-hole sew-thru pearl was engraved and portions of the design stained. $6.50.

7. This fancy-edged pearl is carved to resemble a FLOWER and embellished with a paste stone. $1.00.

8. Engraved abalone with the lines of the design pigmented. $3.00.

9. An abalone two-hole sew-thru with a leaf and flower design engraved, then stained. $1.25.

10. An engraved white pearl, lines pigmented and abalone inserted at the center; a "whistle" button. $1.75.

11. CONCH SHELL with gilding. Scarce. $5.00.

12. A PORTRAIT engraved on white pearl, lines filled with black pigment. This is classed as a miscellaneous pictorial design. $27.50.

13. A dark pearl, carved with a paisley design; two-hole sew-thru. $2.00.

14. A scalloped white pearl with a design produced by machining; a scalloped and pierced smoky pearl piece is inserted at the center. $1.50.

15. A design of BIRDS and foliage on iridescent pearl. This type of decoration is secured by applying a paper print to a pearl button that has been sized. The paper is dampened and removed, leaving the picture, which is later varnished. When these buttons are found the design is often not intact. $3.50.

16. Two-hole sew-thru, cameo-carved and pierced on one side, showing a house, tree, and lady on balcony. $4.50.

17. A painted pearl, showing a PAISLEY design; two-hole sew-thru. Many of these, when found have lost some of the decoration but if in good condition they make a colorful arrangement. $1.00.

18. A carved, two-hole sew-thru with a BUCKLE design. $2.00.

19. A dark pearl, four-hole sew-thru, with a carved design of the AMERICAN FLAG. $10.00.

20. An INSECT (grasshopper), cameo cut, with feet engraved. $3.00.

21. A dark pearl, four-hole sew-thru, carved with a HORSESHOE design and a border of looped semicircles. $4.00.

22. COWRIE SHELL, carved with a conventional flower design. Rare. $5.00.

23. SNAIL SHELL with abalone, inlaid. $1.00.

24. Pierced and carved, two-hole sew-thru, showing a SCENE. $2.50.

25. SNAIL SHELL with smoky pearl, laminated. $1.00.

26. A concave, dark pearl with a pierced design. $.75.

PLATE 99

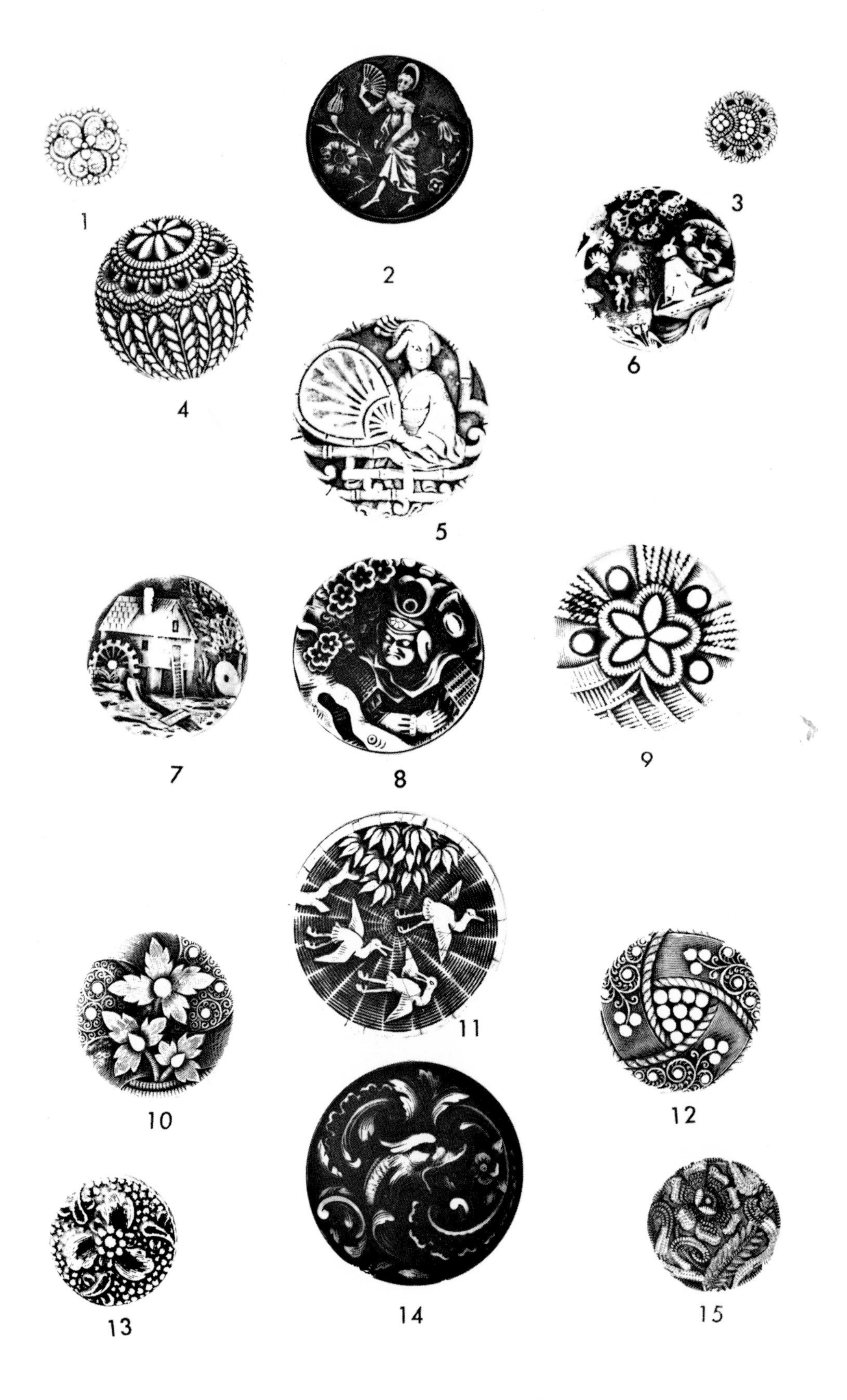

PLATE 99

SEPIA TINTED MILK GLASS

These buttons are of sepia tinted milk glass. In the glass classification of the N.B.S. the style is called Victorian and other opaque glass buttons in various colors, which usually have gold or silver decorations, come under the same heading.

Some transparent glass is made up in the same style and is also called Victorian. These of sepia tinted milk glass are unusually rare.

1. A flower form resembling a TRILLIUM, outlined by a beaded and scalloped border and accented by the sepia tint. $.50.

2. MERVEILLEUSE, a woman of the Directoire period, sometimes called a Lady Fop. Her dress is typical of this period and the button, heavily tinted, has also a floral decoration. $12.50.

3. A small button with CRESCENT AND STAR motif. $.50.

4. Many of these buttons have a surface resembling FABRIC or handwork such as crochet or tatting. This one has the appearance of a crocheted ball. $8.00.

5. MME. CHRYSANTHEME. $15.00.

6. ORIENTAL THEATER. A figure is seen performing on a stage as two oriental ladies watch from a theater box. $12.50.

7. A MILL SCENE. The tinting makes this button resemble a cameo. $12.50.

8. GENGHIS KHAN, famous conqueror of Tartary, Persia and China, 1160-1227. This same representation of Genghis Khan can be found in brass and in black glass with various lusters. $15.00.

9. A conventional FLORAL design. $8.00.

10. Another FLORAL with lacy ribbon ornamentation in the background. $9.00.

11. THREE CRANES FLYING. $15.00. This same design is common in brass.

12. Conventional design. $8.00.

13. Another FLORAL with three petals, resembling a trillium. $3.50.

14. A beautiful large sized DRAGON. $14.00.

15. A FABRIC design with floral motif. This one is also tinted with silver and pink. $5.00.

PLATE 100

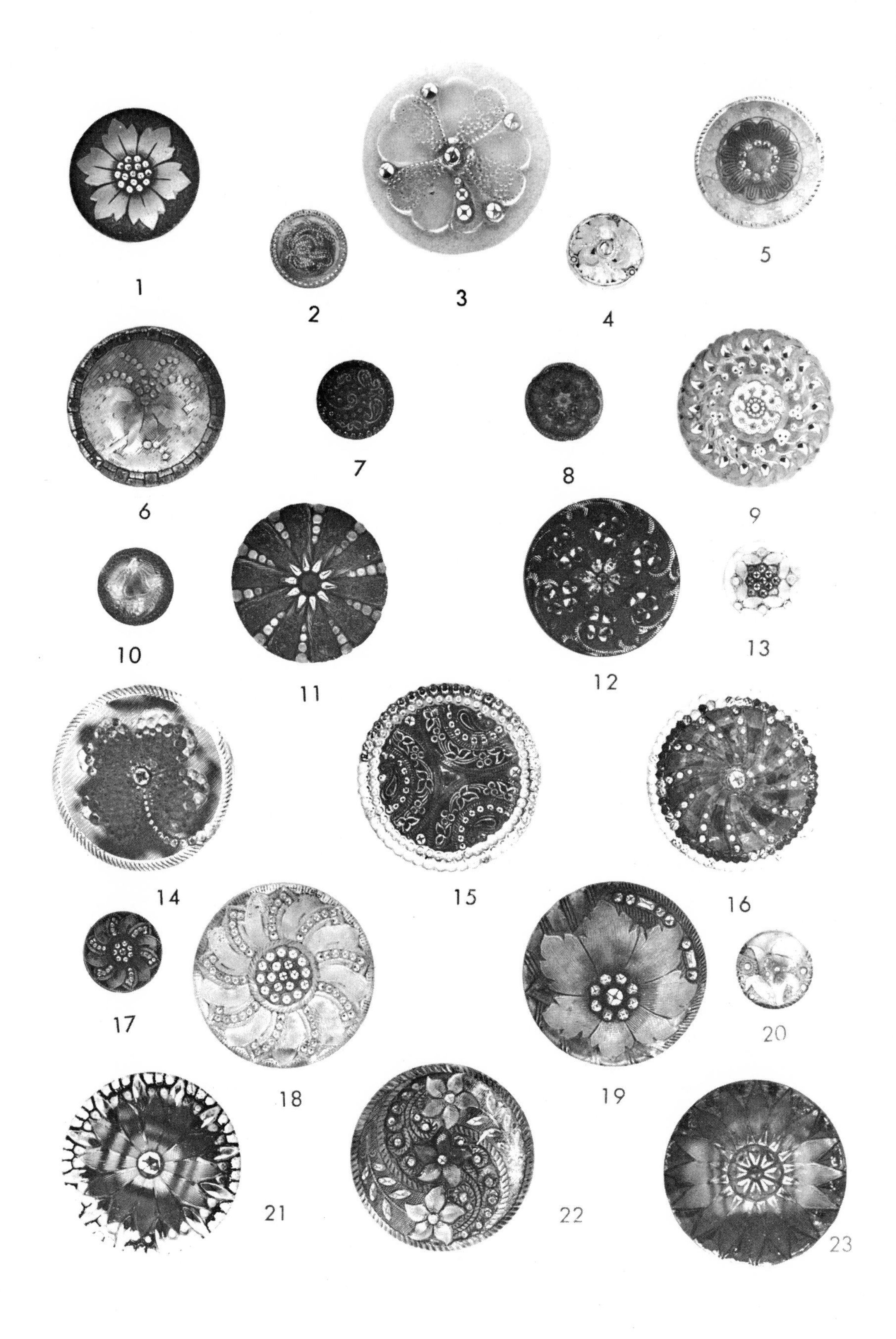

PLATE 100

LACY GLASS

In the early days of button collecting, "lacy glass" was thought to have been made at Sandwich and was called "Lacy Sandwich" by some. However, original cards were later found, that were marked, "Austria". Almost no imports were marked in this manner until after 1891 and as the Sandwich factory closed in 1888, this origin was considered a mistake.

Although they are not Sandwich glass, they still are beautiful buttons and are not plentiful in their original condition. Many collectors and dealers at one time removed the colored paint from the backs to make them look more like Sandwich glass. Now when they are found in their original state, they are very desirable.

All lacy glass buttons have lovely molded patterns on the front with often, touches of gilt or silver luster. The backs are often painted with colors, if the face is clear. Then a foil covering or darker coating of paint is added. They are found in green, red, blue and amber glass as well as clear.

1. This face is of clear glass with silver luster added to the center of the flower and some rose colored paint between the petals. The back is painted with rose color, backed with black. $8.00.

2. The top design is a flower, touched with gilt. The back, pale blue paint, backed with silver. $2.00.

3. A clear glass specimen that has had the paint stripped from the back. The petals of the molded flower design are shaped like hearts. Molded shapes between the petals and representing the stem, are silvered to simulate faceted cut steel trim. Without back paint. Value, $4.00. Painted back in original condition, $18.00.

4. A molded leaf design, backed by silver. $1.00.

5. A clear glass top backed by two shades of gold paint, lighter at the border, and this covered with black. $8.00.

6. Clear glass top with floral design; back covered with silver, then black. $12.00.

7. This small button has a molded paisley design, embellished with black paint and touches of gilt; black back. $2.00.

8. This small button has an intricate design. A rosette, gilded, is centered in a six point star with petal shapes between. The back is painted with rose color and gold. $1.00.

9. Clear glass with a gold painted back, covered by black. The gold paint gives the face the appearance of amber. The wreath which decorates the face is silver lustered. $12.00.

10. Clear glass with back painted with black, around the border only. $1.50.

11. Clear glass, slightly scalloped. The ten point star in the center and the hobnails are silvered. The back is painted a wine red, covered with black. $15.00.

12. Cobalt blue glass with silver luster touches; back painted with the same shade. $15.00.

13. Clear glass with a square center design. Molded forms, touched with silver luster, to simulate cut steels. Pale blue paint, covered with black on the back. $2.00.

14. Clear glass with a floral design which has heart-shaped petals that are filled with tiny hobnails; center and beaded stem are gilded; back is painted gold color. A rope shaped border. If perfect, $18.00.

15. Clear glass with leaf and berry wreath designs, and paisley designs that are gilded; simulated cut steels that are silvered. The back is painted green, covered by black. $15.00.

16. Clear glass, back painted with blue and gold, alternating between the silvered hobnails of the pinwheel design. Colored paint, covered with black. $12.00.

17. and 18. Two sizes in the same pattern; clear glass with a molded pin wheel design, touched with silver; back painted with gold, covered with black. Small, $2.00, Large, $18.00.

19. Amber glass top with silver luster trim that simulates cut steels. The back is painted with gold, then black. Very lovely. $18.00.

20. Clear glass, backed with blue and covered with black. $2.00.

21. and 23. Both buttons have geometric designs painted in several colors on the back, before the black was added. These colors show through the molded designs of the clear glass fronts. $18.00 each.

22. A lovely swirled floral design with back coated with silver, then black. $18.00.

PLATE 101

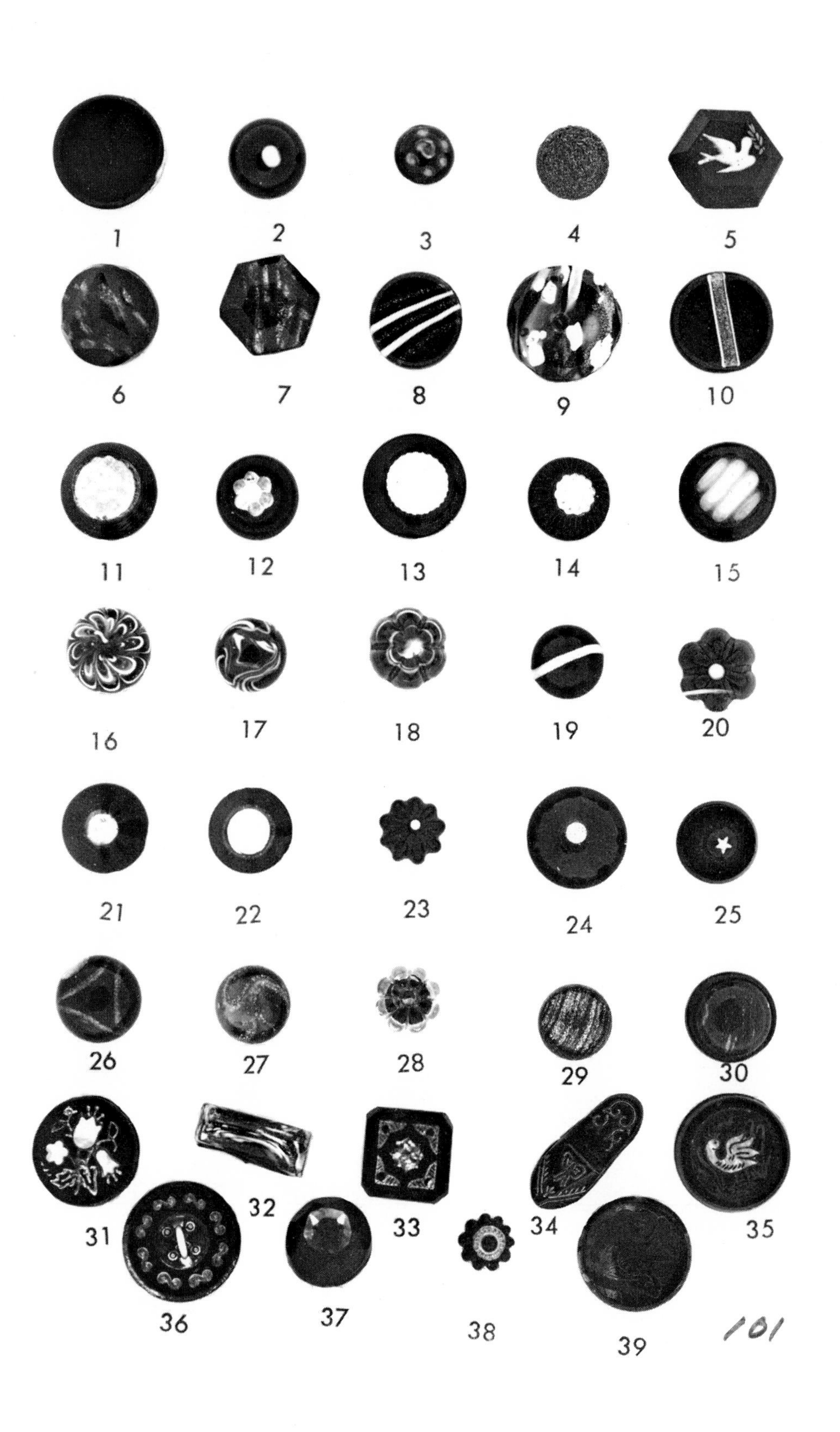
1
2
3
4
5
6
7
8
9
10
11
12
13
14
15
16
17
18
19
20
21
22
23
24
25
26
27
28
29
30
31
32
33
34
35
36
37
38
39
101

PLATE 101

BLACK GLASS

True jet is a rich black variety of lignite, a carbonized vegetable substance similar to bituminous coal. Jet was used in Britain in prehistoric times; jet beads and rings of the Bronze Age having been excavated there. The monks of Whitby abbey, on the Yorkshire coast, used jet for rosary beads and it is here at Whitby that jet was later mined and the craft of making jet ornaments flourished.

When Prince Albert, Consort of Queen Victoria died, the widowed Queen dressed herself in deep mourning which she continued to wear until her death in 1901. She made jet her favorite jewel and covered herself with masses of it. Other women of the world adopted the same fashion but since jet was quite costly, beads, buttons and other ornaments were made of black glass and substituted for jet as costume accessories.

This has led to some confusion as black glass has been called "jet" and many uninitiated button collectors are not aware of the difference. True jet buttons are extremely rare but can be identified by several tests, the simplest of which is the static electricity test. This and other simple tests have been described by Esther Woodard in the Florida State Button Bulletin for December 1966.

Many lovely black glass buttons were produced during the Victorian Era, and we illustrate examples of them on the following pages. We have tried to keep our descriptions in accord with the Black Glass Classification of the N.B.S., as prepared by Jane Ford Adams.

ROW I, OVERLAY TRIM. (1) banded, $.50. (2) dotted, $.50. (3) floral, $.75. (4) salt, $.75. (5) painted, dove of peace, $1.50. (this is also an odd geometric shape.)

ROW II, GOLDSTONE TRIM. (6) faceted top, $.75. (7) hexagon shape with goldstone trim, $.75. (8) white inlay with goldstone, $.75. (9) Hit and Miss (white, red, yellow, green, blue and goldstone; whistle type). $.75. (10) barred with goldstone and white, $1.00.

ROW III, GLASS ON GLASS BODY, (11) coronet. (13) fancy topped milk glass coronet on black glass base. (14) rayed base with clear coronet top. (15) melon top. $.75 each.

ROW IV, (16) Nailsea, loops and swirls of white and brown in overlay trim, $2.00. (17) swirls of white and brown, $.75. (18) slag, $.75. (19) barred with white, $.50. (20) a fancy contoured shape; fluted with opalescent white tip. $.75.

ROW V, (21) a cone with foil tip (clear glass tip, having foil underneath). $.75. (22) a cut-off cone with white top, circled by goldstone, $1.00. (23) low fluted, with white tip, $.75. (24) dotted foil trim, $.75. (25) star shaped foil trim, $1.50.

ROW VI, PAPERWEIGHTS, ETC. (26) ball shape with goldstone swirls and blue, green and red foil on sides, $2.00. (27) goldstone, black and yellow glass under clear glass dome, with black base, $2.00. (28) a radiant (clear glass body with black glass fused at the shank). $3.00. (29) ball with bands of green and goldstone, $2.00. (30) black glass base with top striped with goldstone, black and red. $2.00.

ROW VII, (31) pearl inlay, leaves in gold outline, $.75. (32) Hit and Miss Paperweight, log shaped with black, white and goldstone set-up under clear glass dome, black glass base, $3.00. (33) tile, $.75. (34) realistic slipper, $5.00. (35) watch crystal in black glass frame. $3.50.

ROW VIII, (36) four-hole, silver luster trim, $.50. (37) TINGUE, faceted black glass ball with top of gold foil under clear glass, centered by red glass. $27.50. (38) metal embedded trim, a fluted shape, also banded with white, $1.00. (39) wafer; thin, concave, green lustered black glass with metal backing, dragon design on face, $3.50.

Values of these buttons range from $.50 to $30.00. Many such as the Nailsea, Tingue, Radiant, Watch crystal, and Wafer have become quite scarce and therefore sell rather high.

PLATE 102

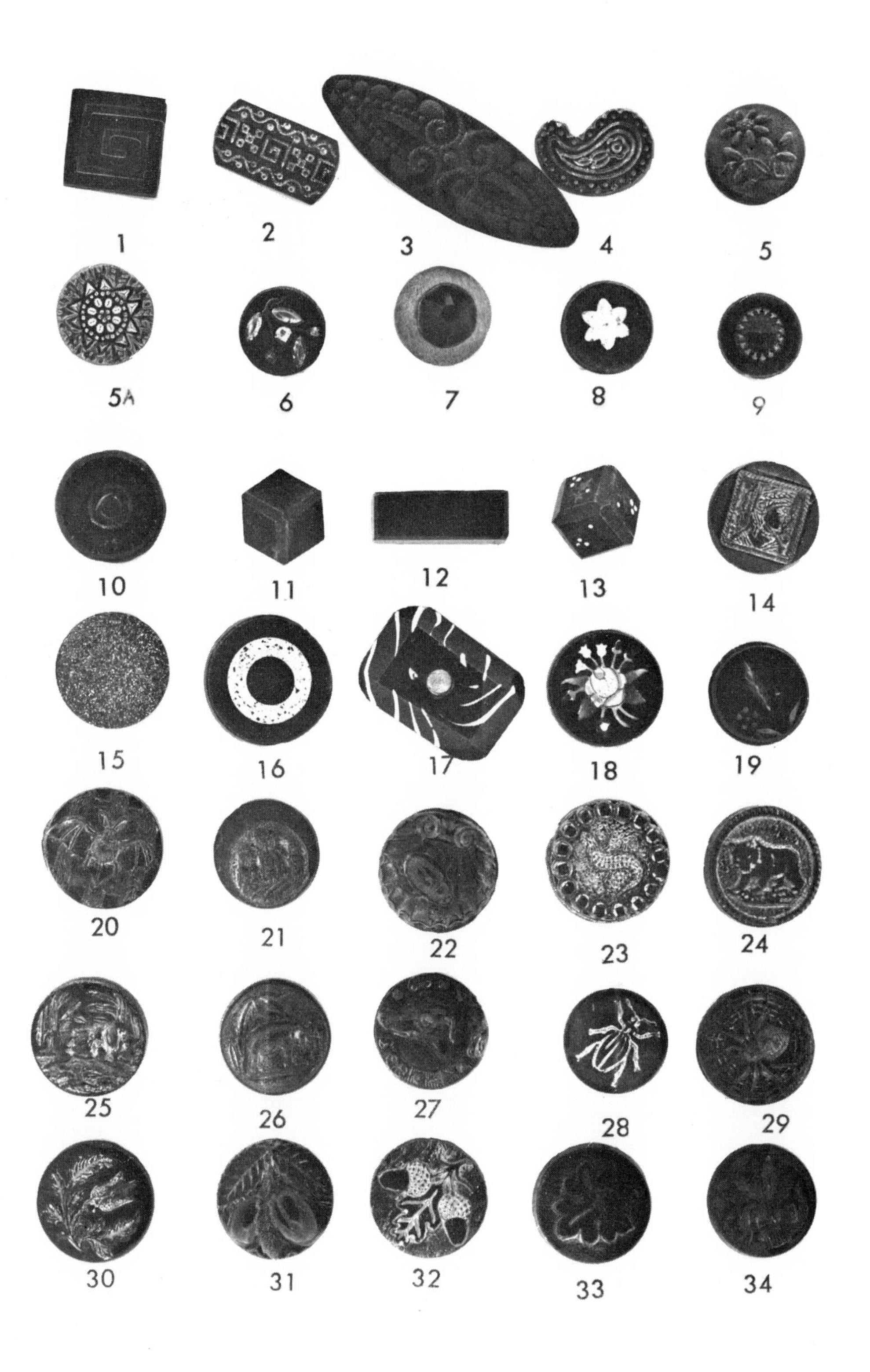

1
2
3
4
5
5A
6
7
8
9
10
11
12
13
14
15
16
17
18
19
20
21
22
23
24
25
26
27
28
29
30
31
32
33
34

PLATE 102

BLACK GLASS

1. A SQUARE SHAPE, showing the Greek key pattern. $.50.
2. RECTANGULAR SHAPE with the Greek key pattern, outlined in gold. $.35.
3. A shape called a BAR BUTTON, a molded design outlined by "cord". $1.00.
4. A PAISLEY SHAPE, design outlined with gold and red, border gold lustered. $2.00.
5. A MODIFIED BALL with floral design, iridescent luster. $.50.

5a. LACY silver-lustered center in a brass frame. $.50.

6. METAL TRIM, cut steels mechanically attached. $.50.
7. CLOTH, with faceted black glass center. $.50.
8. METAL ESCUTCHEON which is a six-point steel star, with dull background. $.50.
9. A STEEL CUP with center which is a faceted black glass "jewel" in a prong setting. $.75.
10. A FOUR-HOLE SEW-THRU. $.50.
11. A CUBE. 12. A RECTANGLE. 13. A CUBE with grape design on the sides done in white paint and gold luster. These three buttons illustrate shapes with geometric contour. Value of each, $.75.
14. A gold lustered cameo-like head, with silver lustered background, recessed in a square frame. $1.00.
15. SALT. $.50.
16. A TILE. $1.00.
17. A RECTANGULAR SLAG button with a pin shank. $1.50.
18. A TILE, the floral decoration in colors of green, white and red. $1.00.
19. A design of WHEAT, done with white, green, blue and gold. $.75.
20. A BAT, copper lustered. $2.00.
21. THREE OWLS ON A BRANCH. The crescent border is bright black. The owls and their background have iridescent luster and the owl's eyes are red with black pupils. Scarce. $2.50.
22. A BEETLE in a shell shape. Iridescent luster. $1.50. This can be found with different luster finishes.
23. A LIZARD, silver lustered. $1.00.
24. BEAR, outlined in gold and a gold background. $2.00.
25. RUNNING PIG, background parti-gold lustered. $1.50.
26. AN ELEPHANT under a palm tree, all black. $3.00.
27. WHIPPET DOG'S HEAD, molded in very high relief. $1.25.
28. A BUG, outlined in silver luster on a modified ball that has a dull finish. $.75.
29. SPIDER on his web. Portions of the web are gold lustered. $1.00.
30. A ROSEBUD AND LEAVES, multilustered with gold, green and red. $.50.
31. PLUMS, with iridescent luster, quite purple on the plums. $1.50.
32. ACORNS and oak leaf, partly silver lustered. $1.00.
33. A GRAPE LEAF molded in high relief with stippled background. All black. A swirl-back button. $.50.
34. WHEAT, tied with a bow. All black. $.75.

PLATE 103

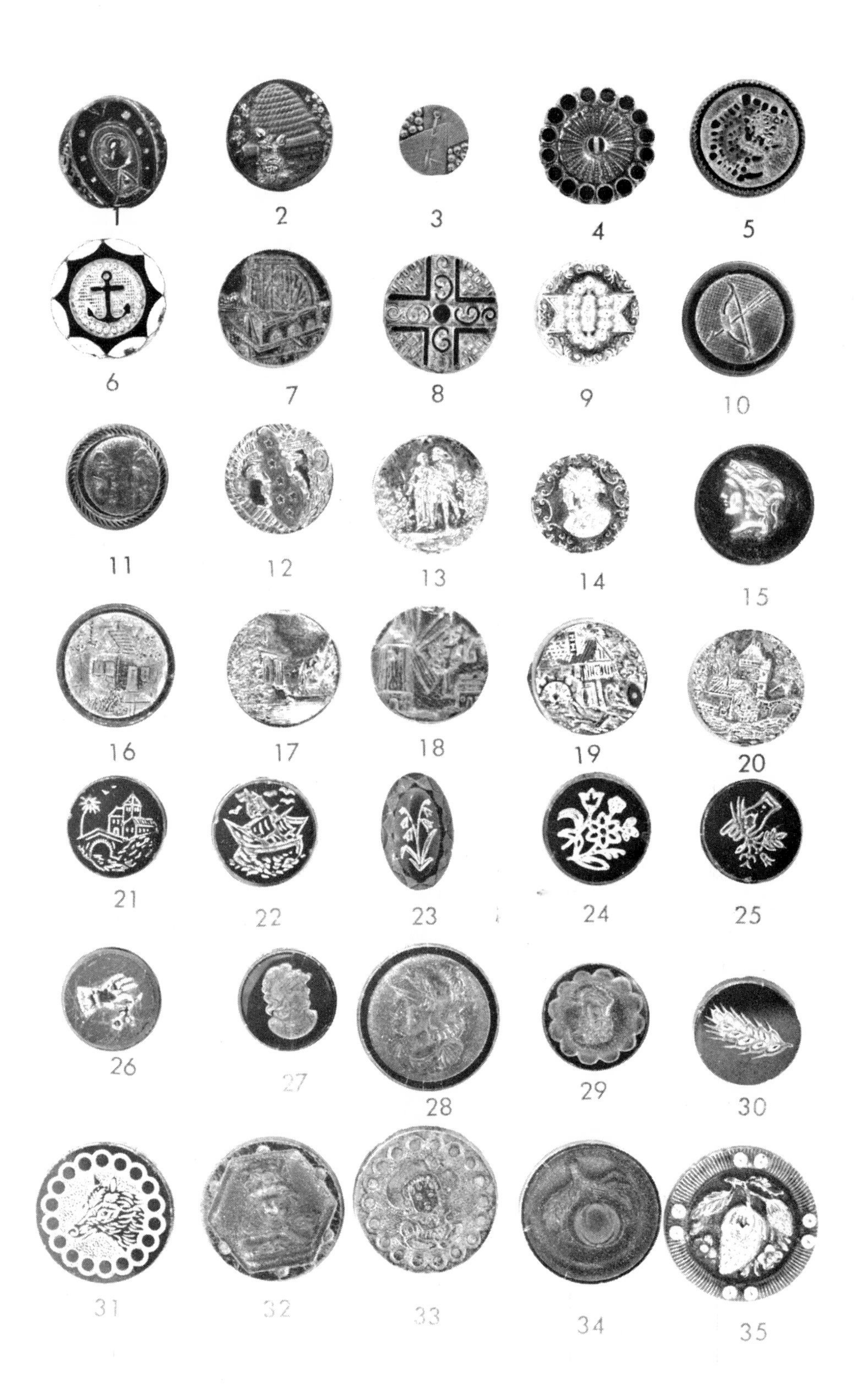
1
2
3
4
5
6
7
8
9
10
11
12
13
14
15
16
17
18
19
20
21
22
23
24
25
26
27
28
29
30
31
32
33
34
35

PLATE 103

MISCELLANEOUS BLACK GLASS PICTORIALS

These buttons are PICTORIALS showing people, objects, plant life, heads and scenes.

1. A HORSESHOE, gold lustered with some black showing, a two-hole sew-thru. $.50.

2. BEEHIVE, dull black with flowers around the hive, touched with gold luster. $.75.

3. A PIN, all black. $.50.

4. A SCREW HEAD forms the center, copper lustered. $.75.

5. BIRD'S CLAW, gold and iridescent luster. $2.00.

6. AN ANCHOR, silver lustered with some black showing. (parti-lustered). $.75.

7. AN IRRIGATION WHEEL, iridescent luster. This can be found with the other lusters, also. $3.00.

8. A CROSS "quarter-pierced", iridescent luster with black showing to outline the design. $1.00.

9. BUCKLE. This has an attractively molded border. Silver lustered. $.50.

10. A textured background with molded BOW AND ARROW in relief, touched with outlines of gold luster. $1.00.

11. PIERROT AND PIERRETTE, the same design that appears on metal buttons. The figures, crescent and border are in bright finish; background dull. $1.50.

12. SOL AND LUNA, silver lustered. $1.00.

13. TWO FIGURES, silver lustered. $1.50.

14. A CAMEO-LIKE HEAD, molded with fine detail on costume and headdress, and nice scroll border. Silver lustered with the background tinted pink. $1.25.

15. A flat black glass button with brass escutcheon-type CLASSICAL HEAD. $1.50.

16. A molded SCENE showing a small house, gold lustered. $1.00.

17. "THE SHRINE OF WILLIAM TELL", silver lustered. $1.25.

18. A scene showing a WINDMILL, iridescent luster. $1.75.

19. A MILL SCENE, the recessed portions filled, before firing, with white paint. A few touches of yellow and pink were also used. $.75.

20. A silver lustered scene showing CASTLE, MILL etc. $.75.

21. A SCENE, showing palm tree, bridge and building done with gold outline. $.75.

22. A SAILING SHIP, done in gold outline. $1.00.

23. A FLORAL design in gold outline, oval shape, concave center, faceted rim. $.50.

24. A FLORAL design done with silver outline. $.50.

25. A HAND, holding flower spray, in gold outline. $1.00.

26. AN INTAGLIO design, of a HAND holding a flower spray between thumb and first finger, the design filled with gold luster. $1.25.

27. MINERVA HEAD, an intaglio design. The head is in dull finish and the surrounding areas in bright, accenting the head. $.75.

28. A CAMEO-LIKE HEAD in the medium size, dull finish with a bright rim. $1.50.

29. CAMEO-LIKE HEAD OF HENRY OF NAVARRE, bright scalloped border. $1.00.

30. An intaglio design of WHEAT, filled with silver luster. $.75.

31. This row is made up of medium sized buttons, all of which are scarce. The head of a FOX, with silver lustered background and outlining, black showing for the dotted border and rim. $2.00.

32. VICTORIAN CHILD'S HEAD, deeply recessed in hexagonal frame. $2.00.

33. "LITTLE JULIA", a Kate Greenaway design, silver lustered with some black showing. $3.00.

34. AN APPLE, molded in high relief, background deeply concave, dull. $1.00.

35. STRAWBERRY, flowers and leaves; silver lustered. $1.00.

PLATE 104

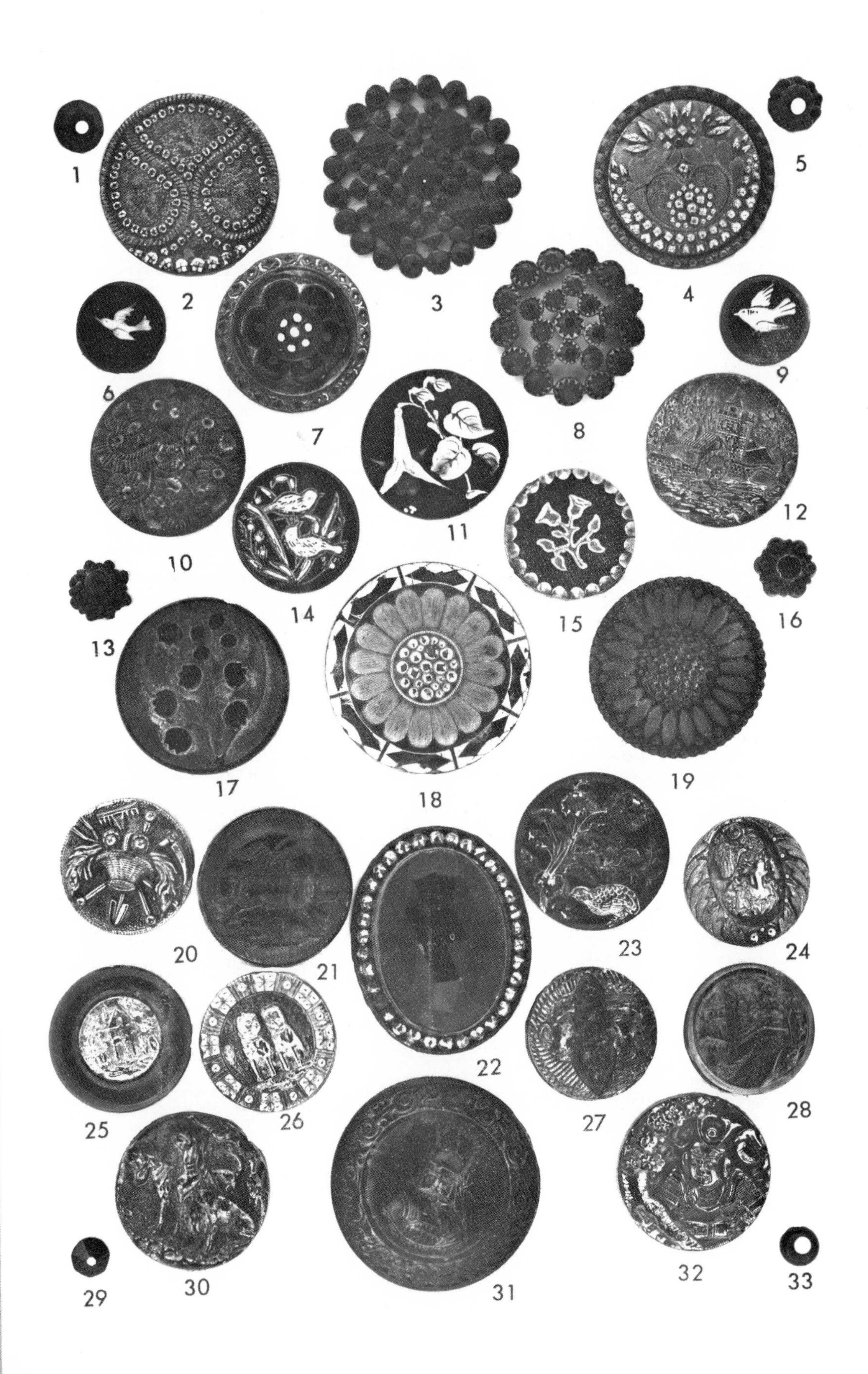

1
2
3
4
5
6
7
8
9
10
11
12
13
14
15
16
17
18
19
20
21
22
23
24
25
26
27
28
29
30
31
32
33

PLATE 104

BLACK GLASS

1. A CONE shape, tipped with white. $.50.
2. This is a button that is lustered to simulate fabric and trimming. The background is multilustered in sliver, yellow, blue and red. A silver lustered "cord" twists around and forms a PAISLEY design. Other outlining is done with silver lustered, faceted forms that resemble cut steels. $2.00.
3. PASSEMENTERIE. Pieces of black glass are attached to a metal back to form the design. $4.00.
4. A lacy molded center with a green-gold luster, brass rim and metal back. $3.50.
5. A "charm string molded" swirl-back with white dot. $.75.
6. A white painted bird on a branch, outlined in gold. $1.50.
7. A molded flower center, with painted white dots, set in a brass rim. Tin back and pad shank. $1.50.
8. Faceted black glass "jewel" cluster, set with prongs. $2.50.
9. Another white painted bird with no branch. $1.50.
10. Molded to represent tatting, the "thread" is gold luster and the background is tinted pink, blue and orange. $2.00.
11. PLANT LIFE. A lovely fuchsia, painted with white and gold. $2.00.
12. A PICTORIAL; a castle, mill and mill wheel, gold lustered. $2.00.
13. BEADED with black glass. $.50.
14. BIRDS on flower branches (animal life), painted in white and gold outline. $2.00.
15. An intaglio floral design, silver lustered. Rim also silver lustered. Since some black shows, this is called parti-lustered. $.75.
16. Charm string mold with swirl back. $.50.
17. LILY OF THE VALLEY molded with a bright finish in a concave background which has a dull finish. Plant life. $1.75.
18. This large, molded, daisy with faceted center and border is silver, full-lustered. $2.50.
19. An all black daisy, molded. Petals are a dull finish; center and border, bright. $2.00.
20. A pictorial showing GARDEN EQUIPMENT; full silver luster with a pink tint. $1.75.
21. RUNNING PIG, medium size, molded design with dull finish, background bright. $3.00.
22. A faceted black glass "jewel" in a collar setting with a cut steel border. $2.50.
23. A molded design on a flat background, showing a QUAIL under a flowering bush. Bird and stems are gold lustered, flowers have touches of white paint. This identical design can be found in other colors of opaque glass. $1.50.
24. A CAMEO-LIKE HEAD, silver lustered. $2.00.
25. A composition button with a silver lustered, black glass mill scene in the center. $1.50.
26. TWO BULL DOGS, medium size, silver lustered. $3.00.
27. SOL AND LUNA. Silver lustered with a pink tint, medium size. All black glass pictorials in the medium size, as well as the large size are scarce. $2.50.
28. A concave button showing a castle scene, medium size, iridescent luster. $2.50.
29. A diminutive cone with faceted sides and white tip, swirl back. $.50.
30. HOUNDS OF ST. HUBERT. Molded in quite high relief, silver lustered. $3.50.
31. A CAMEO-LIKE HEAD OF ODEN in a dull finish, concave center. The animals and other designs have a bright finish. $10.00
32. GENGHIS KHAN. This is another design that can be found in various lusters and in opaque glass, other than black glass. This is silver lustered. $4.50.
33. A round diminutive ball with white dot, probably a glove button. $.50.

PLATE 105

PLATE 105

CERAMICS

1. This a specimen of enamel-painted faience made in Copenhagen. It is signed with a crown and three bars. The white porcelain background is left to form the flower, which is outlined with green and the stem, leaf and border are of the same green; the rest of the background is a deep blue. Rare. $35.00.

2. A glazed ceramic disk with self shank. Background and back are black with a polychrome transfer of PLAYING CARDS. $45.00.

3. A glazed ceramic disk with self shank; polychrome painting with silver background; black and white transfer. These figures are SKATING and three similar buttons, not shown, illustrate activities of the three other seasons. $35.00.

4. Eighteenth century; porcelain center with polychrome FLORAL decoration in red, yellow and green; gold bead border; set in gilt rim. $45.00.

5. An early SATSUMA, polychrome painting with gold encrustation. The background shows the cream colored body with crackle glaze, characteristic of Satsuma ware, over which is painted a Japanese scene and in the foreground are many tiny gold dots, typical of the older Satsumas. The back is signed. $35.00.

6. A glazed ceramic with self shank, having a beautiful polychrome painted design of CHERUBS AND FLOWERS; gilt border, fired. $35.00.

7. Eighteenth century Dresden with an unusual shank, made with four holes which required a curved needle for sewing it to fabric. The decoration is hand-painted and called an Audubon bird. $37.50.

8. A flat porcelain disk with an ivory painted surface and outline designs. The round decoration is a polychrome painting with a gold background, a CHINESE LADY in pink and blue robe is about to pick a white iris. $35.00.

9. A sepia transfer of a GREEK HEAD on a black background, set in brass rim with brass back and shank. $25.00.

10. Glazed ceramic disk with monochrome transfer of a large BEE; brass rim and back. $35.00.

11. One of a set which illustrates several of Aesop's Fables, this being, "THE FOX AND THE STORK". It is hand-painted on porcelain in lovely colors; self shank. $37.50.

12. An eighteenth century framed porcelain with a scene of CASTLE and trees, hand-painted and fired; enclosed by a gilt border; the scene is in black and white. $50.00.

All buttons shown on this Plate are from the collection of Zula Fricks Brown.

PLATE 106

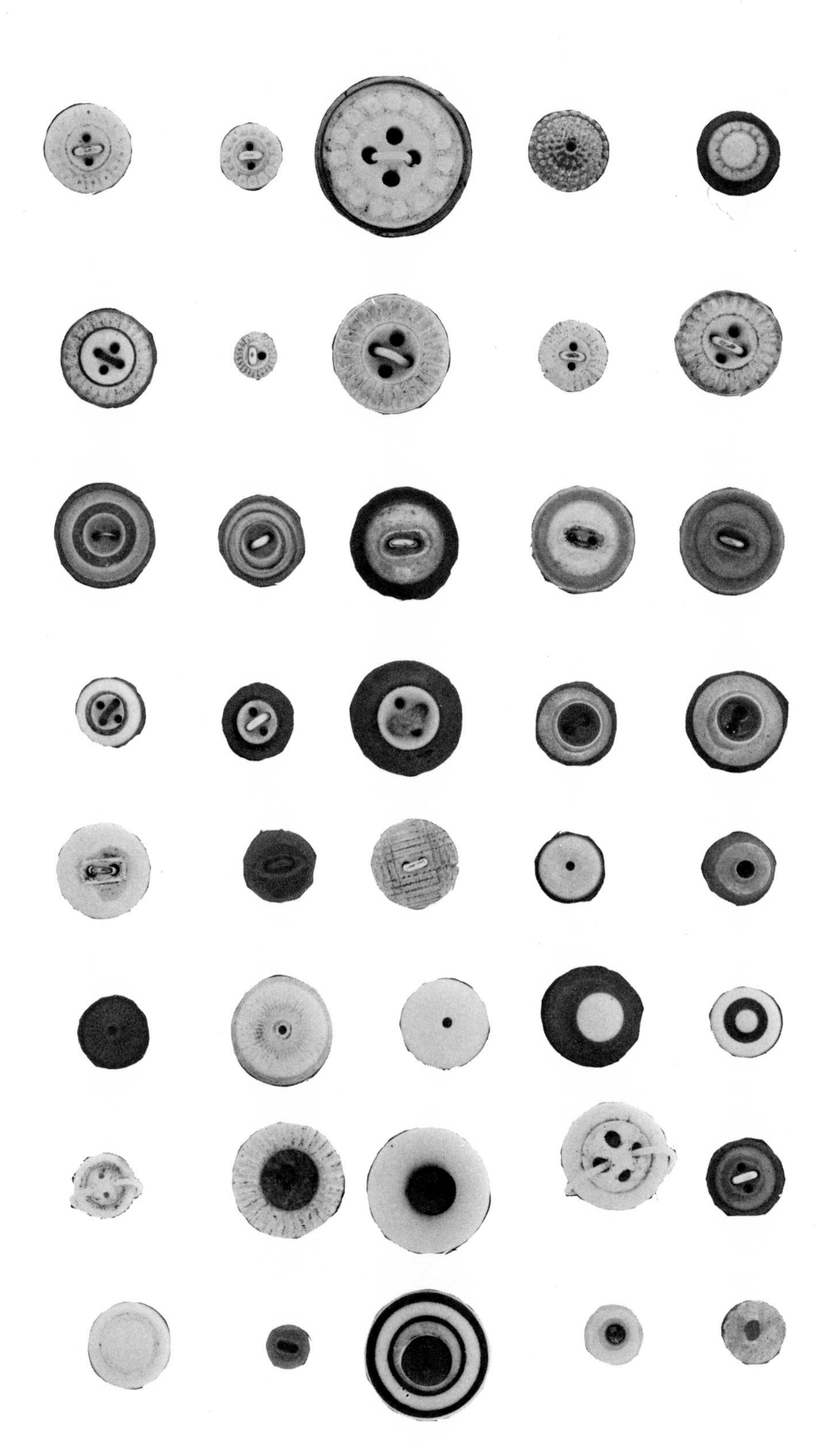

PLATE 106
CHINA ASSORTED

We give you here a "sampling" of the different types of china buttons, other than calicoes and stencils, which follow. Many collectors like to specialize in these interesting little ceramic buttons and any one type can become a fascinating study.

From Left to Right:

1. The first row are all HOBNAILS. No. 1 and 2 are four-hole sew-thrus, lustered; values, $.50 and $.25.

3. The medium size with metal rim. $10.00.

4. Hobnail whistle, metallic luster, medallion with lacy center. $.75.

5. Hobnail Gaiter, white boss, white hobnail band, lavender rim. $1.50.

6. This row are PIECRUST BUTTONS. This one is white with green trim; banded around edge, over side; solid band around center. $.50.

7. A diminutive, lustered, white three-hole. $.25.

8. All white, lustered. $.35.

9. Saw-tooth rim, all white. $.25.

10. Banded around edge and over side with light green, body white. $.50.

11. HOLLOW-EYE, two holes contained in a round hollow. Gray with blue rings. $.25.

12. The same type as No. 11, more rings. $.25.

13., 14., and 15. are MOUNDS, a molded rim enclosing a raised center which has two holes in an oval eye. Tan body, brown rim; white body, blue rim; all blue with a lustered ring between mound and rim. $.25 each.

16., 17., and 18. are INK WELLS. The centers of 'hese are deep like an old fashioned ink well and the sides slope. We show three sizes with different trim, solid colors can also be found. $.25, $.15 and $.25.

19. and 20. are DEEPWELLS, beige with brown rim and beige with lavender. They can be found in a great variety of colors. $.75 each.

21. Smooth Top, plain opaque white body with plain luster finish and boxed oval eye. "Boxed" means straight ends. $.35.

22. A FISHEYE, solid orange. $.35.

23. A PATTERN-EYE, the pattern being a cross; opaque white with plain lustered surface. $.50.

24. A white WHISTLE with orange rim. $.50.

25. A HIGHDOMED WHISTLE, this one is all blue. $.75.

26. A WHISTLE, low convex fluted with raised rim, orange. $.50.

27. A WHISTLE with convex white body, raised rim that here is orange. $.75.

28. White, medium height, convex, rimless WHISTLE. $.35.

29. and 30. are BULL'S EYES. All of these gaiter buttons have smooth tops, rounded and metal shanks. They can be found in pink, light blue, dark blue, orange, brown, wine, purple and black, combined with white. There are 15 distinct patterns. There is one exception to the color combined with white; this is like the last button on this Plate, which is tan, bordered by brown. It can also be found with tan center, bordered by pink, purple, orange, or green. The value of Bull's Eyes runs from $.25 to $.75, depending on size, color and pattern. Some patterns are very scarce and therefore more costly.

31. Called a BIRDCAGE due to the shape of the shank, which can be seen here. This has a smooth convex top, trimmed with a band of orange. $1.00.

32. A BIRDCAGE, a fluted white top with mottled center. $1.50. This type can also be found with lavender, blue, brown and black, as well as different mottled tones. Rarely one finds colored flutings.

33. The much sought after IGLOO, the name given to it by button collectors because of the igloo shaped shank. This has a black decoration. The one directly below has two rings of black. There are 17 different patterns listed (see N.B.B. September '59). Value of this specimen, $27.50.

34. An all white BIRDCAGE with smooth, convex top. $1.00.

35. An all blue body with brass rim. $2.50.

36. An all white GAITER BUTTON of a fancy shape with smooth high dome. $.50.

37. Diminutive gray body. OVAL EYE. $.25.

38. Described above, an IGLOO. $37.50.

39. Turquoise blue SHOE BUTTON with pin shank. $.75.

40. See Bull's Eyes above. $.75.

PLATE 107

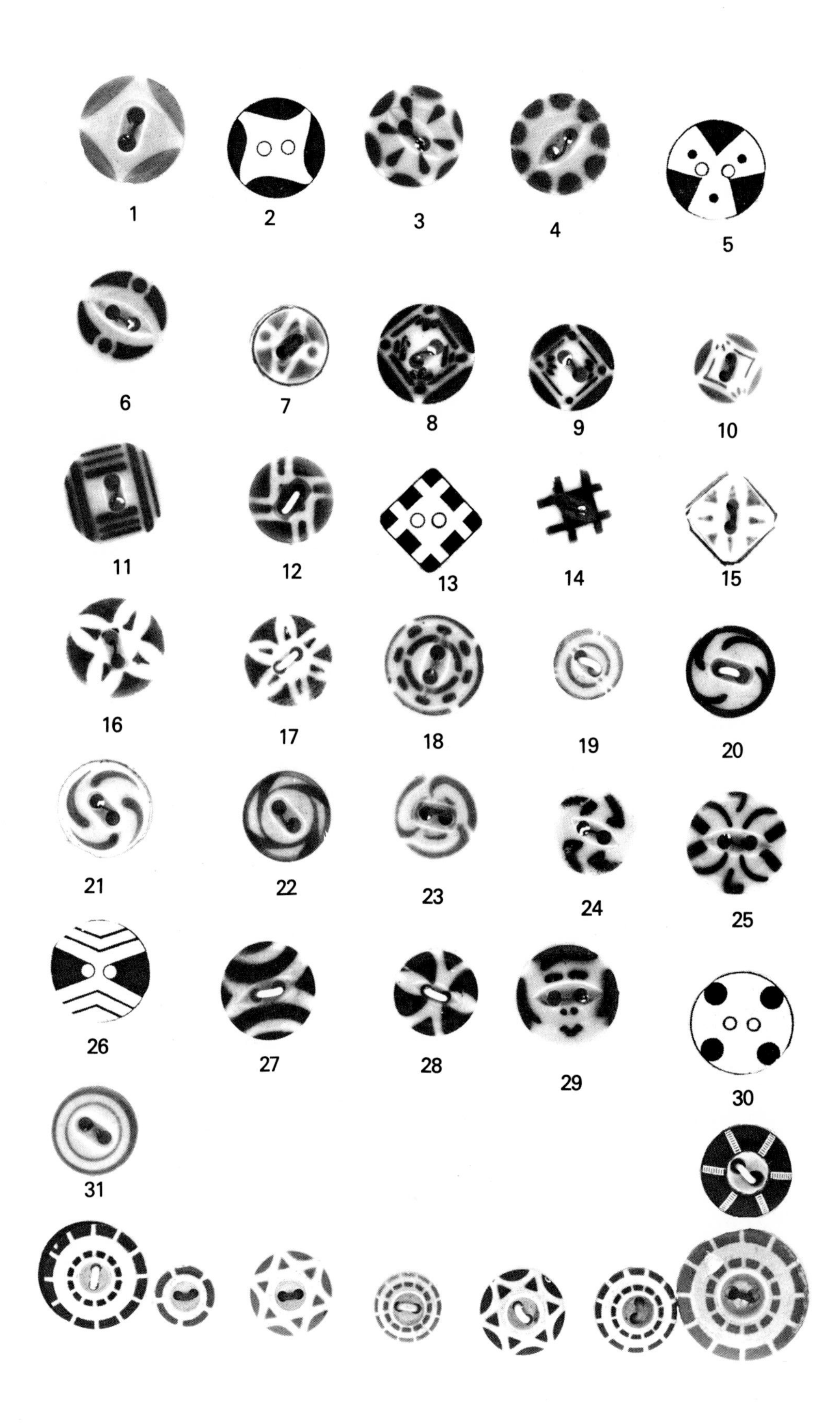

1
2
3
4
5
6
7
8
9
10
11
12
13
14
15
16
17
18
19
20
21
22
23
24
25
26
27
28
29
30
31

PLATE 107

CHINA STENCILS

We show you here the Tabulated List of China Stencil Buttons as compiled for the N.B.B. by Helen Schuler and Jane F. Adams in September, 1961. Some collectors add more to this chart but finding each of these sometimes proves difficult.

The body color of Stencils is usually either pure white or an ivory white. The colors used in the decorations are black, red, orange, lavender, light blue, dark blue, light green, dark green, dark brown, deep lavender, pink and yellow.

The only two shapes, round and square, are shown here. All have two holes, only and these are enclosed, in either fish-eye, oval-eye or boxed slot. The patterns are not applied completely by stencils as first believed, but by hand decoration as well. The Catalog of China Stencils by the authors mentioned above (N.B.B. September '61) states, "The name stencil signifies a style, not a technique".

Prices range from $.25 for the smallest size, to $.75 for the largest. The "difficult to find", of course sell higher.

The unnumbered buttons at the bottom of this Plate are aluminum stencils; values range about the same. Scarce colors are priced higher.

1. This is about the most common stencil and can be found in about every color. The one shown here has the oval eye.
2. This has boxed holes, can be found in red, dark blue and yellow.
3. All colors except pink and yellow; fisheye; ivory body.
4. Ivory body, fisheye, all colors except yellow, pink, light blue and lavender.
5. Difficult to find, ivory fisheye body. No light blue, pink, lavender, or yellow.
6. Found most often in black but also in red, orange, brown, blue and green. Ivory, boxed holes.
7. Ivory with boxed holes; a scarce pattern, found in green, black, lavender and pink.
8. Plentiful. White, oval-eye body, all colors except pink, light blue, yellow and dark brown.
9. White body, oval-eye, found in all colors except light blue, light green and light brown.
10. White body, oval-eye, all colors except dark brown, yellow, deep lavender and pink.
11. Ivory body, oval-eye, all colors except yellow, deep lavender, pink and light green.
12. Ivory body, oval boxed eye, all colors except yellow, dark green and light brown.
13. Ivory body, fish-eye, not plentiful, found in red, orange, light blue, dark blue and light green.
14. White, fish-eye, found in all colors except lavender and yellow.
15. White body, fish-eye, all colors except yellow, pink and dark blue.
16. White, oval boxed eye, all colors except yellow and dark brown.
17. Both white and ivory, oval eye, all colors.
18. Ivory, fisheye, all colors except yellow, pink and light brown.
19. White, oval-eye, found only in black and green.
20. Ivory, oval-eye, every color except pink.
21. Ivory, oval-eye, all colors except yellow, pink, and dark blue.
22. Ivory, oval-eye, all colors except light brown, pink and dark blue.
23. Ivory body, oval boxed eye, all colors except the lavenders, yellow, pink, and dark green.
24. Ivory, fisheye, only found in black and dark green.
25. Ivory, fisheye, all colors except pink, the lavenders and yellow.
26. Amost impossible to find. White with pink decoration.
27. Ivory, fisheye, all colors except yellow, lavender, pink, and light brown.
28. Ivory, fisheye, all colors except yellow and pink.
29. Ivory, fisheye, comes in black only.

30. and 31. Ivory oval-eyes, some collectors do not include these two types.

The metal stencils which follow have a patent date which is March 24, 1931. The patterns shown are called, "Single broken band, Two broken bands, Star with straight points". (See N.B.B. January '62).

PLATE 108

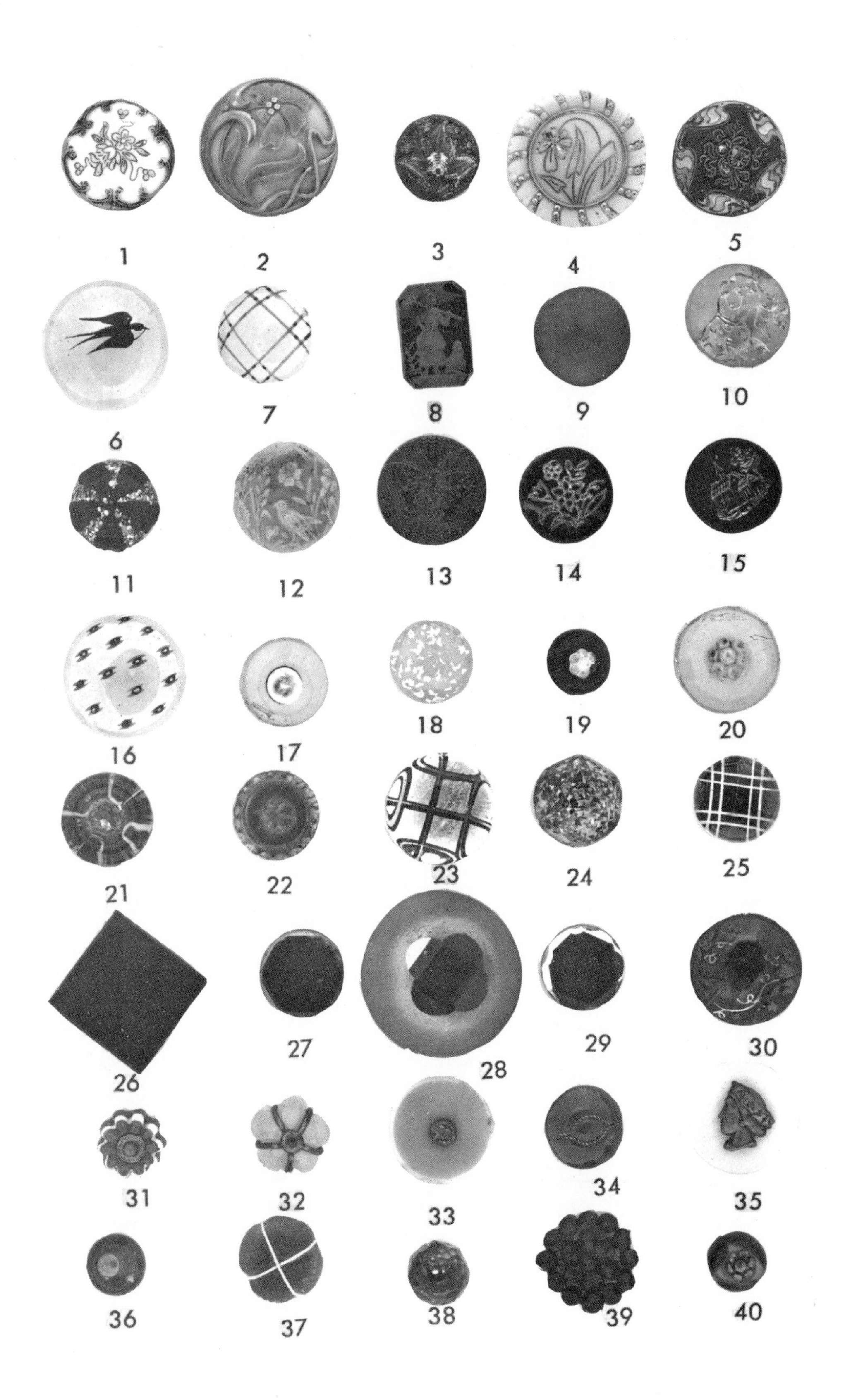
1
2
3
4
5
6
7
8
9
10
11
12
13
14
15
16
17
18
19
20
21
22
23
24
25
26
27
28
29
30
31
32
33
34
35
36
37
38
39
40

PLATE 108

GLASS, CLEAR & COLORED

1. A VICTORIAN. White milk glass (opaque), the floral design and border molded in the face, then outlined with gold luster and color added to enhance the design. $1.00
2. A Victorian of opaque caramel with molded flower and stem design, painted with gray and gold luster. $2.00.
3. A small Victorian of opaque chocolate, molded design touched with gold and white. $.75.
4. Turquoise Blue Victorian, opaque, floral design molded, then outlined with gold and given touches of pink. $3.00.
5. Opaque, cobalt blue Victorian, center design outlined in gold and given touches of pink and blue. The border is gold with molded designs filled with light blue. $1.00.
6. A painted and fired BIRD on a clam broth, medium sized button. $2.00.
7. Design painted in blue, green and black on clambroth (opaque). $.75.
8. A design of a GIRL WITH RAKE painted on tortoise (a mixture of brown and amber which simulates tortoise shell.) A rectangular shape with cut corners. $1.50.
9. Green, frosted. $1.00.
10. Frosted camphor glass with molded pictorial design of DOG WITH BIRD, outlined in silver luster. $2.00.
11. Opaque chocolate with FROSTED WHITE DESIGN and polished panels. Scarce. $2.50.
12. Opaque caramel Glass, lustered, with molded pictorial design of BIRD, flowers and foliage. A Victorian. $2.00.
13. BUTTERFLY, molded in red glass with iridescent luster. $6.00.
14. Tortoise with floral design, outlined in gold. $1.00.
15. Red glass with BUILDING and tree outlined in gold. $1.00.
16. Clambroth with black TRANSFER. $1.00.
17. Opaque milk glass (white) CONE WITH FOIL TIP. The tip is clear glass, backed by foil. $1.00.
18. Opaque turquoise blue with FOIL TRIM. $2.50.
19. A CORONET, transparent cranberry with clear glass top, backed by foil. (Glass with glass). $1.50.
20. A CORONET of white glass (opaque) with clear glass top. $1.00.
21. A PAPER BACK. These buttons resemble Kaleidoscopes but the paper with the design lies, completely exposed, against the glass, not covered by a metal plate. This one is a sew-thru which is quite rare. From the collection of Prudence Crawford. $5.00.
22. A FOIL METAL BACK. These are like Kaleidoscopes but have no pattern under the glass, only colored foil. This one has a molded clear glass top with a star design in the center and a scalloped border. The foil is red, metal disk applied to the back. $2.00.
23. A KALEIDOSCOPE, rare in this size. The design is in black and gold plaid on silver. The transparent glass dome has straight sides like a drum. The metal reinforcement covers the back. $3.00.
24. A KALEIDOSCOPE with high faceted dome. White underneath that is sprinkled with red, green and gold. $2.50.
25. A low domed KALEIDOSCOPE with plaid design, black and white on red, under the clear glass. Metal back. $2.50.
26. A square WAFER of amethyst glass with a metal reinforcement at the back which holds the shank. $5.00.
27. A MIRROR, genuine looking glass with a gold tint, metal back, beveled edge. $1.00.
28. A medium sized Mirror with a faceted center of clear looking glass and wide outer border that is frosted. Metal back, high dome. $5.00.
29. A MIRROR of clear looking glass with a faceted rim, metal back. $.75.
30. A rare convex, ruby glass WAFER with a metallic sheen and a painted design of a bird and foliage. The back is concave and a metal reinforcement fits into this and is cemented to the back. The center of this metal backing is slightly cone shaped and encloses the metal shank. From the collection of Prudence Crawford. $8.00.
31. Cobalt blue opaque fluted shape, banded by white overlay trim, and metal trim, embedded. $1.75.
32. Light green opaque glass METAL BOUND. This also has a pin shank (a pin head on the front and a loop shank on the back are connected by a stem which goes through the center of the button.) $4.00.
33. SHEET OVERLAY, rare. White opaque glass is overlaid with a "sheet" of opaque green, thin, flat and the same size and shape as the underlay. A metal reinforcement at the back and a pin shank, as described above. In this specimen the pin head is like a SCREW HEAD. $7.50.
34. Opaque green with a metal embedded BRACELET. $3.00.
35. Opaque white glass with an ESCUTCHEON, which is a classical head, connected through the glass to the shank. $1.00.
36. A transparent green glass ball shape with a pin shank. $.75.
37. THREAD BOUND molded blue glass. The fluting holds the thread in place and it passes under the metal plate of the shank at the back. $3.00.
38. A faceted transparent blue glass ball. $.50.
39. PASSEMENTERIE. Ruby glass simulating garnets. Faceted pieces of glass are riveted to an openwork, metal frame. Very rare. $10.00.
40. AN OPAQUE BALL of green and blue with an ornamental pin head, connected with shank. $.75.

PLATE 109

1
2
3
4
5
6
7
8
9
10
11
12
13
14
15
16
17
18
19
20
21
22
23
24
25
26
27
28
29
30
31
32
33
34
35
36
37
38
39
40

PLATE 109

GLASS, CLEAR & COLORED

1. A BLOWN GLASS ball, blown loop shank, pink. $.75.
2. CRACKLE glass ball, clear. $.75.
3. Amber LACY GLASS with gold outline design. $.75.
4. Opaque green, FLUTED with band of white overlay trim. Swirlback. $.75.
5. A ball shape with overlay trim, designated as BIRD'S EGG. $1.00.
6. Ruby glass cone DOTTED with overlay trim. Swirlback. $.75.
7. Green glass cone, DOTTED AND BANDED with white overlay trim. Swirlback. $.75.
8. Opaque gray body with design of darker gray, LOOPED with chocolate brown and goldstone. $1.50.
9. OVERLAY TRIM illustrating PLANT LIFE; a modified ball of light blue with a satin finish, flower done in polychrome, stem goldstone. $3.00.
10. SLAG (not true slag) with a chocolate brown base and overlay trim of lighter brown, white and goldstone. Swirlback. $.75.
11. Opaque, cream-colored base with SWIRLS of chocolate brown. $1.00.
12. Opaque milk white glass MULTI-TIPPED with black. $1.00.
13. SPIRAL PINWHEEL. This is a twentieth century paperweight made by Jacques Israel. The pinwheel is in shades of pink and blue. This is backed by threads of latticinio, in which he has incorporated goldstone. The set-up is under a clear glass dome. $12.00.
14. VENETIAN. A rare type. This has a clear glass base with swirled back and wire loop shank. The top is gold lustered and overlaid with loops and swirls. In the center is a dot of light blue opaque glass. $12.00.
15. OVERLAY SHEATH. The core is of clear glass and twisted threads of gray glass with a silver luster are wrapped tightly around it so that it is only visible at the base. $12.00.
16. A DEWDROP, clear glass with blue glass fused to the ribs at the back. $6.50.
17. A GLORY. Looking straight into these buttons one sees a shape like that of a morning glory chalice. The dome is smooth and the back has molded ribs similar to those of a Dewdrop. Colored glass is fused at the shank; in this button the color is amber. $6.50.
18. A REFLECTOR. These have molded backs and tops, this one molded to show a cross. Colored glass is fused at the shank, only. In this the color is dark amber. $5.00.
19. and 20. These are also REFLECTORS but smaller and lower than No. 18. The tops have different molded designs. No. 19 has green glass reflecting through the top from the fused bit at the base while No. 20 has amethyst. $4.00 each.
21. The buttons described in the row above all belong to the class of RADIANTS. No. 21 is a RADIANT also but UNNAMED. It is molded on top with ribs and is frosted so that it is almost translucent but a dot of light blue glows dimly through the surface. $3.00.
22. One of the UNNAMED RADIANTS with a different molded design from No. 21. The other glass used is white and one must look closely to realize that this is indeed a RADIANT. $3.00.
23. A paperweight with a set-up that is a CROSS-SECTION OF CANE; clear glass dome. $3.00. Twentieth century.
24. A paperweight with clear glass dome and SET-UP OF CANES TWISTED. (Green and white). $6.50.
25. A beautiful paperweight made by Thure Erickson (1913-1963). He used lovely flower set-ups and in some, as in this, delicate glass threads of FILIGREE. $50.00.
26. A paperweight with a base set-up of silver FOIL, over opaque glass, with a clear glass dome, decorated with green dots. $4.00.
27. A set-up of blue metallic foil at the base covered by a high blue glass dome. $3.50.
28. A FLORAL PAPERWEIGHT made by Erickson. The lovely base set-up is on cobalt blue opaque glass which is sprinkled with goldstone. The pink rose has delicate green tendrils. $50.00.
29. AN OUTLINED GLORY, the aristocrat of the Glory family. The top is a clear glass dome and the back is fluted, by molding. Cranberry glass is fused, almost filling the cone at the base and a band of white is laid around the cone of the back. Seen from the top, this band outlines the red in the fluted shape of the back ribs. $20.00.
30. An Erickson paperweight with a base set-up of black glass with SPIRALS of green under a clear glass dome. $25.00.
31. A SULPHIDE PAPERWEIGHT made by Israel. The set-up is a molded angel's head, under a cranberry glass dome. $22.50.
32. A SWIRL paperweight. Clear glass dome, set-up of blue and white swirls. $5.00.
33. Opaque milk glass with pink ROSE and swirls of goldstone. $4.50.
34. PEBBLED. A blue set-up under a berry-shaped clear cap. Found in other colors. $5.00.
35. PEACOCK'S EYE. Blue glass base with a blue foil disk, surrounded by green foil forming a center set-up. Clear glass cap. $10.00.
36. Called a log shape. A base set-up is made with white milk glass that has HIT-AND-MISS flecks of blue and goldstone embedded in it, under glass. $5.00.
37. A base of amber glass with flecks of white embedded, under a clear dome. $5.00.
38. A foil set-up on white glass that represents a BUTTERFLY; clear glass dome. $10.00.
39. Similar to No. 37. Pink flecks embedded in white milk glass for the set-up. Clear glass dome. $5.00.
40. Same construction as No. 39 with goldstone, as well as pink, glass embedded in the white set-up, oblong shape, clear dome. $5.00.

PLATE 110

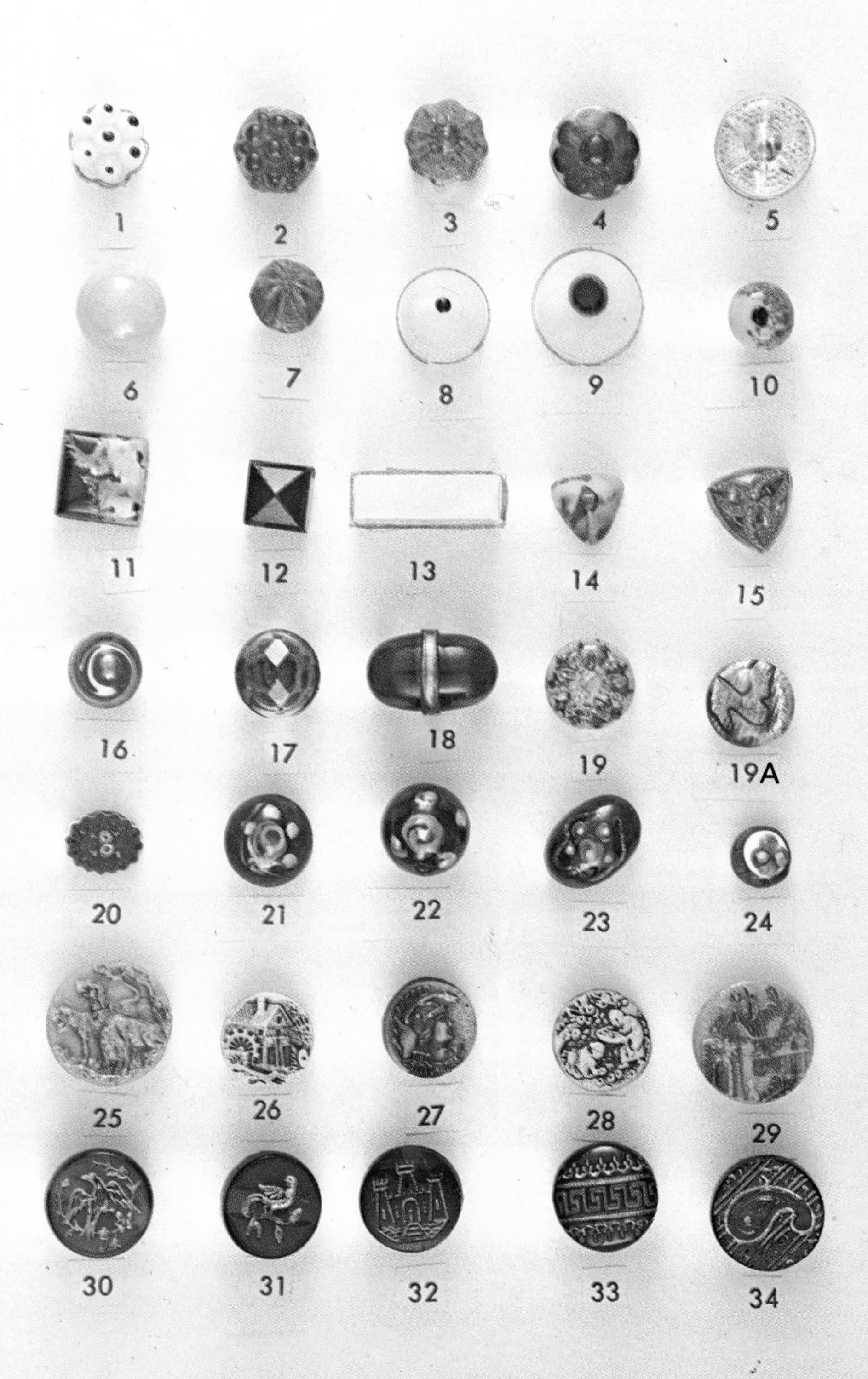
1
2
3
4
5
6
7
8
9
10
11
12
13
14
15
16
17
18
19
19A
20
21
22
23
24
25
26
27
28
29
30
31
32
33
34

PLATE 110

GLASS, CLEAR & COLORED

1. A fancy contour shape, milk glass, opaque white, black MULTI-TIPPED. Swirlback. $1.00.

2. Amethyst glass in a FLUTED SHAPE. Swirlback. $1.00.

3. Transparent AMBER GLASS, a fluted cone. Swirlback. $.75.

4. RADIANT-LIKE shape in transparent amethyst glass. $3.50.

5. A clear glass DEWDROP shape. The name comes from the low dome on the top. $1.00.

6. Opaque turquoise blue BALL. Plate shank. $1.00.

7. An amber MODIFIED BALL shape with staple shank, sometimes called an ANTIQUARIAN. $.75.

8. White milk glass CONE, tipped with black. Swirlback. $1.00.

9. CUT-OFF CONE, opaque white milk glass with black tip, circled by goldstone. Swirlback. $1.00.

10. A REALISTIC SHAPE, representing a PEAR. Yellow, opaque glass with a mottled red "cheek". Pin shank. $1.00.

11. A POPPER button, opaque glass in shades of blue. KEY SHANK, found only on this type button. Square shape. $.50.

12. A GEOMETRIC SHAPE. Chocolate opaque glass, swirlback, loop shank. A cube. $.75.

13. Another geometric shape, a rectangle of opaque clambroth. Loop shank. $.75.

14. A POPPER of opaque yellow, mottled with green, red and goldstone. A key shank. $.50.

15. Transparent pink TRIANGLE. A popper with key shank. $.75.

16. A ball shape with pin shank, with white swirl overlay trim. $.50.

17. Transparent amber glass, modified ball shape with faceted top. $.75.

18. A transparent CYLINDRICAL SHAPE, bound with metal to which a loop shank is attached. $1.00.

19. Clear glass with molded top and back. The inverted areas on the back are filled with pigment, in this case, brown. $1.00. Called a Painted Back.

19a. A paperweight with clear glass dome that has LOOPED OVERLAY TRIM of brown. The set-up is foil, backed by amethyst glass. $2.50.

20. CRANBERRY GLASS, transparent, fluted, banded by white and with overlay trim, consisting of twin pink roses and green leaves. $2.50.

21. Opaque cobalt blue with overlay trim of pink rose, green leaves and swirls of goldstone. $2.00.

22. Chocolate brown ball with overlay trim of pink rose, green leaves, dots of goldstone and touches of white. Opaque. $2.00.

23. Cobalt blue with white dot and floral decoration. $2.00.

24. Opaque cobalt blue with overlay trim of rose and leaves, bordered by loops of goldstone. $2.00.

25. This row is made up of opaque glass pictorials of a type called VICTORIANS. This one is of caramel with gold luster, molded and showing the HOUNDS OF ST. HUBERT. $3.00.

26. Sepia-tinted milk glass showing a MILL SCENE. $2.00.

27. Molded caramel glass, with sepia-tint; head of MINERVA. $2.00.

28. Sepia tinted milk glass. AN ORIENTAL GARDEN SCENE. $2.00.

29. Caramel with a sepia tint. A DWELLING WITH SMALL DOG sitting by the steps. $1.00.

30. This row shows all RUBY GLASS, transparent. This is decorated with a BIRD, outlined in gold. $1.00.

31. An INTAGLIO design of a bird, the design filled with gold. $1.00.

32. A CASTLE, outlined in gold. $1.00.

33. The molded design on this is the GREEK KEY border. It is filled with blue paint and the straight lines and outer border are gold. $1.00.

34. The PAISLEY design and background lines, outlined in gold. $.75.

PLATE 111

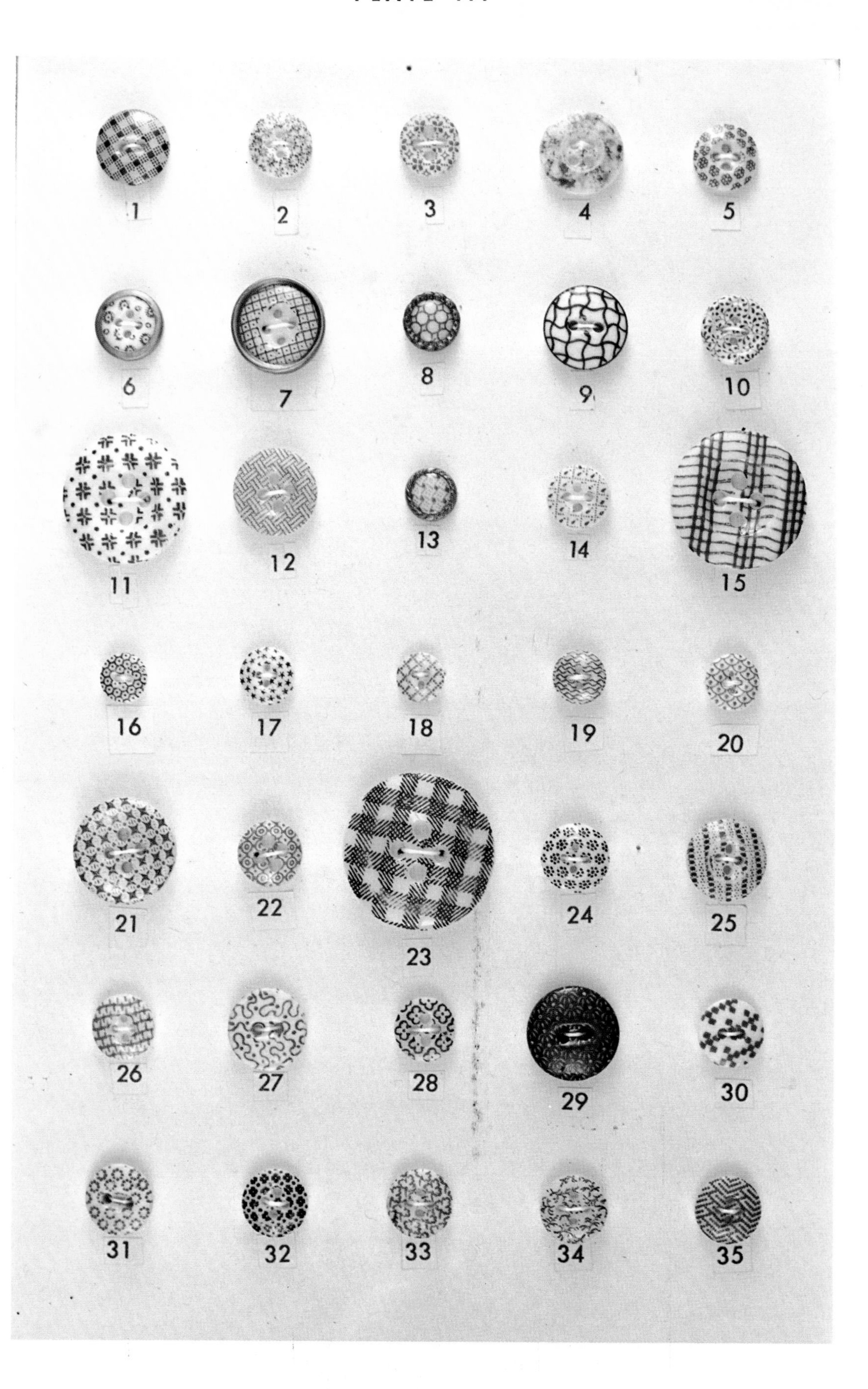

1
2
3
4
5
6
7
8
9
10
11
12
13
14
15
16
17
18
19
20
21
22
23
24
25
26
27
28
29
30
31
32
33
34
35

PLATE 111

CALICOES

1. #55, luster, black on tan, on white body. ½", two-hole. $2.00 to $2.50.
2. Unlisted. Two color, blue and brown, regular size. $3.00 to $4.00.
3. #149, orange, regular, $1.00 to $1.50.
4. #193, multi-colored, "knob" center, 9/16", $1.50.
5. #156, red, regular, $.75 to $1.00.
6. #17, green, brass rim, regular, $8.00.
7. #171, brown, brass rim, 5/8", $12.00.
8. #2, blue, jeweled, 3/8", $12.00.
9. #318, purple, two-hole, Note outer ring, 9/16", $6.00.
10. #122, green, rolled rim, regular, $2.00 to $3.00.
11. Unlisted, red, medium. $18.00.
12. #237, blue, 9/16", $1.25 to $1.50.
13. #64, pink, jeweled, diminutive, $12.00.
14. #255, green, regular, $.75 to $1.00.
15. #299, blue, medium 7/8", $18.00.
16. #71, purple, two-hole diminutive, $1.50 to $2.00.
17. #110, brown, inkwell, diminutive, four-hole, $2.00.
18. #34, green, three-hole, diminutive, $1.50 to $2.00.
19. #92, saucer, brown, four-hole, diminutive, $1.50 to $2.00.
20. #105, pink, four-hole, diminutive, $1.00 to $1.25.
21. #69, brown, saucer, 11/16", $3.00.
22. #9, orange, saucer, regular, $1.50 to $2.00.
23. #252, purple, medium 1", $20.00.
24. #44, black, inkwell, regular, $.75 to $1.00.
25. #182, blue, inkwell, 9/16", $2.50.
26. #277, pink, regular, $1.50 to $2.00.
27. #313, red, two-hole unlisted body shape, 9/16", $4.00 to $5.00.
28. #306, green, regular, $1.00 to $1.50.
29. #146, white on blue, solid body color, two-hole, 9/16", $1.50.
30. #176, red, two-hole, regular, $2.50 to $3.50.
31. #43, lavender, two-hole, regular, $2.00.
32. #175, black, regular, $.50 to $.75.
33. #192, red, regular, $1.50 to $2.00.
34. #263, black, regular, $1.00 to $1.50.
35. #47, purple, regular, $.50 to $.75.

From the collection of Dorothy Lloyd.

PLATE 112

1
2
3
4
5
6
7
8
9
10
11
12
13
14
15
16
17
18
19
20
21
22
23
24
25
26
27
28
29
30
31
32
33
34
35

PLATE 112

CALICOES

Nos. 1 thorugh 25 are all four-hole dish type calicoes.

1. #6, regular, $.75 to $1.00.
2. #137, green, 5/8", $1.00 to $1.25.
3. #60, orange, regular, $1.00.
4. #97, red, 9/16", $1.50.
5. #227, green, regular, $.35 to $.50.
6. #173, black, 5/8", $1.25 to $1.50.
7. #102, pink, regular. $1.50.
8. #116, purple, medium, 7/8", $18.00.
9. #141, green, regular, $.50 to $.75.
10. #90, brown, 11/16", $1.50 to $2.00.
11. #170, red, regular, $1.50 to $1.50.
12. #18, lavender, 9/16", $1.25.
13. #70, orange, 9/16", $1.50 to $2.00.
14. #140, red, 9/16", $1.00 to $1.50.
15. #302, green, regular, $.50 to $.75.
16. #39, black, regular, $.20 to $.35.
17. #101, brown, 5/8", $1.50.
18. #3, green, regular, $.75 to $1.00.
19. #219, black, 5/8", $1.00 to $1.50.
20. #26, pink, regular, $.20 to $.35.
21. #58, green, 9/16", $1.50 to $2.00.
22. #152, black, regular, $.35 to $.50.
23. #285, red, medium, 7/8", $18.00.
24. #157, green, regular, $.50 to $.75.
25. #169, blue, 5/8", $2.00.
26. #125, brown, 9/16", inkwell, $2.50.
27. #38, two-hole luster, pink on pearl, $2.00 to $2.50.
28. #128, green, two-hole, 1/2", $2.00.
29. #125, purple, 9/16", inkwell, $2.50.
30. #298, green, 5/8", saucer, $3.00.
31. #120, green saucer, $1.00 to $1.50.
32. #36, brown, medium, $18.00.
33. #96, black, diminutive, $.75 to $1.00.
34. #107, brown, medium, $18.00.
35. #50, blue, regular, $.50.

All buttons owned and described by Dorothy Lloyd.

PLATE 113

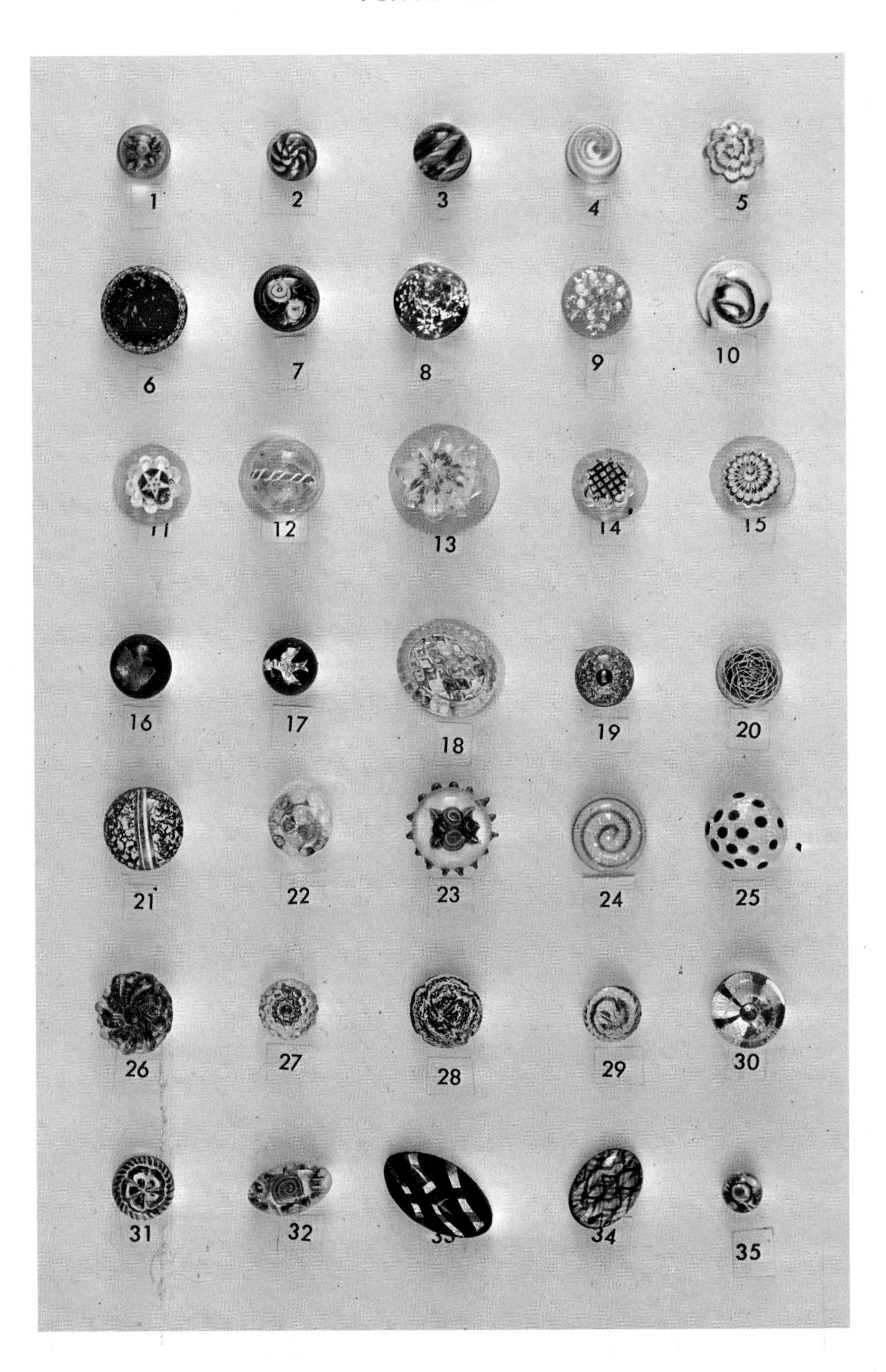
1
2
3
4
5
6
7
8
9
10
12
13
14
15
16
17
18
19
20
21
22
23
24
25
26
27
28
29
30
31
32
34
35

PLATE 113

PAPERWEIGHTS

Paperweight buttons are tiny glass specimens of creative art that resemble the old desk paperweights and are made in much the same manner. A true paperweight must have a cap or crown which is usually of transparent glass. This covers the decorative portion which is called a "set-up". The set-up is preformed and then fused to the cap. The first were made at about 1840. Most of the buttons shown here are from this period and are from the collection of Agnes Smith. Paperweights are built, not blown.

1. This has a blue glass base with the pink ROSE set-up built upon it. Green leaves and goldstone add to the arrangement. Clear glass cap. $7.50.

2. TWISTED blue and white CANES form the base set-up for this diminutive paperweight. Clear glass cap. $6.50.

3. TWISTED CANES again on a white base, with transparent cap. $7.50.

4. Another diminutive with a base set-up of white with SPIRALS of blue and goldstone. Clear glass cap. $5.00.

5. A base set-up of white glass with SPIRALS of pink laid on; covered by a molded, transparent glass cap in a fluted shape. $6.00.

6. A black glass base set-up with red metallic FOIL sprinkled over the top surface; transparent cap and salted rim. $5.00.

7. TWIN ROSES on a green glass base set-up; a low cap of transparent glass. $7.50.

8. A faceted cap of clear glass with a base of blue, sprinkled with silver FOIL. $4.00.

9. Turquoise blue base with silver FOIL; clear glass cap that is molded and tipped with white. $8.50.

10. Milk white base with SPIRALS of blue and goldstone. Clear cap. $3.50.

11. A CANE cross-section on white milk glass base forms the set-up. The cap is molded in a fluted shape. $12.00.

12. This set-up is TWISTED CANE, completely enclosed by clear glass, swirled at the base. $5.00.

13. A SPATTER design of pink on opaque white forms the base set-up; the cap is transparent glass, molded in a fluted shape. $6.50.

14. Another fluted cap with base set-up of opaque white overlaid with blue and dots of pink. $7.50.

15. A molded clear glass cap, cone shaped with base set-up of opaque white with blue SPIRAL. $10.00.

16. and 17. These two buttons have center set-ups of FOIL, a butterfly and a bird, set on opaque black glass and covered by transparent caps. $10.00 each.

18. A base set-up of opaque white, SPATTERED with blue and goldstone; a fancy-molded cap, oblong shape. $5.00.

19. Green glass base, SPATTERED with goldstone, clear glass cap with metal pin head embedded. $4.50.

20. Cobalt blue base with white FILIGREE form the set-up, cone shaped, faceted cap of clear glass. $6.50.

21. Base set-up of green glass SPATTERED with white and a center bar of goldstone and white canes. Low clear glass dome. $5.00.

22. Molded glass dome in a berry shape over a set-up of opaque white with blobs of pink at the base. This is called PEBBLED. $5.00.

23. A FLORAL set-up on a base of opaque white; clear glass cap with sides tipped with turquoise blue. $17.50.

24. Opaque white base, sprinkled with silver FOIL; clear glass dome with a spiral of blue. $5.00.

25. Opaque white base, sprinkled with silver FOIL; clear glass dome with dots of amethyst. $5.00.

26. Base of green glass, SPATTERED with goldstone; fancy molded cap. $5.00.

27. A fancy molded cap, PEBBLED, with set-up at base of opaque white with spirals of red. $6.50.

28. The same type of set-up as No. 27, with blue SPIRALS; fancy molded dome. $7.50.

29. A SPIRAL of blue on white forms the base, fancy molded cap. $5.00.

30. A silver FOIL design laid on red glass forms this base set-up. The cap is molded in a shape called, "dimpled and beaded". $5.00.

31. Another fancy molded cap with a base set-up of blue with SPRIALS of white. $6.50.

32. Opaque blue base with ROSE and goldstone loops; clear glass cap, oval shape. $5.00.

33. Black glass base with strips of silver and colored FOIL laid on. Molded transparent glass cap. $5.00.

34. Black glass with colored FOIL base set-up, clear cap, oval shape. $4.00.

35. Diminutive with transparent cap over turquoise blue glass with rose set-up. $2.50.

PLATE 114

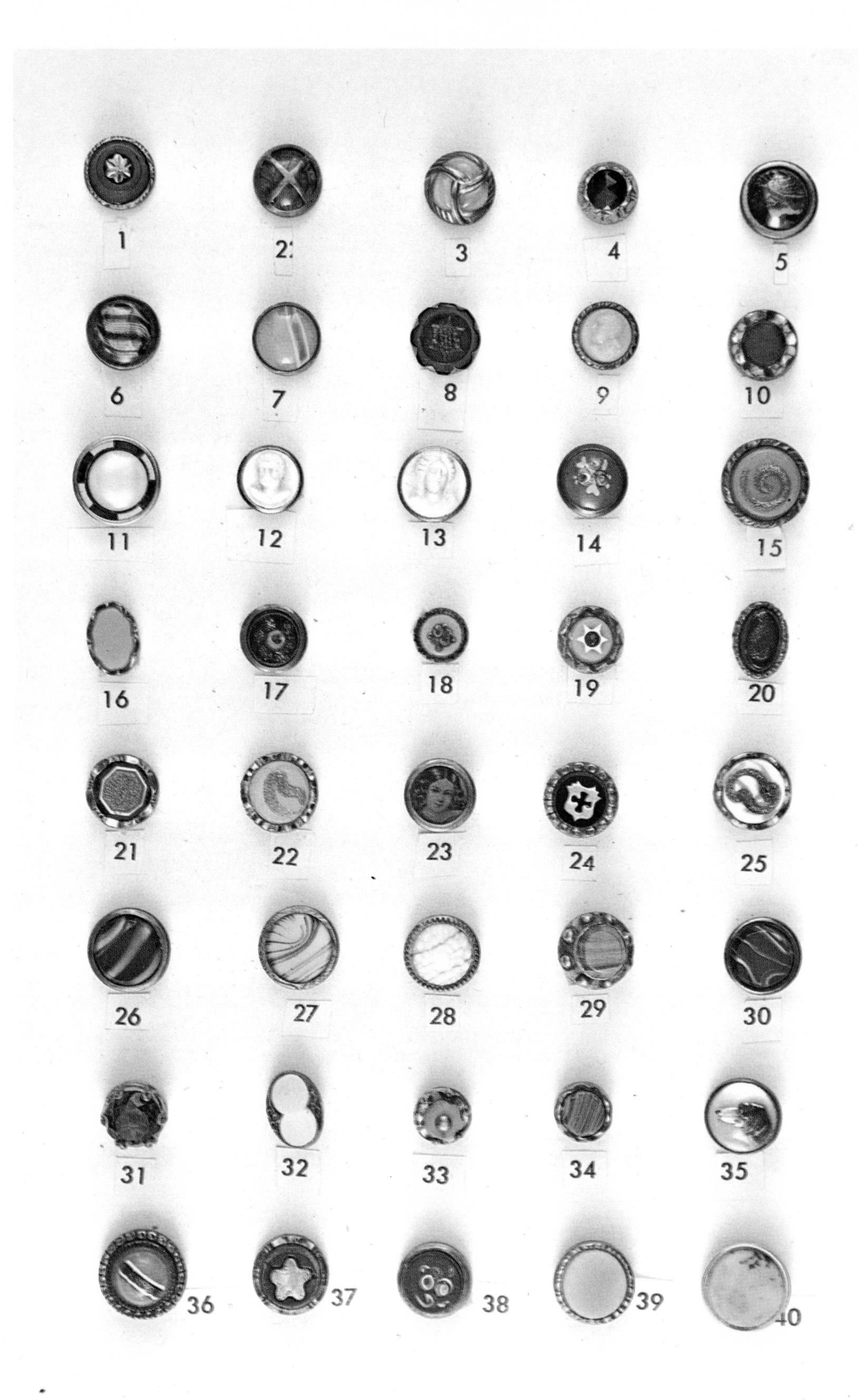
1
2
3
4
5
6
7
8
9
10
11
12
13
14
15
16
17
18
19
20
21
22
23
24
25
26
27
28
29
30
31
32
33
34
35
36
37
38
39
40

PLATE 114

WAISTCOATS

The vest, or waistcoat made its first appearance about 1660, in France. It was a long garment with sleeves, which reached to the knees. The coat, worn with it, was slightly longer. This fashion was introduced in England by Charles II. During the eighteenth century the vest sleeves disappeared and the vest, itself, became shorter, with the corners cut away. These waistcoats were very elaborate, made of satin, velvet, damask and other richly embroidered materials. These all had fancy buttons, sometimes as many as forty that sparkled down the front.

The early colonists in American dressed simply but when they became well established, they soon sent to England and France for pretty buttons. Portraits of men of the Colonial period show elaborate waistcoats being worn and many like these are being preserved in our museums. The custom of having a fancy waistcoat prevailed for years and even the poorest farmer had a special, finer one for his best attire. Many of our early colonists were frugal in speech; speaking briefly, they clipped their words and slurred their vowels. The word waistcoat was shortened, in some regions, to Weskit and thus we often hear these charming little "jeweled" buttons that adorned their waistcoats, called Weskit buttons, or simply Weskits.

1. Brown opaque glass center with brass escutcheon. $.75.
2. Cranberry glass crossed by metal bands. $1.00.
3. Opalescent glass with brass bands attached to the border. $1.00.
4. Faceted green glass with wider, chased border. $.50.
5. Norwalk pottery center. $.75.
6. Opalescent glass center with threads that resemble latticinio. $1.50.
7. Opaque green with overlay of white and pink. $1.00.
8. Molded green glass with a star design, brass prongs. $.75.
9. A molded head, opaque pink glass. $1.50.
10. Ruby glass center with flat top and straight sides. $1.00.
11. Center of pearl with enamel border, rim gold plated. $1.00.
12. A man's head, molded in high relief, opaque white. $2.00.
13. Molded head of Jenny Lind. $2.00.
14. Opaque glass with painted floral decoration, fired. $1.00.
15. a larger style, turquoise blue opaque glass with swirl of goldstone. $1.00.
16. Oval shape, prong-like setting, opaque turquoise blue. $1.25.
17. Preformed rose with dots of goldstone embedded in opaque blue glass, $1.25.
18. Twin roses and green leaves, preformed and embedded. Prongs. $1.25.
19. A preformed cane design, embedded in opaque glass. $1.25.
20. Oval shape, ruby glass with goldstone, embedded. $1.00.
21. Overlay. First black glass, then white and on top, goldstone, cut in an octagon shape. $2.00.
22. Clambroth glass with goldstone embedded. $.75.
23. A tin type, showing a child's head. Made during the Civil War period. $2.50.
24. Molded black glass, the shield is sunken and painted, making the cross stand out in relief. $1.25.
25. White milk glass with swirls of turquoise and goldstone. $1.00.
26. Slag, taken from a sample card of 1845. $1.00.
27. Another slag of the same age. $1.00.
28. Molded hobnails on white milk glass with streaks of pink and green. $1.00.
29. Slag in a collar setting with heavy, molded brass border. $1.00.
30. A Scotch agate, gold filled rim. $1.00.
31. Faceted ruby glass, $1.00.
32. An oval shape with twin opaque glass centers that have a grape leaf design. $.75.
33. Opaque turquoise blue glass with a pin shank. $.75.
34. Pink slag. Both this and No. 33 are diminutive buttons. $.75.
35. A high convex glass, molded on the back in intaglio and filled with paint. $2.00.
36. Ball shaped opaque turquoise blue with overlay of white and goldstone. $1.00.
37. Star escutcheon on amethyst glass, pin shank. $1.00.
38. Preformed pink roses, green leaves and goldstone, embedded in black glass. $1.50.
39. Opaque pink. $1.00.
40. Moss agate, gold filled rim. $2.00.

INDEX

—D—

—E—